Industrial Control

ELECTRONICS

MATTHEW MANDL
Technical Institute
Community College
Temple University

Industrial Control

ELECTRONICS

PRENTICE-HALL, INC.
Englewood Cliffs, N.J.

Library of Congress Catalog Card No.: 61-11816

Current printing (last digit):
11 10 9 8 7 6 5 4 3

Printed in the United States of America

45940-C

Preface

Industrial Control Electronics is intended to serve as a foundation for the study of all aspects of industrial electronics and control, including basic circuitry, control devices, transducers, relays, and solid-state gates, as well as the practical equipment associated with these items. Throughout the text particular emphasis has been placed on commercial and industrial circuits and devices, so that the reader can associate the theoretical aspects of automation and control with equipment in actual use. Numerous cross references have been incorporated to indicate associated discussions, related topics, or similarities in circuitry and industrial devices.

The initial chapters contain introductory material on control signals, solid-state devices, amplifiers, and oscillators, and serve as a summary and review of basic material required for the more advanced discussions which follow. Subsequent chapters deal with reactors, generators, power supplies, transducers, and other such items used in industrial electronics. Later chapters cover gating and switching, motors, servomechanisms, magnetic amplifiers, and appropriate circuitry. The final chapters relate to commercial equipment used in counting and indicating. Also, various industrial package units are covered to show practical applications of error detection, circuit and machine control, and related practices.

Standard symbols and electronic diagrams are employed throughout the book so that those who have previously studied standard electronic fundamental textbooks or who have had practical experience in radio and television circuits will encounter no difficulty in following the discussions when referring to the schematics. Comparable industrial symbols are given in the Appendix for reference purposes, should such symbols be encountered in current literature or in field practices.

Grateful acknowledgment is made to the numerous manufacturers of industrial electronic controls, indicators, and other commercial equipment for their permission to use photographs and data included herein.

MATTHEW MANDL

Yardley, Pennsylvania

Contents

Industrial Control
ELECTRONICS

1

Control Signals and Devices

INTRODUCTION

Of paramount importance in all the circuits used in industrial electronics is the waveform of voltage or current known as the *signal.* The signal may consist of a pulse, a squarewave, or a sinewave, which must be amplified or modified in some specific manner by the circuit in question. Because the signal is of such special significance in industrial electronics, a knowledge of the characteristics of the various signal types is essential.

Because each type of signal waveform has characteristics peculiar to itself, the amplifying or control aspects of a circuit depend to a considerable degree on the type of signals which it handles. For instance, power values and calculations are not the same for a sinewave as for a pulse train, and an amplifier which will pass a sinewave signal of a certain frequency may be unable to reproduce faithfully a squarewave signal or a pulse train. The different signals are discussed summarily in this chapter for review purposes and to establish the proper foundation for a clear understanding of the circuits involved in industrial electronics. Vacuum tubes, transistors, and diodes receive the same summary treatment as a foundation for subsequent discussion of circuit applications of these devices.

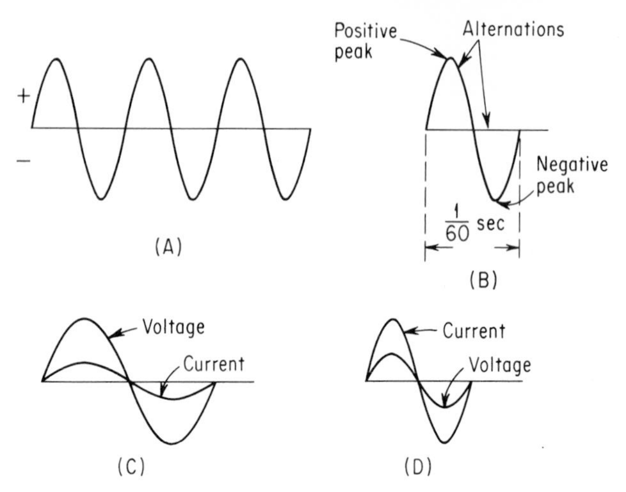

Fig. 1-1. Sinewave characteristics

THE SINEWAVE

A sinewave signal is illustrated at A of Fig. 1-1. This type of signal is characterized by having positive and negative segments known as *alternations* as shown. Two successive alternations as shown at B comprise a *single cycle.* If one cycle occurs in $\frac{1}{60}$ of a second, the signal is said to have a frequency of 60 cycles per second.

The sinewave type of signal is a common one; it is the type making up the alternating current (a-c) in power mains. Sinewave signals having various frequencies are found in industrial applications. Signals between approximately 30 and 20,000 cycles per second are known as *audio signals* because they fall within the audible range when converted from their electric representation to audible sounds from a loudspeaker. The simple sinewave signal, however, does not have musical characteristics, since no overtones or harmonic frequencies are present.

Both the voltage and current waveforms can be shown simultaneously, as at C. At D the current is higher in amplitude than the voltage. Voltage is in phase with the current at both C and D. Because a-c is at its peak amplitude only briefly, it cannot do the same amount of work which could be done by d-c having a value equal to the a-c peak. Thus, to find the *effective* voltage it is necessary to multiply the peak voltage by 0.7 as shown in the formula:

$$\text{effective voltage} = 0.707 \times \text{peak}$$

The effective value is also known as the "rms" value after "root-mean-square," which is named after the mathematical derivation of the effective value of voltage. The effective value indicates the amount of a-c which is as "effective" as d-c. Thus, if the a-c power main is rated at 120 volts, the peak amplitudes reach values of approximately 169 volts. To find the peak voltage if the effective value is known, the following formula is used:

$$\text{peak voltage} = 1.41 \times \text{effective}$$

When the voltage and current are in phase, the amount of power consumed is ascertained by multiplying the effective value of voltage by the effective value of the current being consumed by the load device:

$$P = E_{\text{eff}} \times I_{\text{eff}}$$

In a-c, the voltage is not always in phase with the current. At A of Fig. 1-2, for instance, the current is shown lagging the voltage by 90 degrees. Similarly, the voltage could also lag the current. At B, the voltage and current are shown out of phase by 180 degrees. Obviously, when current and voltage are not exactly in phase, maximum power cannot be realized. The amount of power which is consumed will depend on the angle which exists between the voltage and current phase conditions. Either inductance or capacity is instrumental in causing a phase difference between voltage and current. At C, for instance, an inductance is shown in series with a resistor. An inductance, by itself, is capable of causing a 90-degree phase displacement between current and voltage, with current lagging (voltage leading). When some resistance is present, however, the angle of phase difference will be less than 90 degrees. This is shown at D, where a triangle has been constructed and the resistance shown along the horizontal line and the reactance (X_L) of the coil shown in the vertical plane. The reactance is found by use of the formula:

$$X_L = 2\pi fL$$

As shown, if the frequency and the inductance value are known, these values are multiplied by 2π, or 6.28.

For the triangle shown at D, the hypotenuse is indicated as being 5 by the conventional mathematical formula using electrical symbols:

$$Z = \sqrt{X_L^2 + R^2}$$

Use of this formula gives a Z (impedance) value of 5 ohms. This 5-ohm value indicates the combined opposition to the flow of a-c produced by both the reactance of the coil and the resistance of the resistor. For the circuit shown at E, the same value of impedance (5 ohms) would be obtained. For the circuit shown at F, where both the inductance and the capacity have similar reactance values, one reactance value cancels the other, leaving only resistance in the circuit.

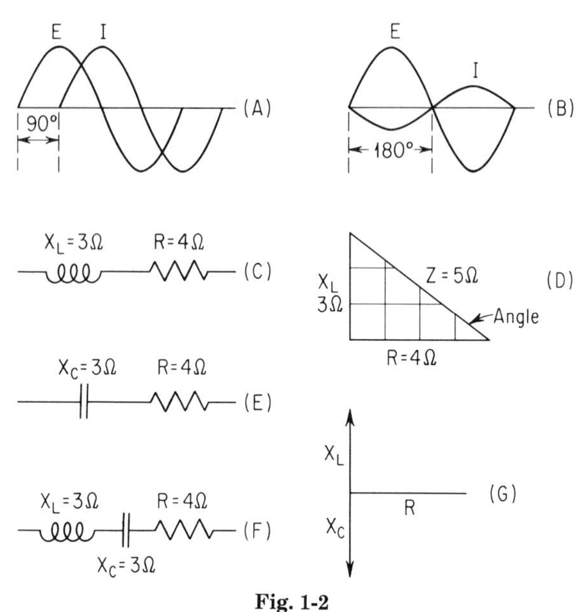

Fig. 1-2

Under this condition voltage and current would again be in phase. This is known as *resonance,* and it establishes a highly selective circuit used extensively in radio-frequency tuning circuits.

When an out-of-phase condition occurs, the formula given earlier for power is only the *apparent power;* the true power is less by virtue of the phase difference existing between voltage and current. To find the true power, the apparent power ($E \times I$) must be multiplied by the cosine of the angle which is established at the triangle shown at D. This is a trigonometric function; first the tangent is found by dividing the X_L value by R, and then the cosine is found by use of appropriate tables of trigonometric ratios. If there is no phase difference between voltage and current, there is no phase angle and hence the cosine is 1. Thus, the apparent power ($E \times I$) becomes the true power. With a phase angle existing, however, the cosine of the angle will be less than 1, and in consequence the formula for power (P) will give a power value less than that which would be obtained by multiplying voltage by current. Hence, the following formula is utilized:

$$P = E_{\text{eff}} \times I_{\text{eff}} \times \cos \phi$$

If, for instance, the cosine of the angle is 0.5, any multiplication of voltage by current would produce a value of power only half of what it would be if voltage and current were in phase. Thus if 50 volts are applied, and a load device draws 10 amperes, the power, for a cosine of 0.5, becomes:

$$\text{power} = 50 \times 10 \times 0.5 = 250 \text{ watts}$$

The manner in which phase differences affect the power factor is discussed more fully later.

THE SQUAREWAVE

Another type of waveform frequently encountered in industrial electronics as well as in other electric circuits is the squarewave shown at A of Fig. 1-3. The squarewave, like the sinewave, has sections which are alternately positive and negative. Unlike the sinewave, however, it does not show a gradual incline and decline of the alternation. Instead, there is an abrupt change. For waves of this type (as well as the pulses described next) the sharp rise of the waveform is known as the *leading edge,* and the sharp decline of amplitude is known as the *trailing edge.* The square (or sometimes rectangular) shape of the waveform has led to the name *squarewave.*

Unlike the sinewave, which consists of a single frequency, the squarewave is made up of a number of signals having frequencies which are related. Thus, a squarewave is made up of a fundamental frequency, plus a number of harmonically related, higher frequencies. Hence, a squarewave is made up of a fundamental frequency signal, a third harmonic having one-third the amplitude of the fundamental, a fifth harmonic having one-fifth the amplitude of the fundamental, and so on for a number of harmonic components. For a pulse whose fundamental frequency is only a few hundred cycles per second, the significant harmonics which contribute to the waveshape would range up to about the twenty-fifth. For squarewaves having a higher fundamental frequency, however, many more harmonic component signals are present.

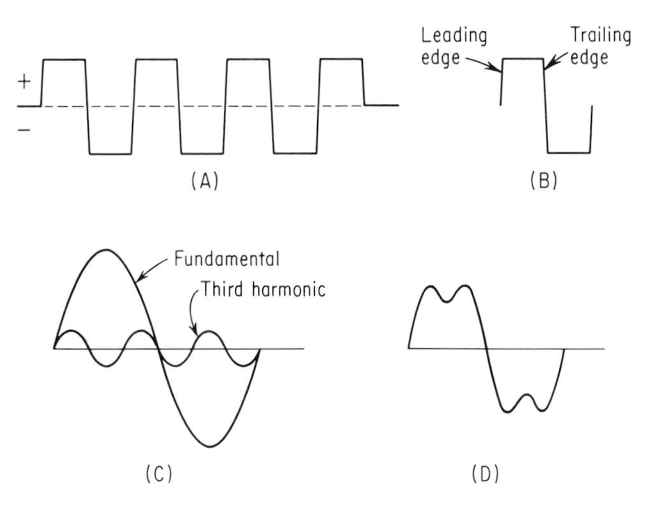

Fig. 1-3. The square wave

As shown at C, when a third harmonic component is added to a fundamental, the gradual incline of the fundamental waveshape is made more steep because of the in-phase conditions which occur for the two signals near the rise time and decline time of the fundamental. At the peak of each fundamental alternation, however, the third harmonic component is out of phase and hence will subtract from the peak amplitude. The resultant waveshape is as shown at B, which represents the addition of the two signal amplitudes. As successive odd harmonics are added to this composite waveshape, the sides of the waveform become more steep and the top becomes flat until eventually the waveshape shown at B is obtained.

Because a squarewave is composed of a number of odd harmonics, it is necessary to retain such harmonics when passing a signal of this waveform through various circuits; otherwise the waveshape of the squarewave will be altered, as described more fully later in this chapter. Thus, in order to retain the squarewave formation, an amplifier or circuit having *wideband* characteristics must be employed; in contrast, the *narrowband* type of amplifier could be utilized for the sinewave type of signal. (A *wideband* amplifier is one capable of passing a wide range of signal frequencies, whereas a *narrowband* amplifier passes only a relatively narrow range of frequencies.) When a squarewave has sharp leading and trailing edges, the peak power is virtually the effective power, since there is no gradual incline and decline as with sinewaves, and the peak power is present almost constantly.

THE PULSE

At A of Fig. 1-4 is shown a series of signals known as *pulses*. These have a single polarity and can be positive as shown at A, or can be negative. As with the squarewave, the leading and trailing edges of the pulse have a sharp rise time, but unlike squarewaves, the repeti-

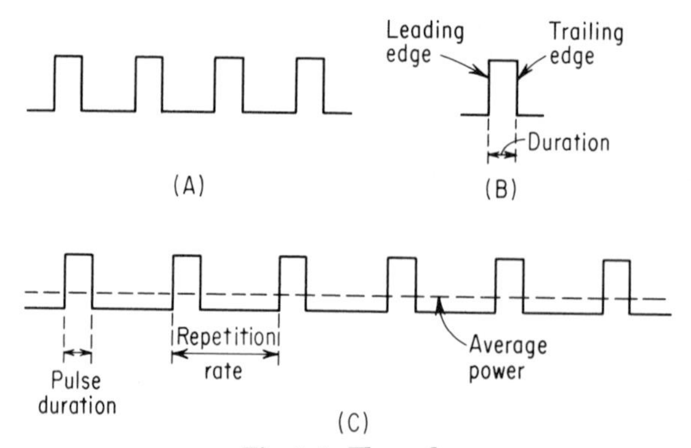

Fig. 1-4. The pulse

tion rate of pulses is not related to the width of the pulse. Hence, the pulse has characteristics which differ considerably from those of the squarewave.

The pulse, unlike the squarewave, is made up of *both* odd and even harmonics. Hence, to retain the shape of the pulse, the circuits which handle this signal must have characteristics which will pass most of the harmonic component frequencies involved.

Because the pulses are of single polarity, they can occur at various repetition rates, such as 100, 2000, or 50,000, or any other rate per second. With a squarewave, the repetition rate is of a fixed value established by the duration of the individual alternations, whereas with the pulse, the repetition rate can be altered as desired.

Because the repetition rate of a pulse of a given duration may be altered, it is obvious that the amount of power represented by a train of such pulses will also change if either the repetition rate or the pulse duration (or both) is altered. To ascertain the amount of power in a train of pulses, it is necessary to know both the duration of each pulse and the repetition rate. When the duration of a pulse is multiplied by the repetition rate, a value is obtained which is known as the *duty cycle.* The duty cycle is utilized to determine the average power of a train of pulses. This is done by multiplying the duty cycle by the peak power of the pulse. Thus, if a pulse having a duration of 2 microseconds has a repetition rate of 1000 per second, and the peak power is 500, the average power is:

$$\text{duty cycle} = 0.000002 \times 1000 = 0.002$$
$$\text{average power} = 0.002 \times 500 = 1.0 \text{ watt}$$

A few of the lower-frequency signal components of a pulse can be lost without appreciably changing the shape of the pulse. Hence, the loss of a fundamental frequency need not appreciably alter the waveshape of a pulse. To ascertain the approximate frequencies which an amplifier must be capable of handling in order to pass a pulse without undue distortion, the formula known as the *base frequency* is utilized:

$$\text{base frequency} = \frac{1}{\text{duration}}$$

Solving for the base frequency will indicate the frequency which the amplifier should be capable of passing for retaining significant harmonic components. Assume, for instance, that a train of pulses occurs at a repetition rate of 5000 per second, and that each pulse has a duration of 1 microsecond. The base frequency then becomes 1 megacycle and, in consequence, an amplifier or other circuit through which this pulse is to be passed should be capable of handling frequencies from the repetition rate of 5000 cycles per second up to the base frequency of 1 megacycle. Regardless of the repetition rate of the 1-microsecond pulses, the base frequency would still be 1 megacycle, because the repetition rate has no bearing on the harmonic content of the pulse. Thus, if the 1-microsecond pulse had a repetition rate of 200 pulses per second, the upper frequency which the amplifier should be able to pass must still be 1 megacycle in order to pass the pulses without undue loss of higher-frequency components.

THE SAWTOOTH

Another type of waveform often used for control purposes (such as the control on the electron beam in an oscilloscope) is the sawtooth waveform shown in Fig. 1-5. The sawtooth waveform, as shown, is characterized by a gradual incline in amplitude, and an abrupt decline. The sawtooth waveform is discussed more fully in the chapter on oscillators, where applications are also covered.

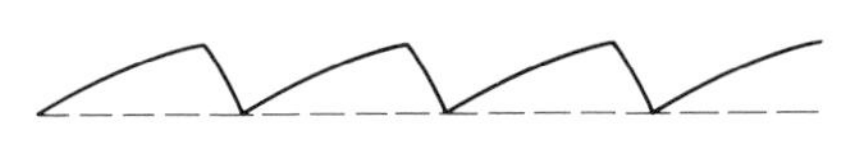

Fig. 1-5. The sawtooth signal waveform

SIGNAL DISTORTION

The factors involved in signal distortion are of considerable importance in industrial electronics. Often, in the design of electronic equipment, precautions must be taken to minimize distortion which may result in certain circuits. On the other hand, there are occasions where it is necessary to introduce distortion deliberately with respect to signal waveforms in order to accomplish certain desired results. Distortion factors for sinewave signals differ somewhat from those for squarewave and pulse signals.

Consider, for instance, the waveforms shown at A of Fig. 1-6. Two signals are shown, one having a frequency twice that of the other. Assume, for instance, that the signal having the highest amplitude is a 1000-cycle signal. If such is the case, the lower-amplitude signal is then a 2000-cycle signal, because it has twice as many cycles as the other. If these two signals are applied to a common terminal of an amplifier or other circuit, the resultant will be the point-to-point addition of the two signals. For instance, at the point marked "1," an in-phase condition prevails and hence the amplitude of the resultant waveform is higher here as shown at B. For the section marked "2," an out-of-phase condition is present and hence there is a decline in the amplitude of the resultant as also shown at B. Thus, when the entire composite signal is shown, it appears as at B. The waveform at B may be considered as a distortion of a pure sinewave since it con-

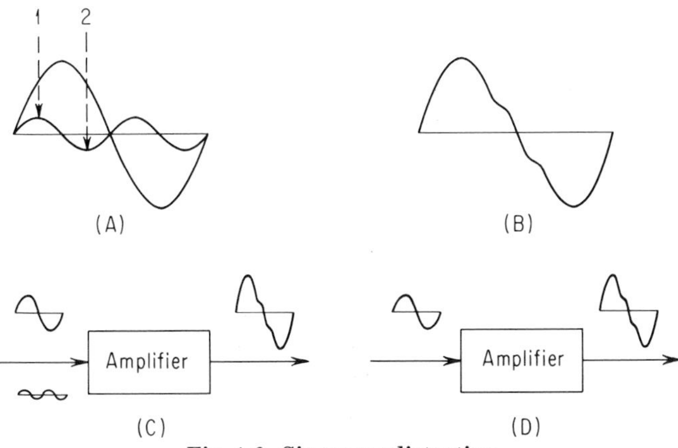

Fig. 1-6. Sinewave distortion

tains not only a fundamental frequency but a second harmonic component.

Relating these two signals to a practical case of amplification, assume that both the 1000-cycle signal and the 2000-cycle signal are applied simultaneously to an amplifier as shown at C. The result would be an amplified version of the two as shown at the output. This is a case where the distortion of a sinewave is a desirable and natural result of an amplifying process. The two signals could have been the music from two different instruments, the duty of the amplifier being to reproduce both instruments in an amplified version. Here, in the strict sense of the word, there has been a blending or combining of the two signals rather than a distortion of them. Consider, however, the case shown at D where a single frequency of 1000 cycles has been applied to an amplifier. At the output, instead of a single amplified signal, a waveform is reproduced which indicates a fundamental plus a second harmonic component. In this instance, *the amplifier* has added a second harmonic signal to the amplified version of the fundamental signal which was applied to the input. In consequence, the original signal has not only been amplified, but has been distorted in the process by the amplifier. This is an undesired result as compared to the amplifying process shown at C, even though the output signal waveform in each instance is identical.

In audio amplification work it is rare to encounter a pure sinewave; most of the signals are of the so-called "distorted" type because they contain a number of harmonic components as well as a blending of the various musical instruments or other audible sounds which enter the microphone. Each musical instrument, also, produces a complex type of waveform which is a composite of the fundamental frequency produced by the musical instrument, plus the harmonic content of the musical tone. When, however, the amplifier or other circuit adds signals in addition to the ones being amplified, the output is then considered to be a distorted version of the input signal. When the amplifier does not add undesired signals, the output is not considered distorted, even though the waveforms which are present are not pure sinewaves but consist of complex waveforms.

Because squarewaves and pulses are made up of a fundamental frequency plus a number of harmonic components, distortion of the squarewave or pulse can occur quite readily in circuits by virtue of the losses of some of the higher-frequency signal components which might occur. Losses result from series or shunt reactances made up of inductances and capacitances. Reactances, when present, will influence sinewave signals also, but only by diminishing their amplitude. The sinewave signal, having only a single frequency, is not affected with respect to its waveshape by virtue of the loss of other frequency components. A squarewave or a pulse, however, will have its shape altered considerably if a number of the harmonic components are lost during the transit of the squarewave or pulse through a circuit or other electric network.

Combinations of resistance, inductance, and capacity affect the waveshapes of squarewaves and pulses because of the time constant involved. The time constant, indicated as "RC," is the value which results when the resistance in a circuit is multiplied by the capacitance. This gives the time constant of the circuit, with the resistance in ohms and the capacity in farads. The time constant of a circuit composed of inductance and resistance is equal to L/R. In the latter instance, the inductance value is in henrys and the resistance value in ohms.

The time constant can be indicated in graphic form by showing the charging curves for a capacitor or inductance as in Fig. 1-7. This chart is known as the *universal time constant curve* and indicates the portion of maximum voltage or current for any particular time constant involved. Each curve illustrated indicates the amplitude changes of current and voltage in inductors as well as capacitors. As shown, each curve changes in an exponential manner. Curve A, which has for its beginning the lower left-hand corner of the graph, represents the exponential voltage rise in a capacitor when energy is first applied through a resistor. This particular curve represents the inductive current in a coil.

Curve B, which starts at the upper left, represents the manner in which the current flows when voltage is first applied to a circuit composed of a resistor and a capacitor. It also indicates the inductance charge current. For the capacitor, the current flow is at a maximum initially and the current gradually decreases as the volt-

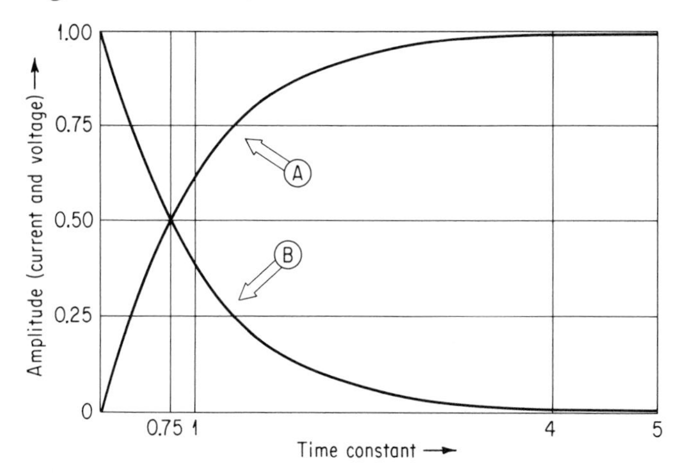

Fig. 1-7. Universal time constant curves

age across the capacitor builds up. Hence, momentarily there is a virtual short across the power source, because the capacitor draws all the current that can be furnished by the battery or other charging device.

In a circuit composed of resistance and capacitance, the time constant (RC) is the time required for the capacitor to reach a charge of approximately 63 per cent of its final charge value. As an illustration, assume a capacitor has a capacity value of 0.01 microfarad and there is a 10,000-ohm resistor in series with it. When the battery potential is applied, the capacitor would be charged to 63 per cent of its full value in 100 microseconds ($10{,}000 \times 0.01$ microfarad). After the elapse of five time constants, the capacitor is considered to be fully charged with the circuit current having dropped to zero. For a circuit composed of an inductance in series with a resistance, the time constant would be 0.002 for a 10-henry inductance and a 5000-ohm resistance, which would indicate the inductance charged to 63 per cent of its full value.

The effect which the time constant of a circuit has on a squarewave or pulse depends on the nature of the circuit. At A of Fig. 1-8, for instance, a resistor (R_1) is shown in series with the signal which is to be applied to an amplifier, and the capacitor (C_1) is shown from the signal-carrying wire to ground. Such a capacity may not be a physical unit, but could be present in circuit wiring or between other signal-carrying components such as vacuum tubes (or transistors) and ground. If the time constant of resistor R_1 and capacitor C_1 is long, pulse distortion will result as shown at A. With the capacitor of a fairly large value, it would take an appreciable interval of time for a full charge to build up. Hence, when the pulse is applied to the in-

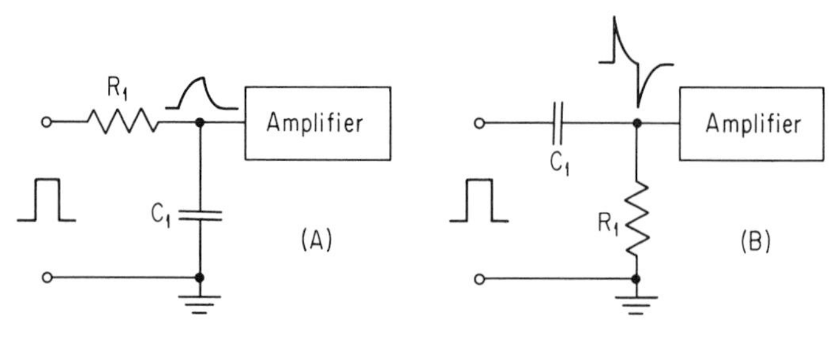

Fig. 1-8. Pulse distortion

put, the sudden rise of voltage representative of the leading edge will not be felt at the amplifier immediately, because current flow through the capacitor is high initially and the voltage build-up is gradual as shown. During the flat-top portion of the pulse, the long time constant of the circuit results in the gradual rise of voltage. Before five time constants have been reached, the flat top of the pulse ends and the trailing edge of the pulse arrives at the input. Now the voltage across the capacitor will start to decline, but again it will follow the time-constant curves. In consequence, the waveform which appears at the amplifier is a distorted version of the pulse applied at the input of the circuit.

The long-time constant network composed of R_1 and C_1 at A of Fig. 1-8 is often referred to as an *integrator* circuit. It can be considered as a low-pass type of filter network, because it will pass the low frequencies through to the amplifier, but will shunt the higher-frequency components by virtue of the low reactance of capacitor C_1. Hence, the high-frequency components of the pulse are diminished because of the low reactance of C_1, but the lower-frequency components of the pulse find a higher reactance for C_1 and are not diminished to as great an extent as by the higher-frequency components. To eliminate the undesired effects of integration in a circuit of this type, the time constant must be shortened. If stray or shunt capacities are present in the circuit, the obvious solution would be to reduce the capacitance value of C_1 and minimize any other shunt capacities as much as possible. This means separating wires from the chassis as much as possible and also dressing away signal-carrying wires from other wires or metallic objects which can act as a capacity to ground between the signal-carrying wire and the chassis.

When the positions of R_1 and C_1 are reversed as shown at *B* of Fig. 1-8, and unit values are such as to produce a short time constant, distortion again occurs. This distortion, however, differs from that in the circuit shown at A. For the network composed of C_1 and R_1 at B of Fig. 1-8, capacitor C_1 could be the coupling capacitor existing between amplifier stages, and R_1 the usual input resistor. If the capacitance of C_1 is insufficient, the short time constant which results will have an adverse effect on the pulse waveform as shown. When the leading edge of the pulse occurs, the sharp rise in voltage immediately charges capacitor C_1 to its full value and in consequence there is a sharp flow of current through R_1 and then an abrupt decline of current through the latter resistor as capacitor C_1 reaches its full charge value. Then, for the remaining interval of the flat top of the pulse, no current flows through R_1 for the signal, because C_1 is fully charged. When the trailing edge arrives at the input, the voltage of the input pulse signal declines abruptly to zero. Capacitor C_1 will then discharge through resistor R_1, and the current flow through the latter is now in a direction opposite to that which occurred originally. Thus, the short burst of current through R_1 establishes a sharp negative spike of signal at the amplifier input. Consequently for every pulse which is applied to this circuit, there will be a double-spike signal applied to the amplifier.

The short-time-constant circuit shown at B is often referred to as a *differentiating* circuit. It can also be considered as a high-pass filter, because the reactance of C_1 is low for the higher-frequency components of a pulse and hence will pass such components readily through the amplifier. For the lower-frequency components of a pulse, however, the reactance of C_1 is much higher and hence the lower-frequency signal components will be diminished and will not pass through as readily to the amplifier. To prevent differentiating of the pulse and the resultant distortion, the value of capacitor C_1 must be increased to lengthen the time constant. With a sufficiently high value at C_1, there will be a low enough reactance present for the various frequency components of the pulse so that virtually all of them will be passed without undue attenuation. On occasion, differentiating is deliberately employed in industrial electronics in order to procure the sharp spikes which result from this circuit. This type of waveform is useful where the leading edges only are desired for triggering and gating purposes.

Sawtooth waveforms are also composed of the fundamental frequency plus harmonic components. Losses of higher-frequency components will result in distortion of the sawtooth signal and reduction of the sharp changes from maximum to minimum amplitude. To prevent such distortion, just as in the case of squarewaves and pulses, circuits must be utilized which will pass all the frequency components which make up the waveform.

VACUUM AND GAS-FILLED TUBES

One of the most common signal-handling devices is the vacuum tube. It comes in a variety of shapes and sizes and is used for converting a-c to d-c (rectifier), for amplification of a signal, for the generation scillator), as well as for the gating and switching of

n tube contains a cathode which is brought to a high
that electrons are emitted (thermionic emission).
(negative charge) are usually caused to flow to a
) by making the latter positive to take advantage of the
basic electronic principle of the attraction between unlike poles or charges. Another variety of tube is the gas-filled type, which has special applications as detailed in subsequent chapters. Both the vacuum tubes and the gas-filled tubes come in many shapes and sizes as shown in Fig. 1-9. Some have a glass envelope, some metal (which is grounded for shielding purposes), and others are composed of both metal and ceramic materials. Typical of the latter is that shown in Fig. 1-10, which has a height of 4.75 inches and can produce a plate output power in excess of 1500 watts.

Another metal-ceramic tube is a special type developed by RCA known as the *Nuvistor.* Containing neither mica nor glass, the tube

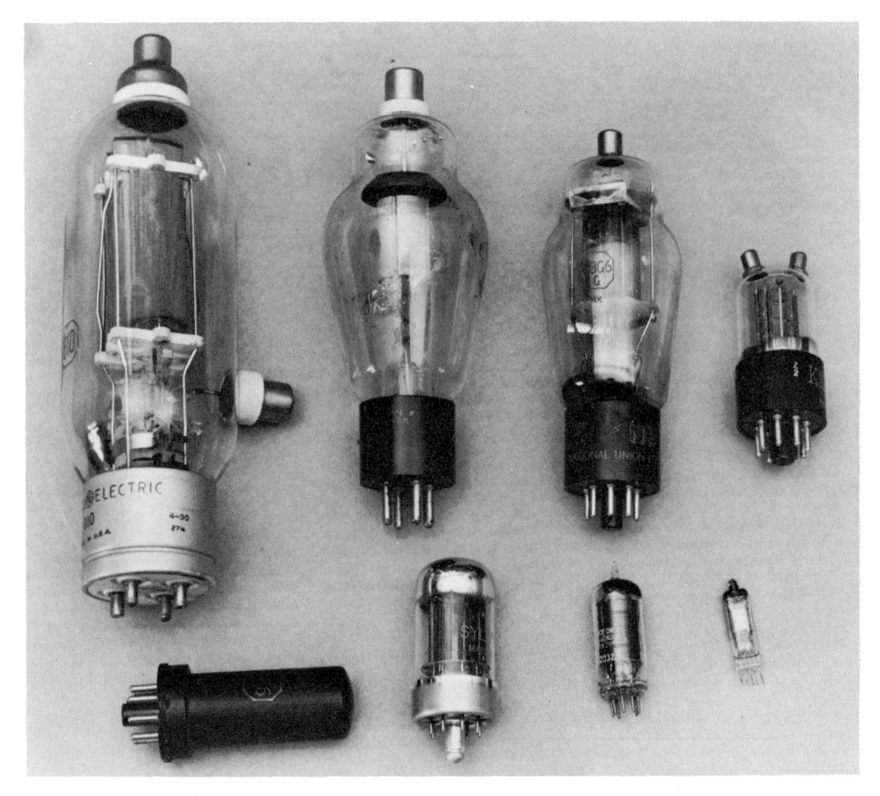

Fig. 1-9. Various tube types

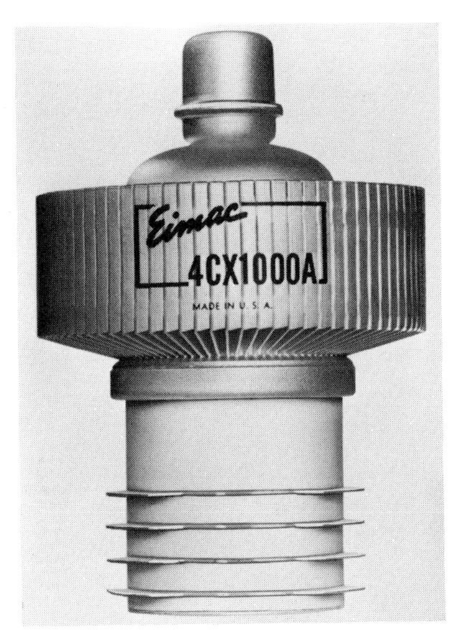

Fig. 1-10. Eimac 4CX100A ceramic power tetrode

is high-temperature processed in brazing and vacuum-exhaust furnaces to reduce residual gases which would affect tube performance. The result is a rugged tube able to withstand extremely high temperatures (it continues to function up to 660°F, and down to −320°F). Because of its ability to perform under abnormal environmental conditions, its applications include automation, electronic computers, and industrial electronics.

The two-element tubes are called *diodes* and consist of a cathode and an anode. The cathode is the active electron-emitting element and can be directly or indirectly heated. In the latter case, even though a separate filament is employed, the tube is still a diode. The *triode* consists of a cathode, grid, and anode; the *tetrodes* and *pentodes* have additional grid elements. Many multi-element tubes are also employed for specific circuit applications. Typical symbols are shown in Fig. 1-11. The gas-filled tube symbol is identified by a dot as shown.

TRANSISTORS

Transistors are solid-state devices having no anode plate or grid and cathode wires and are formed from germanium or silicon, with the addition of other elements to produce what are designated as P (positive) and N (negative) sections, as more fully described in the next chapter. Such sections are chemically bonded together to form P-N or N-P combinations for diode applications, and P-N-P or N-P-N for

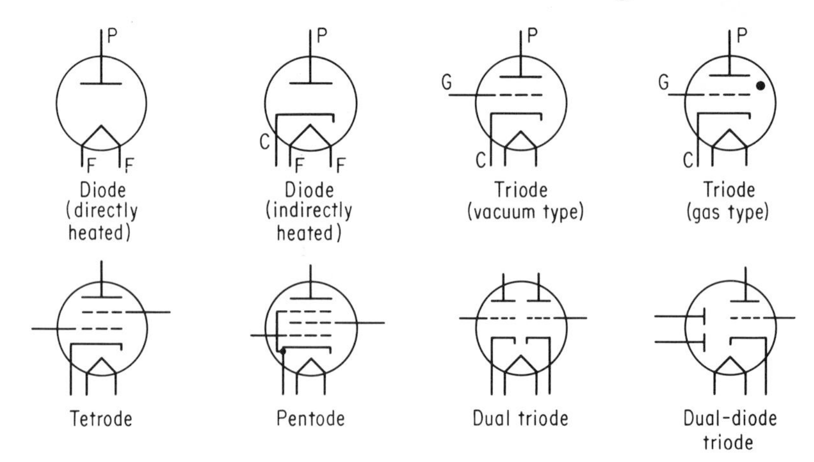

Fig. 1-11. Tube symbols

triode applications. Compared to vacuum tubes, the transistors require much less power for operation in either an oscillator or an amplifier and, comparatively, are much smaller. They are fairly rugged and have an exceptionally long life, although they are surpassed by some vacuum tubes with respect to signal-power handling and high-frequency operation. Because of their advantages with respect to size and operational power, and because they can perform all the functions of vacuum tubes with respect to the generation and amplification of signals, they are extensively employed in computers for automation and in other industrial electronic applications. (Symbols and basic operational theory are given in the next chapter, and special types of transistors are covered in subsequent chapters.)

SOLID-STATE DIODES

Diodes of various types are frequently employed in industrial electronic circuitry, and the symbol for the solid-state diode differs from the vacuum-type, just as the transistor symbol differs from the vacuum-tube type. (See Fig. 1-12.) The usefulness of the diode lies in its ability to pass current in one direction while limiting current flow in the other direction. In a vacuum tube the condition is ideal; the tube will pass current in one direction (low resistance) but not in the other (infinite resistance). In the solid-state diodes, however, there is appreciably less than

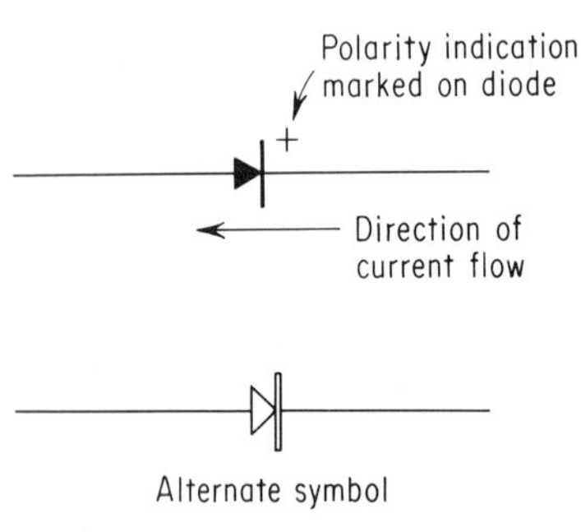

Fig. 1-12. Solid-state diode symbols

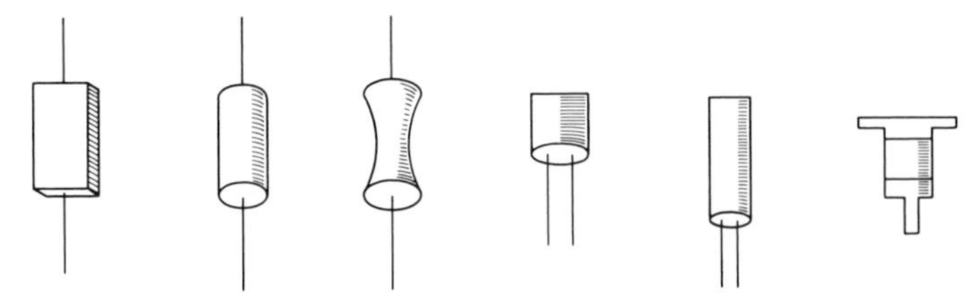

Fig. 1-13. Typical low-power diode shapes

infinite resistance in the reverse direction and hence the device is not perfect with respect to passing current in only one direction. There is sufficient difference, however, between the amount of current passing in its low-resistance direction (forward) and that which passes in its high-resistance direction (reverse), to permit extensive applications in various branches of electronics. Typical diodes are illustrated in Fig. 1-13.

Germanium Diode

Small germanium diodes are used primarily to handle low-current, signal-type waveforms such as encountered in the detectors of AM, FM, and television receivers, and in some switching and logical gate circuitry of computers. The germanium diode is in the same semiconductor class as the transistor, being composed of the basic germanium element and chemically altered by the addition of another element to form a P-N junction.

Fig. 1-14. Selenium rectifiers

Selenium Diode

Selenium diodes have been used extensively as rectifiers in power supplies for converting a-c to d-c (the principles of which are described in Chapter 6). The selenium diodes are made up of stacks of individual rectifier plates. The latter can be copper, aluminum, or magnesium, on one side of which is deposited a crystalline semiconductor layer of selenium. Such diodes have a high internal capacitance and hence are limited in their usefulness to lower frequencies. They have been put to extensive use in radio and television receiver power supplies where several-layer, small types handle several hundred milliamperes of current. They have also been used in battery chargers, where they handle several amperes of current. Many multi-layer, larger types have also been employed in industrial electronic applications, handling currents up to several thousand amperes. Typical selenium diodes are shown in Fig. 1-14. Since the advent of the silicon diode with its many advantages, the selenium diode has been used less frequently in modern equipment.

Silicon Diode

Silicon diodes have also been manufactured in miniature sizes for low-current signal-handling in radios, computers, and other electronic circuits. Most of these are similar in basic construction to the germanium diodes discussed earlier. For handling power from low to very high values, the newer-type silicon junction semiconductor diode is extensively employed in various branches of industrial electronics. Besides its application in rectification, it is also utilized in regulation, switching, and other applications, to be discussed later in this book.

Typical silicon diodes are shown in Fig. 1-15. On the larger types a threaded mounting stud is provided so that the unit can be bolted to the chassis. The flared flange present in some types forms what is known as a *heat sink,* and this heat-dissipating principle is also used in some power transistors. The flat section of the flare is pressed against the metal chassis when the unit is bolted to the latter, and thus the heat which is generated is drained off. With the heat sink, semiconductors can operate at higher current ratings.

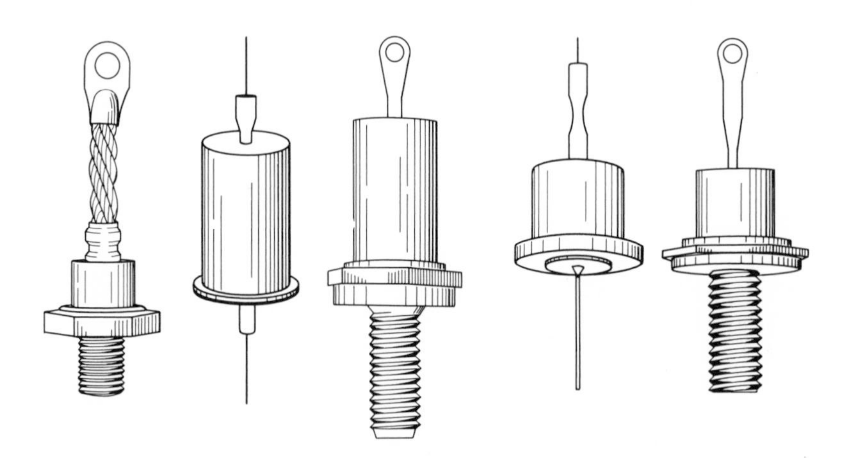

Fig. 1-15. Silicon diodes

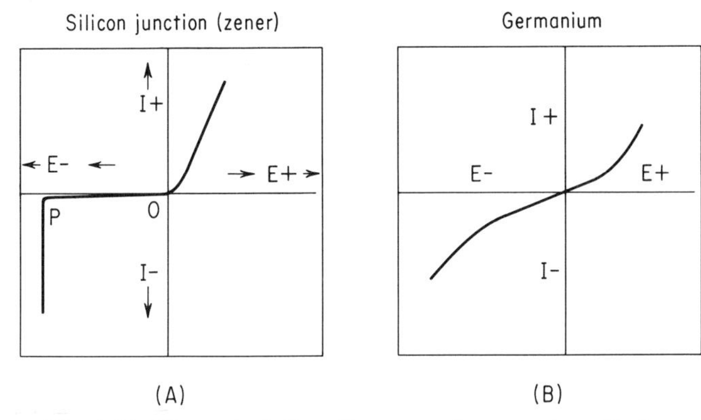

Fig. 1-16. Characteristics of zener and germanium diodes

For comparable ratings, the silicon rectifiers are much smaller than the selenium types, are able to pass much higher currents, and have greater efficiency. The reverse current flow in the silicon types is so low that it compares favorably with the ideal characteristics of the vacuum tube. In low-current silicon diodes the reverse current is only a few *microamperes,* whereas in the higher-current types it passes only several milliamperes in the reverse direction, while conducting hundreds of amperes in the forward direction.

An important feature of the silicon junction diode is the unusual breakdown characteristic of the unit. This is shown at A of Fig. 1-16. On the forward bias side the silicon diode behaves in a fashion similar to the germanium diode shown at the right at B, though with lower resistance and a much higher current-passing capability as the voltage is increased. When reverse voltage is applied (starting at the zero point) the resistance of the unit is high, and for the smaller units only a few microamperes of current flow. As the reverse voltage is increased, only a slight conduction change occurs (in contrast to the pronounced change evident at B for the germanium diode).

As the reverse voltage is gradually increased, a critical point is reached where suddenly the resistance drops to a low value and current shoots up from a few microamperes to several milliamperes (point P on the graph). Despite the current increase, the voltage drop across the diode remains practically the same as before the breakdown, making the device extremely useful for voltage regulation, as illustrated in Chapter 6, and for other applications subsequently described.

The breakdown is not damaging, as would be the case with an ordinary germanium diode, transistor, or vacuum tube. The breakdown occurs because at a certain amplitude of applied reverse voltage the latter is sufficient to penetrate the diode's internal semiconductor barrier (explained more fully in the next chapter) and the device becomes a conductor in the reverse direction. After removal of the reverse voltage the internal barrier region reforms itself.

The breakdown point is known as the *zener* region, and this breakdown point can be regulated closely during manufacture by control of the resistivity of the silicon structure. The zener point can be set at one or two volts or several hundred volts as required. Silicon diodes which are processed so as to have a specific zener point are known as *zener diodes.* In ordinary silicon rectifiers, the zener point is made sufficiently high to be beyond the peak inverse voltage at which the unit is rated. (The peak inverse voltage is the maximum amplitude of the voltage which has reverse polarity characteristics, that is, inverse to the voltage causing normal conduction.)

SILICON-CONTROLLED RECTIFIER

The silicon-controlled rectifier differs from the ordinary silicon diode by virtue of its combining some of the characteristics of both the solid-state diode and the transistor. It has a special "gate" lead placed beside the usual cathode lead and hence has three terminals instead of the usual two for the normal diode. Fig. 1-17 illustrates the General Electric C35 silicon-controlled rectifier. The threaded terminal is the anode, and this section is bolted to the chassis, with the flange acting as a heat sink. This particular unit has a width of slightly over a half-inch, and a height of about one and one-half inches. It will handle voltages up to 400 and load currents up to 16 amperes; in switching circuits it will operate at speeds between 10 and 20 microseconds. Thus, this device in rectification and switching applications is far superior to ordinary solid-state diodes and transistors.

Fig. 1-17. GE C35 silicon diode

The silicon-controlled rectifier has characteristics similar to the gas-tube thyratron (discussed in Chapter 8); hence a signal applied to the gate will cause conduction, and the latter continues even after the signal is removed. In Fig. 1-18 the comparative construction of the silicon diode (at A) and the silicon-controlled rectifier (at B) is

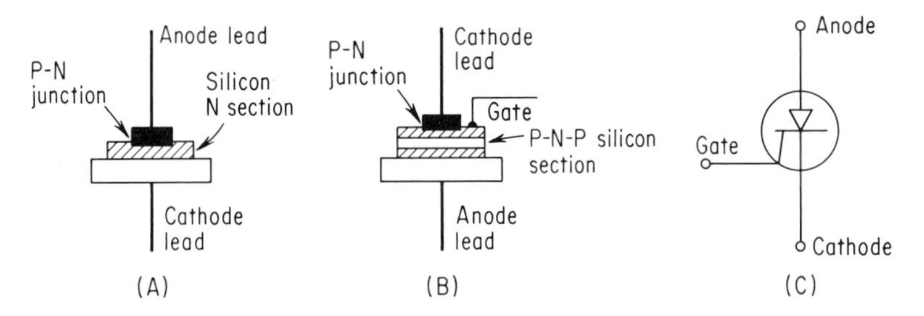

Fig. 1-18. Silicon versus silicon-controlled rectifier

illustrated. The symbol used by GE is shown at C. Additional data are given in Chapter 8.

The RCA and Bell Laboratories version of this solid-state device is known as the *Thyristor*; the Westinghouse unit is called the *Trinistor.*

TUNNEL DIODE

In 1958 the Japanese scientist Leo Esaki published a report entitled "New Phenomenon in Narrow Germanium P-N Junctions." * This report opened the door to the development of a new semiconductor diode device, which in many respects is superior to both the transistor and vacuum tube in circuit applications such as amplifiers, oscillators, switching devices, bistable circuits, and detectors. This device is known as the *tunnel diode* and it is capable of operating at much higher signal frequencies than the transistor. In addition, the unit is considerably smaller and the associated circuit is simple. In switching devices the tunnel diode is over one hundred times faster than some transistor types and at the same time requires less operating power. Also, the tunnel diode is not susceptible to temperature changes and hence, unlike the transistor, its operating characteristics remain stable during wide variations in temperature. Either germanium or silicon can be employed for fabricating the tunnel diode. Either type will operate at temperatures considerably higher than silicon diodes or germanium and silicon transistors. The silicon tunnel diode operates at temperatures slightly over 600°F. Unlike transistors, the tunnel diode resists the adverse effects of nuclear radiation and hence finds important applications in this field. Radiation affects semiconductor diodes and transistors by altering their internal resistance and increasing the inherent noise level. Such damage does not occur for the tunnel diode, and in this respect it is superior to transistors by a ratio of 1000 to 1.

* *Physics Review,* Vol. 109, p. 603

The tunnel diode derives its name from the so-called "tunnel effect" which occurs between the P-N junction. In normal semiconductor diodes an internal potential barrier exists within the junction which has a very high resistance to current flow in the reverse direction. In the tunnel diode the barrier is made extra thin by doping with other elements in excess of the amount used for transistors. The consequence is that an electric particle approaching the barrier suddenly disappears and then reappears virtually instantly (the transfer is at the speed of light) at the other side of the barrier. This can be likened to a situation where the electric particle doesn't have sufficient energy to overcome and penetrate the barrier, but rather "tunnels" beneath the barrier. Because the electric charge which tunnels through the barrier does so at approximately 186,000 miles per second, the operational characteristics of the tunnel diode are much faster than the transistor, where electric charges move through barriers at a comparatively slow speed. Hence, the tunnel diode operates at frequencies ranging up to thousands of megacycles.

As compared to ordinary diodes, the tunnel diode can amplify because it has a negative-resistance characteristic, to be more fully explained in the next chapter.

HALL-EFFECT DEVICES

E. H. Hall, a Harvard University physicist, in 1879 discovered an effect which has been named after him and is known as the *Hall effect.* The Hall effect relates to the behavior of current flow under the influence of a magnetic field perpendicular to the conductor. The basic function is illustrated in Fig. 1-19 where a conductive slab is shown. In the absence of a magnetic field, the electrons which constitute

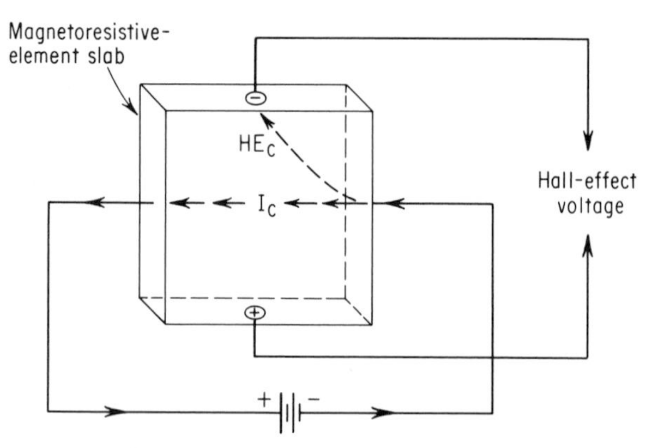

Fig. 1-19. Principles of the Hall effect

current flow progress through the conductor in a steady, straight, conventional flow; this constitutes what is referred to as the *controlled current.* When a magnetic field is now applied so that the magnetic lines of force are at right angles to the slab, the electrons are forced aside as shown in the illustration. This results in an excess of electrons on that side (negative charge), while on the other side there is a deficiency of electrons creating a positive charge. Thus, the magnetic field is instrumental in creating a potential difference across the edges of the slab opposite to the potential difference applied to cause the controlled current flow. Potentially, this phenomenon has many possible applications in the measurement of the strength of magnetic fields, in measuring devices, and in industry, electronic, and computer applications.

The degree to which the Hall effect occurs depends on the so-called *mobility* of the conduction material. With ordinary conductors the Hall effect is not very pronounced and the voltages set up are of insufficient amplitude to be of much use. With semiconductors, however, the Hall effect is considerably higher and so are the voltages produced, because of the greater mobility characteristic. This is particularly the case with intermetallic components such as indium arsenide and indium antimonide. These components have magnetoresistive characteristics which have permitted practical application of the Hall effect, and in consequence such devices are now available commercially. A basic magnetic amplifier using the Hall effect is illustrated in Chapter 11.

THERMISTOR

A thermistor is a resistor which is thermally sensitive; that is, its resistance value changes with temperature changes. It is basically a nonlinear resistor and is produced in various shapes and sizes. Some appear as small discs, others as small rods resembling resistors, and sub-miniature models have also been produced.

Most resistance elements undergo a slight change in resistance as the element heats, but the thermistor has a considerable resistance change for temperature variations, hence is useful in applications such as temperature control, relay systems, measuring devices, and others as described later. Thermistors are available having either negative temperature-coefficient characteristics or positive temperature-coefficient characteristics. The former have long been employed in series tube circuits of radio and television receivers. With the tube filaments in series, their over-all resistance is lower when cool than after they rise in temperature. When the voltage is first applied, current rises to an abnormal value before the tubes heat up and they may be damaged or have their life shortened. The thermistor is employed in series with a filament string and it has a high resistance when cool. Thus when the voltage is first applied to the string, the high resistance of the thermistor prevents overload. After the heaters of the tubes come up to temperature, their resistance increases and at the same time the resistance of the thermistor decreases to balance out the resistance level. The modern thermistor employs the semiconductor principle, and though it is a two-terminal solid-state device similar to the germanium or silicon diode, it is not a rectifier. Hence, unlike the solid-state diodes, it can be employed in either d-c or a-c circuitry with no regard for polarity.

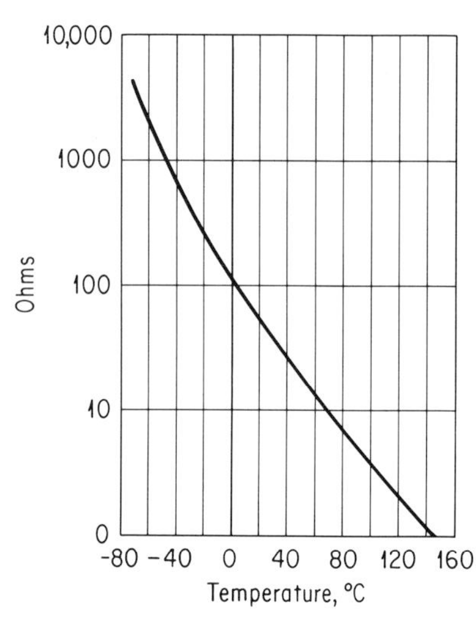

Fig. 1-20. Non-linear characteristics of a thermister

During the initial current flow through the thermistor, there is a lag while the temperature of the thermistor rises. Thus, there is a definite time interval between the application of a voltage and the time when the maximum resistance change occurs. This factor makes the thermistor useful in time-delay applications. A typical use is the time-delay relay illustrated in Chapter 8.

Depending on the type, the resistance of a thermistor may change with as high a ratio as 2500 to 1 for temperature variations between minus 50 to plus 150° C. The resistance change is not linear; that is, it is not a straight-line affair, as can be seen for the curve of a typical thermistor in Fig. 1-20.

Review Questions for Chapter 1

1. What are the basic characteristics of a sinewave type of signal?
2. Briefly explain the factors relating to peak voltage and effective voltage, and explain how each can be calculated by the use of a formula.
3. What is meant by *reactance* and *impedance*. How do these differ from *resistance?*
4. What causes an out-of-phase condition to occur with respect to the voltage and current in a-c? How does this affect power?
5. Briefly explain how harmonics make up the waveshape of a squarewave.

6. Compare the characteristics of a pulse with those of a squarewave. What is meant by the *duty cycle?*
7. Briefly explain how the *average power* of a pulse train can be ascertained by use of the duty cycle.
8. Show by waveform drawings the effects of both low- and high-frequency losses on a squarewave.
9. Briefly explain what is meant by the *time constant* of a circuit. Also explain what is meant by the *universal time constant chart.*
10. Explain briefly the characteristics of an integrator circuit and a differentiating circuit.
11. What circuit characteristics are necessary to pass squarewave or pulsewave forms?
12. Draw the symbols for three different types of vacuum tubes and define all the elements.
13. List the relative advantages and disadvantages of transistors versus vacuum tubes.
14. What is a heat sink and where is it used?
15. Briefly summarize the basic characteristics of a zener diode.
16. Summarize the basic aspects of the silicon-controlled rectifier.
17. Summarize the general characteristics of the tunnel diode.
18. Explain briefly the Hall effect.
19. Compare the characteristics of the thermistor with that of an ordinary resistor and describe one application for the thermistor.

2

Basic Amplifiers

INTRODUCTION

This chapter is a summary of the practical aspects of signal-voltage and signal-power amplifiers as related to industrial electronics, including a comparison of the vacuum-tube and the transistor types. Basic amplifier theory has been held to a bare minimum, since expanded theory is readily available in the numerous books on fundamentals of electricity and electronics.

Specialized amplifiers such as the magnetic and dielectric are covered in detail in a later chapter.

CLASSES OF AMPLIFIERS

Several classifications are applied to amplifiers, one of which is the alphabetical designation that indicates the operational characteristics of the circuit. The chart which follows shows various classes of amplifiers, consisting of Class A, Class AB_1, Class AB_2, Class B, and Class C. The primary factor which influences the alphabetical class of the amplifier is the bias which is applied. In the case of vacuum tubes, the bias potential is the negative voltage which is applied to the grid so that the latter is negative with respect to the cathode. With transistors, the bias refers to the potentials applied to the input circuits (more clearly illustrated later in this chapter).

AMPLIFIER CLASS APPLICATIONS

RECOMMENDED FOR:

Amplifier class	Audio voltage amplification	Audio power amplification	Radio-frequency voltage amplification	Radio-frequency power amplification
A	Yes	Yes	Yes	Yes
AB_1	No	Yes	No	Yes
AB_2	No	Yes*	No	Yes
B	No	Yes*	No	Yes
C	No	No	No	Yes

* Dual-tube operation.

The circuit for a specific vacuum-tube amplifier differs from that of its transistor counterpart, though if given proper bias potentials both the vacuum-tube circuit and the transistor circuit exhibit similar operational characteristics. Thus, the factors discussed for either the vacuum-tube or the transistor amplifiers will apply to both in this chapter.

The Class A amplifier is suitable for low-frequency signals such as audio or pulse waveforms as well as for radio-frequency signals such as short wave, television, or frequency modulation. The Class A amplifier, in the vacuum-tube version, has a bias which makes the grid sufficiently negative so that its characteristics lie between the zero bias point and the cutoff bias point as shown at A of Fig. 2-1. Here, t_c indicates the tube characteristic. The fixed bias level is indicated by e_g, and the applied signal is indicated by e_s.The average current which flows in the tube in the absence of the signal is indicated by i_p, and the signal current which flows is indicated by i_s. For Class A amplification, the bias is set on the linear or straight-line section of the t_c characteristic curve. Hence, the signal which is applied to the grid will vary above and below the bias level and will also operate on the straight-line portion of the tube. Such operation, although not of maximum efficiency, does provide for good fidelity of signal reproduction; hence the class A amplifier is employed extensively for audio or other signal amplification where distortion must be held at a mini-

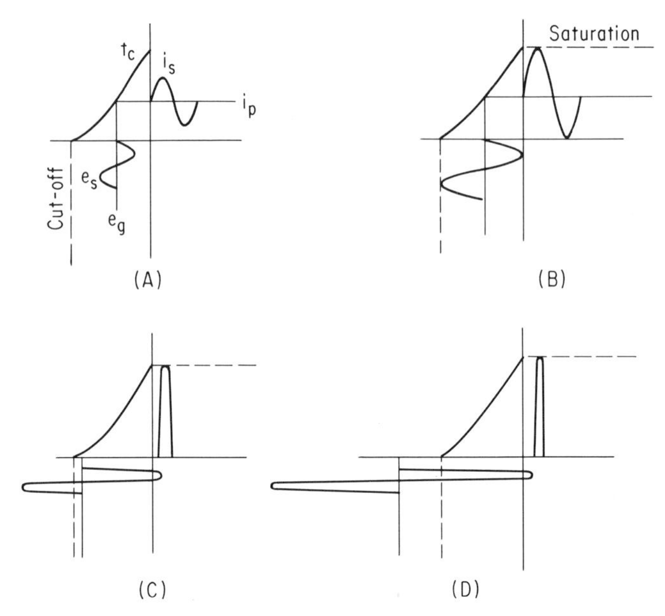

Fig. 2-1. Classes of amplifiers

mum. Efficiency depends on the amplitude of the signal input and the exact bias setting, and averages between 15 and 20 per cent.

Class AB_1 operation is shown at B of Fig. 2-1. This class provides more signal output and operates at higher efficiency than Class A, but distortion is increased somewhat because the input signal e_s has an amplitude sufficient to run near the zero-bias as well as near the cutoff-bias regions of the tube. Usually, the bias is at a higher negative value for Class AB_1 than for Class A. Efficiency is usually slightly over 20 per cent.

For Class AB_2 operation, the bias is increased somewhat over Class AB_1 operation; the signal makes a greater excursion above and below the bias reference level, usually running slightly beyond the cutoff point and also beyond the tube zero-bias level. In consequence, distortion is much greater although efficiency may be over 25 per cent. The subscript "2" indicates that the grid signal is sufficient to overcome the bias on the positive excursions and causes the grid to become positive for a brief interval.

Class B operation provides an efficiency well above 40 or 50 per cent but the distortion factor is much higher. For audio applications, two tubes are necessary to minimize the distortion which would result from use of a single tube. The characteristics for the Class B amplifier are shown at C of Fig. 2-1. The bias is almost at cutoff, and the exact location is chosen by theoretically projecting the straight-line portion of the characteristic curve to the horizontal base line. This is sometimes referred to as *projected cutoff*. In Class B operation, only a positive alternation of the input signal causes plate-current flow as shown at C. In consequence, two tubes are needed to reproduce a full cycle in audio amplification. For radio-frequency amplification two tubes can be used, although one will also function because of the resonant effects of the flywheel circuits which produce the second or missing alternation of the cycle automatically (discussed more fully later on). Since the plate current changes from almost the zero plate-current level to saturation for only one alternation, efficiency of the Class C amplifier is much higher than the others previously mentioned. Only the Class C amplifier has a higher order of efficiency than the Class B amplifier.

The Class C amplifier is useful only for radio-frequency amplification, since only a portion of one alternation is instrumental in causing plate-current flow. Only where resonant circuits are utilized to reproduce a full sinewave is this amplifier useful. The characteristics of this amplifier are shown at D of Fig. 2-1. Note that the bias is well beyond cutoff (usually approximately two and one-half times cutoff). Because of the high negative bias, plate current starts to flow only after the positive alternation of the input signal has reached sufficient amplitude to overcome the cutoff bias level. Plate current flows from the zero level to the saturation level, and because only a portion of the input signal causes plate-current flow, the efficiency of this amplifier is very high, ranging up to 95 per cent in a well-designed circuit. As with Class AB_2 and B, the input signal drives the grid positive, hence grid current flows. In consequence, the grid consumes power and the grid signal which is applied must be able to furnish electric energy to the circuits; whereas in Class A and AB_1 virtually no power is utilized in the grid circuit and a grid voltage is sufficient to cause amplification.

BASIC CIRCUITRY

Basic amplifier circuits are shown in Fig. 2-2. Both are Class A, but they are sometimes known as *grounded-cathode amplifiers* because the cathode of the vacuum tube is either connected directly to ground or is at *signal ground*. At A, a triode, high-vacuum-type amplifier is shown in its basic form. The input signal is applied across the terminals shown, and coupled across the grid and cathode circuit via the coupling capacitor C_1. Resistor R_1 is sometimes referred to as the *grid leak* since it will discharge an accumulation of electrons which may pile up on the capacitor for large signal voltages. The grid is made negative with respect to the cathode by use of the bias potential B_1,

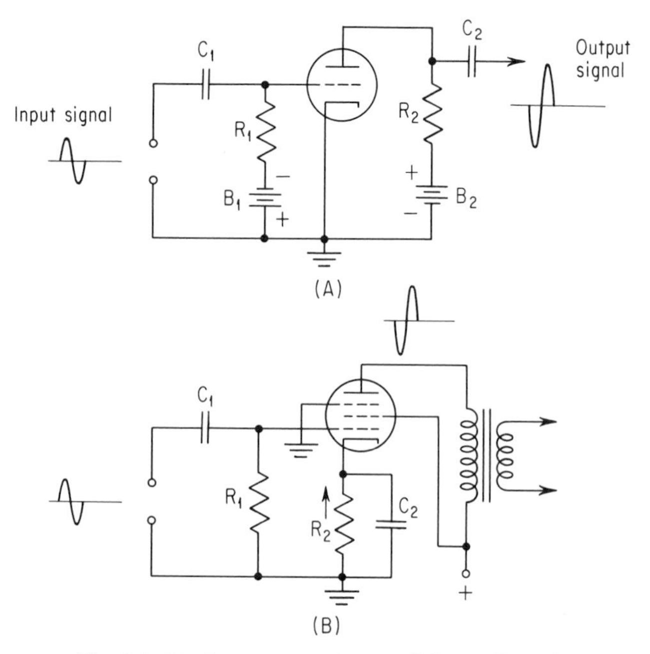

Fig. 2-2. Basic vacuum tube amplifiers (Class A)

in the form of a battery or power supply. The bias, as mentioned previously, establishes the operating point around which the input signal varies. The fixed bias causes a certain amount of current to flow constantly. For a positive alternation of the input signal, the bias level is effectively reduced and more current flows through the tube. Current flow is from plate toward the positive section of the B battery (B_2) and this establishes a voltage drop across resistor R_2. When the current through R_2 changes, it is coupled via capacitor C_2 and to a subsequent stage or device. When plate current increases, the voltage drop across R_2 also increases, and because it is in a negative direction, a negative alternation of the amplified version of this signal occurs. (*Note:* Throughout this text the direction of current flow will be considered to be from *minus* to *plus* to conform to modern electronic theory, as distinguished from the older "conventional" theory of current flow from *plus* to *minus.*)

For a negative alternation of the input signal, the bias increases and less current flows through the tube. The voltage drop across R_2 declines, and the signal becomes less negative (more positive) thus producing the positive alternation of the output signal. The signal-voltage variations across R_2 are above and below the fixed voltage drop which occurs during the absence of a signal at the grid. Hence, signal-voltage variations across R_2 are in the form of a variation of the d-c potential. The signal coupled by virtue of capacitor C_2, however, is a-c in its characteristics because C_2 will pass only the a-c portion of the signal and will not pass the d-c level.

The amplifier shown at A is essentially a voltage amplifier and will give an amplified signal-voltage version of the input-signal voltage. The output signal will be 180 degrees out of phase with the input signal as shown at A. If the amplifier is well designed and operating on the linear portion of the tube, there will be a minimum of distortion with respect to the input versus the output signal.

At B of Fig. 2-2 another version of the Class A amplifier is illustrated. This circuit also couples the signal across grid and cathode by use of a coupling capacitor C_1. The grid leak in this circuit goes directly from the grid of the tube to ground. Bias is established by use of a cathode resistor and bypass capacitor. The plate-current flow through the cathode resistor R_2 is in the direction shown by the arrow, and in consequence a polarity of voltage is established across this resistor as indicated. Since the grid of the tube is placed at ground potential by resistor R_1 (in Class A there is no grid-current flow, hence no voltage drop across R_1), the grid is negative with respect to the cathode by a value established by the voltage drop across R_2. Since the plate-current flow through R_2 will vary in accordance with the signal variations present between grid and cathode, the bias would also vary at the signal rate. Hence, a bypass capacitor, C_2, is placed across the cathode resistor to minimize bias variations.

The amplifier shown at B uses a pentode tube, wherein a screen grid and suppressor grid are present in addition to the normal control grid. A pentode tube could also have been used for the voltage amplifier shown at A, or a triode tube could be used in place of the pentode tube shown at B. The pentode tubes provide a greater degree of amplification and contribute to the over-all efficiency of the circuit. An output transformer is utilized in the circuit shown at B, to minimize the large voltage drop and signal-energy loss which would occur across a fixed resistor. With the low d-c resistance of the transformer, the amplifier can furnish signal power. As with the amplifier shown at A, there is a phase reversal for the signal across the tube. The relative phase of the signal produced at the output terminals of the transformer secondary can be chosen to suit, since a complete phase reversal can be obtained by transposition of the output leads.

A Class B amplifier is illustrated at A of Fig. 2-3. Here, two tubes are utilized for the Class B stage, V_2 and V_3. Vacuum tube V_1, shown in partial schematic form, is a typical Class A amplifier of the type shown at B of Fig. 2-2. The push-pull V_2 and V_3 tubes contribute greater power output and reduce distortion over that available from a single output tube. The dual-tube (push-pull) application can also

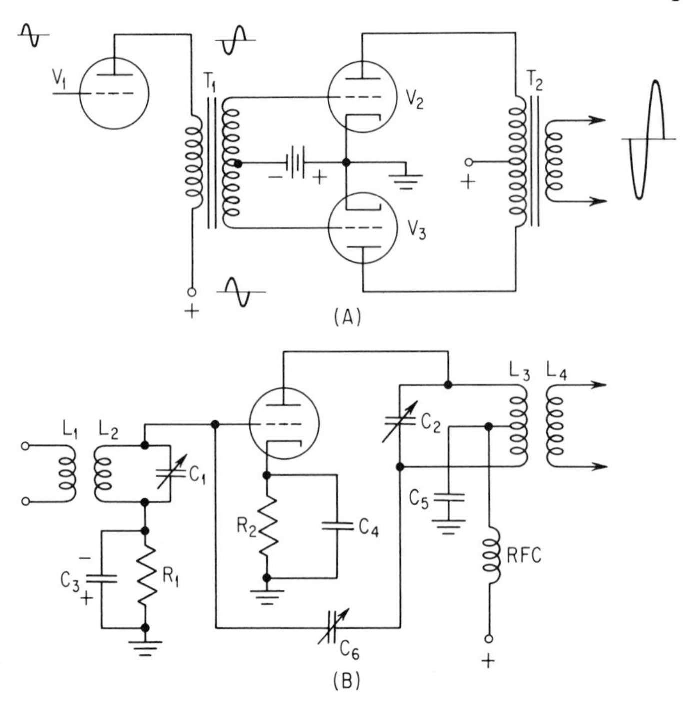

Fig. 2-3. Class B and Class C amplifiers

be utilized for the previous power amplifier shown at B of Fig. 2-2. For Class B operation, a bias potential is applied to both grids of V_2 and V_3 so that tubes are operating near the cutoff value. The type of bias which can be obtained by use of a cathode resistor is not employed for Class B, because of the wide variations in plate-current flow with and without a signal. With no input signal applied to the grids of V_2 and V_3, only a low-value idling current flows through the tubes. When a positive signal alternation appears at either tube, however, high values of current flow through the tube.

For push-pull operation, it is necessary to apply to the grid of one push-pull tube a signal which is 180 degrees out of phase with the signal applied to the other tube. One method for accomplishing this is by use of a tapped transformer as shown at A of Fig. 2-3. Here, the secondary of transformer T_1 has a center tap which is applied to the negative section of the bias battery or bias-voltage source. The other two leads go to the respective grids of V_2 and V_3 as shown. Thus, when the signal is applied to the primary of the transformer by vacuum tube V_1, the signal which appears across the secondary will be split into two sections, the upper signal having a phase relationship which is 180 degrees different from that at the bottom of the transformer secondary. Thus, the necessary phase difference for push-pull operation is present at the grids of V_2 and V_3. In Class A operation both tubes would amplify simultaneously and contribute to the final amplified version. In Class B, however, the tubes operate alternately.

For instance, for the waveforms shown at A, the first alternation of the signal applied to V_2 is negative-going. Consequently, V_2 is cut off, since a negative-going signal increases bias. The first alternation of this signal applied to the grid of V_3, however, is positive-going, hence the bias is reduced, V_3 conducts, and one alternation of signal current flows through the primary of the output transformer T_2. For the second alternation of the signal appearing at the grid of V_2, a positive signal is present and the bias is reduced. Now, V_2 conducts and a plate-current change is felt through the primary transformer T_2. For the second alternation of the signal applied to V_3, however, a negative-going alternation is present which drives the grid into the cutoff region, and V_3 does not conduct. Thus, for Class B, each tube contributes one alternation of the amplified output signal, and the resultant is the amplified sinewave signal shown at the secondary of A in Fig. 2-3.

At B of Fig. 2-3, a Class C amplifier is shown. This is also a power amplifier suitable for r-f amplification only, as mentioned earlier. Here, the input is applied via the transformer from L_1 to L_2. Inductance L_2, in conjunction with capacitor C_1, form a resonant circuit which is tuned to the frequency of the incoming signal. Capacitor C_3 and resistor R_1 comprise the grid capacitor and grid leak. Because any positive polarity of the incoming signal is sufficient in amplitude to drive the grid positive, grid current flows down through L_2 and charges capacitor C_3 with a polarity as shown. The latter, during negative alternations of the signal, discharges across R_1, thus establishing the cutoff bias for the Class C amplifier. Capacitor C_3 filters the ripple component. Although bias beyond cutoff can be obtained in this manner, there would be no bias in the absence of a signal. Consequently, additional bias is provided by use of resistor R_2 and capacitor C_4. This bias, although not sufficient to obtain cutoff by itself, nevertheless provides sufficient bias for protection of the tube should signal absence occur. Without the protective bias, tube currents may run excessively high when no signal is applied to the input circuits.

The amplified signal is developed in the plate resonant circuit consisting of variable capacitor C_2 and inductance L_3. Even though plate current flows only in periodic pulses, the flywheel effect of the resonant circuit causes an interchange of energy between the charging characteristics of C_2 and L_3. Hence, a sinewave type of signal is developed. In r-f amplifiers using resonant circuits, oscillations occur when a triode tube is employed, because of the high value of interelectrode capacities which provide a sufficiently low reactance for coupling purposes between input and output circuits. To eliminate such oscillations, a capacitor, C_6, is employed to apply a portion of the amplified signal to the grid. The neutralizing capacitor applies a signal to the grid which is 180 degrees out of phase with the plate signal. By adjustment of C_6, its value is regulated so that exactly the right amount of energy is fed back to the grid circuit to neutralize the undesired oscillations. If a pentode is utilized to eliminate oscillations, the neutralizing capacitor C_6 can be dispensed with, in which case the B voltage can be applied to the bottom of the resonant circuit consisting of C_2 and L_3. When the neutralizing capacitor is applied to the bottom of the resonant circuit, however, the positive plate potential is applied to a center tap on L_3 as shown. The radio-frequency choke, (r-f-c), prevents leakage of the r-f energy to the power supply by providing a high series-inductive reactance. Capacitor C_5 provides a low capacitive reactance return path for the r-f energy to the cathode of the Class C amplifier. The signals circulating in the resonant circuit are transferred to inductance L_4 by a transformer arrangement between inductance L_3 and L_4. The amplified r-f power is then applied to an antenna, to another Class C amplifier, or to some other appropriate load circuit.

A GROUNDED-GRID AMPLIFIER

The Class A, B, and C amplifiers previously discussed are all of the *grounded-cathode* types. Some of these amplifiers do not appear to have a grounded cathode, because the cathode resistor and associated bypass capacitor were used. The term *grounded cathode,* however, refers to the fact that these amplifiers had the cathode at *signal ground* by reason of a low-reactance cathode bypass capacitor. The grounded-cathode amplifier is the one most commonly used, in both vacuum tube and transistor types.

Another amplifier is the *grounded grid,* illustrated in Fig. 2-4. Here, the grid is shown connected directly to ground, although it could be above ground for d-c by use of a resistor. The signal input is applied across an inductance (L_1) in the cathode circuit. Instead of an inductance, a resistor could also be used for application of the signal. Bias is established by resistor R_1 and the shunting capacitor C_1. The voltage drop of the plate-current flow through R_1 will make the cathode more positive than the grid, hence the grid has a negative potential applied to it for bias purposes. The inductance L_1 is not bypassed because the applied signal input must develop across it.

Because the signal is applied between cathode and ground, there is no phase reversal between input and output signals. Assume, for

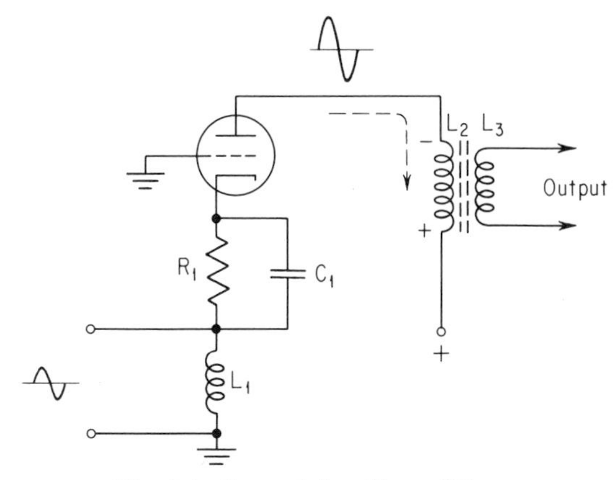

Fig. 2-4. Grounded-grid amplifiers

instance, that the first alternation of the a-c signal waveform applied across L_1 is positive. In the latter instance, the top of L_1 is positive and the bottom negative. Such a voltage drop in the cathode circuits causes the negative bias which exists between grid and cathode to increase, since the positive potential at the top of L_1 makes the cathode more positive than the grid by an additional amount over and above that established by resistor R_1. The increase in bias causes a decrease in the current flow through the vacuum tube causing the plate voltage to rise, hence the amplified signal in the anode circuit coincides in phase with that applied to the input at the cathode. For the second alternation, the top of L_1 becomes negative and the bottom positive. Such a voltage drop opposes that which develops across R_1 and, in consequence, the negative grid bias is reduced and the plate current increases. For an increase in plate current, the voltage drop across the inductance L_2 increases and in consequence plate potential decreases, again following in phase the signal potential applied to the input.

The signal which drops across inductance L_2 is transferred by transformer arrangement to L_3 and so is available at the output. For the circuit shown in Fig. 2-4, inductances L_2 and L_3 form resonant circuits with interelectrode capacities of the tubes as well as stray capacities, hence this type of amplifier is well suited for r-f signal amplification. Powdered iron cores can be used, and if these are in the form of adjustable slugs, the resonant frequency factors of L_2 and L_3 can be varied to tune the circuits. Such an arrangement is used often at UHF and other r-f frequencies. The choice for the grounded-grid amplifier lies in the fact that it needs no neutralization as does the grounded-cathode amplifier. With the grounded grid amplifier there is isolation between the input and output circuits by virtue of the electrostatic fields established by the grounded grid. Hence, there is no energy coupling between the anode circuit and the cathode circuit, and no feedback occurs to cause regeneration and oscillations.

This circuit, however, does have some degeneration caused by the unbypassed inductance L_1 (or the use of an unbypassed resistor in place of L_1). The signal-voltage variations which occur across the cathode inductance L_1 oppose the normal steady-state bias established by resistor R_1, and hence cause degeneration. When a positive alternation occurs across L_1, it increases the negative potential applied to the grid and current though the tube decreases. A current decrease, however, also means a decrease in the voltage established across L_1, shifting the bias to a value which is less negative. Also, for a negative potential across L_1, the bias normally decreases and current through the tube increases. An increase in current through L_1, however, causes an increase in bias, thus opposing the decrease established by the second alternation of the input signal. For an inductance such as L_1, however, the d-c resistance would be low and not much voltage would develop across L_1 by virtue of the plate-current flow through this inductance. When a resistor is utilized, however, degenerative effects increase.

CATHODE FOLLOWER

Another type of circuit often used for specific purposes is that known as the *cathode follower*. The basic circuit of the cathode follower is illustrated in Fig. 2-5. The input signal is applied across the grid and cathode circuits in the conventional manner, but the output signal is taken from across a cathode resistor instead of from a resistor in the anode circuit. If a resistor is employed in the anode circuit, it will normally be bypassed to prevent any signal-voltage variations from developing across it. Capacitor C_1 shown in Fig. 2-5 places the anode at signal ground and prevents the development of any signal voltages in the battery or power supply utilized for the anode voltage.

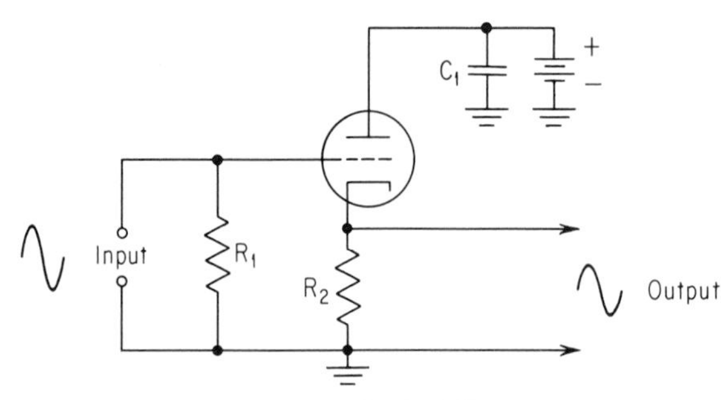

Fig. 2-5. Cathode follower

As was the case with the grounded-grid amplifier, the cathode follower has no phase reversal between input and output signal. For a positive alternation applied between grid and cathode, the plate current increases, and the increase in current through resistor R_2 causes a voltage drop to develop across it which develops the first alternation of the output signal. When the input signal applied between grid and cathode is negative, the resultant bias increase will cause a decline in the plate current through resistor R_2 and the second alternation of the output signal is developed.

The cathode follower has a signal-voltage gain which is less than unity, because of the degeneration which occurs across the cathode resistor R_2. In the absence of a signal, a steady current flow through resistor R_2 would establish a fixed bias. This bias, however, is not stable and will vary in accordance with the variations occurring for the input signal. Consequently, degeneration and loss of gain results for this circuit.

The cathode-follower circuit is useful where it is necessary to step down an impedance without using a step-down transformer. The input impedance to the grid circuit of a cathode follower is high, as with the conventional grounded-cathode amplifier. The output impedance, however, is very low, and can be adjusted to match coaxial cables which have an impedance between 50 and 150 ohms. The advantage of the cathode follower as a step-down transformer equivalent is that there is less attenuation of some of the frequencies than with a transformer. When a transformer is utilized as a step-up or step-down device, high-frequency signal components are often diminished in amplitude because of the distributed capacities which prevail between each wire turn of the transformer as well as between layers. Also, low-frequency signals are attenuated because of the variation in reactance which occurs in a transformer for different frequencies. As signals of lower and lower frequency are applied across a transformer, the inductive reactance decreases proportionately and a smaller voltage drop develops across the transformer. With the cathode follower there is no such signal attenuation for lower frequencies, though some signal shunting may occur for the higher-frequency signal components which cause the capacitive reactances within the tube to have low values and act as a shunt. By the use of tubes having low interelectrode capacities, however, a cathode-follower circuit can handle a wide band of frequencies with a substantially flat response characteristic.

THE GROUNDED-EMITTER AMPLIFIER

The vacuum-tube amplifiers previously discussed have counterparts in the transistor amplifiers. However, before a direct comparison is made between the vacuum-tube and transistor amplifiers, the fundamental factors relating to transistors will be reviewed. As was the case with the vacuum tubes, the basic characteristics of emission and electron theory are omitted because the theoretical physics of the vacuum tube and transistor will be found in standard texts.

The solid-state diodes and transistors utilized in electronics are manufactured by use of the silicon or germanium crystal. Instead of a pure crystal structure, however, certain chemical impurities are added to some crystal structures so that either a P-type crystal or an N-type crystal is formed. The P-type crystal is so named because some of its atoms have one less electron than the normal crystal atoms. In the N-type crystal some atoms have one more electron than the normal crystal atoms. The "P" and "N" designations, however, do not indicate any charge or potential differences, but merely indicate the fact that a P-type crystal has had inserted into it some foreign atoms which differ from the crystal atoms with respect to the number of electrons in the outer atomic shell. Similarly, the N-type crystal has had some foreign or so-called "impurity atoms" inserted which again have a different number of outer-shell or outer-ring electrons with respect to the crystal atom.

During the chemical construction of diodes or transistors, when the P and N sections are combined, some electrons leave the N section and go into the P section. The result is that the N section now has a definite positive charge, because it has lost some of its electrons by giving them up to the P section. The latter now has a net negative charge since it has acquired some electrons from the N section. This is illustrated at A of Fig. 2-6, where a joined (junction) P-N combination is shown. The fact that the N section now has a net positive charge and the P section a net negative charge establishes within this P-N junction a potential difference known as a *potential barrier*. The potential barrier can, in essence, be considered as a small battery having a definite polarity as shown at A. When an external battery (B_e) is connected to this circuit so that the positive terminal of the external battery is connected to the P zone and the negative terminal of the battery con-

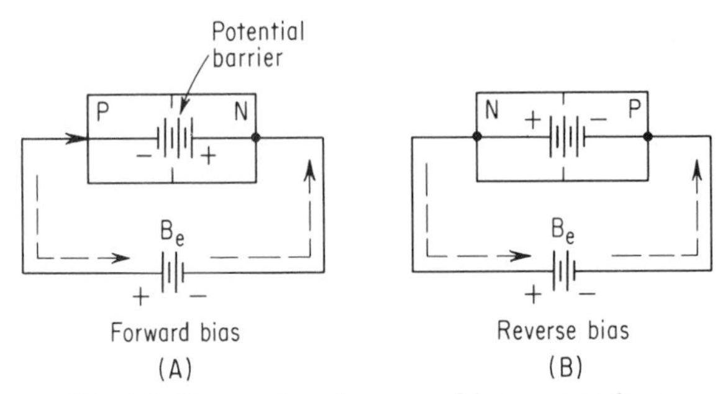

Fig. 2-6. Forward and reverse bias connections

nected to the N zone as shown at A, the connection is known as *forward bias.* A forward bias applied to a P-N section will reduce the internal barrier or internal resistance of the junction, because the current flow created by connecting the external battery is in the same direction as the current flow which would be established by the internal potential barrier as shown. The internal potential barrier would have current flowing from its negative terminal out of the P section while it would draw electrons into the N section to its positive terminal. This direction of current flow, as shown by the dashed arrows in A, coincides with that which would be established by the external battery. Because both potential sources have directions which coincide, a maximum amount of current flow is possible, limited only by the internal resistances which remain for both potential sources, and by the amplitude of the external battery voltage.

At B of Fig. 2-6 the condition known as *reverse bias* is shown. Here, the N-P sections of the crystal structure have been reversed, so that now the external battery (B_e) functions in a manner opposite to the internal potential barrier. The latter again would have a direction such that electrons would flow from its negative terminal out of the P-zone area while electrons would normally be drawn into the N-zone because of the positive barrier potential. This barrier-potential polarity opposes the current flow which would be established by the external battery; but the latter, having a higher potential, would force current to flow through the N-P section. However, because the internal potential barrier offers opposition to such current flow, the internal resistance of the N-P junction is high. Thus, the application of reversed bias raises the internal impedance of an N-P section while the application of forward bias reduces the internal impedance.

The factors of forward and reverse bias are very important with respect to transistors, and follow certain rules which are summarized in the subsequent discussions. Factors relating to the circuits shown at A and B of Fig. 2-6, however, also apply to the ordinary *crystal diodes* which are utilized in industry. Silicon and germanium diodes have a high resistance in one direction and a low resistance in the other direction because of the potential barriers created within the crystal structure. For the circuit at A, the battery connection would cause a high current to flow and the diode can be considered to be in its conducting state. For the circuit shown at B, however, the reversal of the N-P section creates a very high resistance and the diode can be considered to be in its nonconducting state. Actually, however, crystal diodes conduct slightly in the reverse direction as opposed to the absolute nonconduction of the vacuum-tube diodes.

Transistors are formed by combining two P sections and one N section or two N sections and one P section as shown at A and B of

Fig. 2-7. The combining of three such sections forms a triode type of transistor comparable to the triode vacuum tube. For the P-N-P junction shown at A, the terminal which compares to the cathode of a vacuum tube is known as the *emitter.* The emitter shown at the left has an arrow pointing toward the P section so that this transistor symbol can be distinguished from the other type shown at B. The terminal comparable to the plate of the vacuum tube is known as the *collector* and connects to the other P zone as shown at A. The terminal which compares to the grid of a vacuum tube is known as the *base,* connected to the N area at A. When an N-P-N transistor junction is formed as shown at B, the emitter lead has an arrow which points away from the N section. The actual symbols used for the P-N-P and N-P-N transistors are shown at C and D of Fig. 2-7. At C, the emitter is identified by the arrow line. Since this arrow points toward the horizontal line of the symbol, it indicates that this transistor is a P-N-P type. The emitter arrow at D points away from this symbol, hence it indicates that this transistor is an N-P-N type.

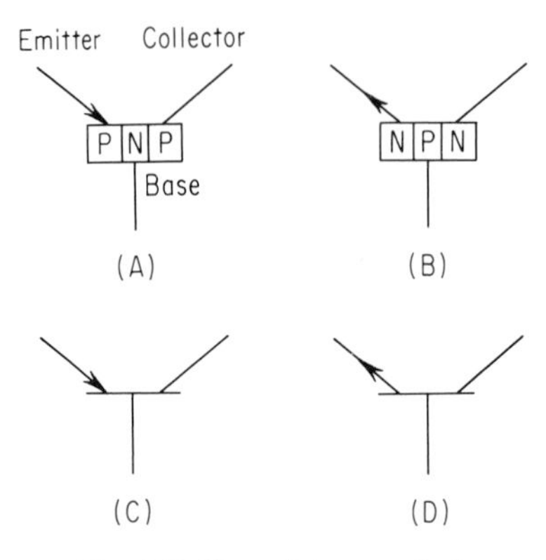

Fig. 2-7. Transistor symbols

The use of an N-P-N transistor in a grounded-emitter circuit is shown in Fig. 2-8. Since the emitter compares to the cathode of a vacuum tube, the grounding of the emitter in this circuit creates a condition similar to that which prevailed for the grounded-cathode amplifier previously discussed. In the collector side, a battery potential is applied to the collector with respect to the emitter which is positive for the collector in a fashion similar to the positive potential applied to the anode of a vacuum tube. For the base-emitter side, how-

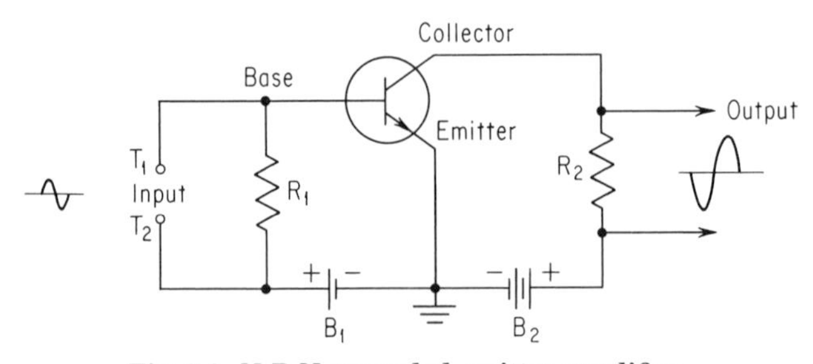

Fig. 2-8. N-P-N grounded-emitter amplifier

ever, a positive potential is applied to the base and a negative potential to the emitter to establish a forward-bias condition at the input of the circuit and a reverse-bias condition at the output. The forward bias established at the input to the transistor causes the latter circuit to have a low internal impedance (approximately 500 to 1000 ohms). On the collector side, the use of reverse bias creates an internal impedance which is quite high, ranging up to approximately 50,000 ohms.

The collector-emitter impedance would normally be much higher, but the forward bias established between base and emitter influences the potential barrier between the collector and base and lowers the impedance of the latter. It is this influence which the base-emitter current and resistance have on the collector base resistance which makes the transistor behave as an amplifier.

When the first alternation of the input signal is applied to the transistor base-emitter circuit, it will establish a positive potential at terminal T_1 and a negative potential at terminal T_2. The potential difference developed across these terminals coincides with that of battery B_1, hence the increase in the total forward bias between base and emitter causes an increase in the current flow through this section and a decrease in the potential barrier. This also causes a decrease in the potential barrier between collector and base, with the result that there is a current increase in the collector-emitter side furnished by battery B_2. Since the current from the latter flows down through resistor R_2, a voltage drop is developed across the latter which is negative in polarity, hence an amplified version of the input signal is developed, having a 180-degree phase difference as was the case with the grounded-cathode, vacuum-tube amplifier.

For the second alternation of the input signal, terminal T_1 becomes negative and terminal T_2 positive. The potential difference across the input terminal is now opposite to that of battery B_1, hence the voltage between base and emitter has been reduced. Since the forward bias has now been decreased, the potential barrier within the transistor increases and less current flows from B_2 through the emitter-collector circuit. In consequence, the voltage drop across R_2 decreases and the collector voltage rises, developing the second alternation of the amplifier output signal as shown. Thus, the triode transistor acts as an amplifier in the same way as the vacuum tube does. The transistor circuit functions on the basis of current changes in the input and output sections, hence it is essentially a power amplifier. Inductors can be used instead of resistors, in place of R_1 and R_2, and conventional transformer-coupled circuits can be employed.

With vacuum tubes, there is no duplicate type of tube with similar characteristics that functions with opposite potential applications as

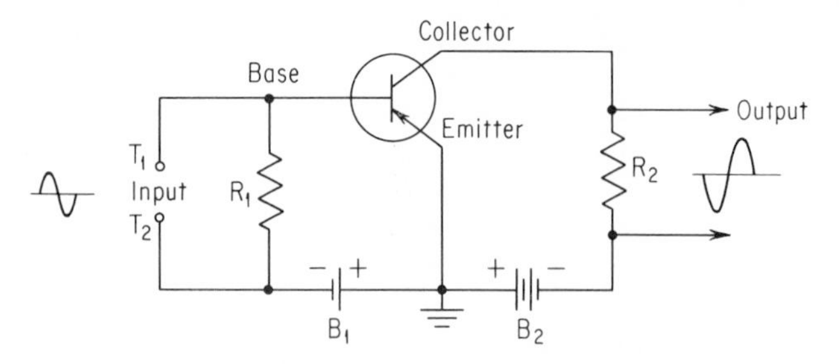

Fig. 2-9. P-N-P grounded-emitter amplifier

with transistors. A circuit similar to the N-P-N grounded-emitter amplifier is that shown in Fig. 2-9, where a P-N-P type of transistor is employed. Here, the circuit is similar except for the reversal of the battery connections. For the input to the transistor, forward bias must still be employed, for this reason: Battery B_1 now has its negative terminal toward the base of the transistor and the positive terminal toward the emitter, because the emitter is now a P section and the base an N section. For the collector side, a negative potential is applied to the P zone and the positive potential to the emitter, establishing the necessary reversed bias which must be used at the output of transistor amplifier circuits. Functionally, the amplifier is similar to the N-P-N type. There is still a phase reversal for the signal at the output with respect to that applied at the input. When the first alternation of the input signal appears at the input, it establishes a potential difference across the input terminals which is such that terminal T_1 is positive and T_2 is negative. This potential difference across the input terminals is opposite to that of battery B_1, and in consequence the current flow in the input circuit is reduced and the internal impedance of the barrier is increased. This results in an increase in the internal barrier between the collector and base circuits, and less current flows from battery B_2. This decline in current means a smaller voltage drop across resistor R_2 and results in the production of a negative alternation of the amplified signal as shown. For the second alternation which appears at terminals T_1 and T_2, the potential difference established would aid battery potential B_1, resulting in an increase in current flow in the base-emitter section of the transistor and a reduction of the internal impedance. This impedance reduction is also felt in the collector side, and more current flows from battery B_2 through resistor R_2. The voltage drop across the latter now increases in a positive direction, producing the second alternation of the amplified output signal. Thus, the P-N-P transistor also functions like the N-P-N transistor as a power amplifier.

A change of the bias polarity at the input circuit alters the characteristic of the transistor circuit and changes it from A to B or from B to C as is subsequently detailed. Reversal of battery B_2, however, will damage the transistor because when forward bias is applied to both the input and output sections of the circuit, excessive currents will flow.

TRANSISTOR CLASS B AMPLIFIER

A transistor can be operated as a Class B amplifier by omitting the forward bias which normally is applied to the base-emitter circuit. The usual reverse bias is, however, still applied to the collector circuit. As is the case with Class B audio amplifiers using vacuum tubes, it is necessary to use two transistors in a push-pull arrangement in order to minimize the severe distortion which results when only a single transistor is employed. For Class B operation in the r-f range, however, as with vacuum tubes, a single transistor is sufficient when a resonant circuit is utilized.

A typical push-pull Class B audio amplifier is shown in Fig. 2-10. Here, two N-P-N transistors are employed, T_2 and T_3. Transistor T_1 is the driver stage which furnishes the input signal. Note that the emitter circuit is grounded directly, as is the center tap of the input transformer. Without the normal forward bias applied to the push-pull transistors, operation without signal input is near the cutoff point. When a signal appears across the secondary of the input transformer, one transistor will conduct while the other will be driven into the cutoff region, similar to vacuum-tube Class B amplifier operation.

Assume, for instance, that the first alternation of the a-c input signal is as shown in Fig. 2-10. With such a signal polarity, the base of transistor T_2 will be positive, while the base of transistor T_3 will be negative. The positive alternation appearing at the base of T_2 is equivalent to the application of the normal forward bias to this

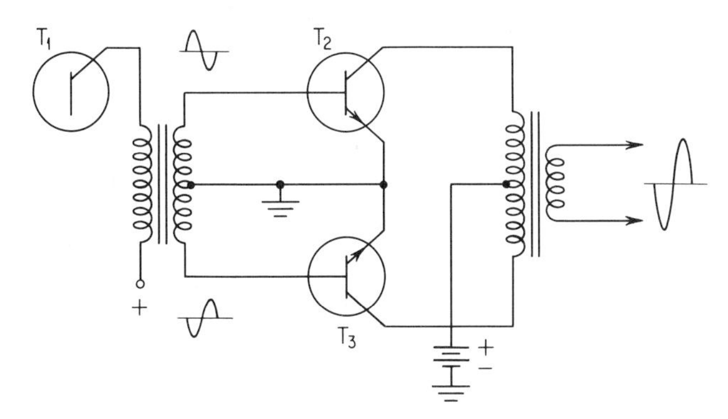

Fig. 2-10. Class B transistor amplifier

transistor, because forward bias for the N-P-N transistor consists of applying a negative potential to the emitter and a positive potential to the base. For transistor T_3, however, the negative potential which appears for the first alternation of the input signal will make the base negative with respect to the emitter. This is in the nature of a reverse bias, and under such a condition transistor T_3 is driven into the cut-off region and no conduction occurs. Thus, one alternation of the amplified signal appears in the output transformer because of the conduction of transistor T_2. For the second alternation of the input signal, the base of T_2 is made negative with respect to its emitter, hence an equivalent reverse bias is applied to the input of T_2 and this transistor does not conduct. The positive alternation appearing at the base of T_3, however, makes the latter positive with respect to the emitter, hence an equivalent forward bias is present here permitting this transistor to conduct. Thus, the second alternation of the amplified signal appears in the output transformer by virtue of the conduction of transistor T_3. Functionally, the operation is identical for P-N-P transistors, although the battery potential would have to be reversed from that shown in Fig. 2-10.

For Class C operation, reverse bias is applied to both the input and output of a transistor as will be shown later in this chapter. As mentioned for Class C amplifiers employing vacuum tubes, the Class C amplifier is suitable only for radio-frequency amplification where resonant circuits are employed, and is not suitable for audio amplification whether or not push-pull operation is used. For operation as Class AB_1 or AB_2, the forward-bias potentials are arranged to secure such operation.

GROUNDED-BASE AMPLIFIER

The transistor counterpart for the grounded-grid vacuum-tube amplifier discussed earlier is the grounded-base amplifier. An r-f amplifier using this type of circuit is shown in Fig. 2-11. As with the

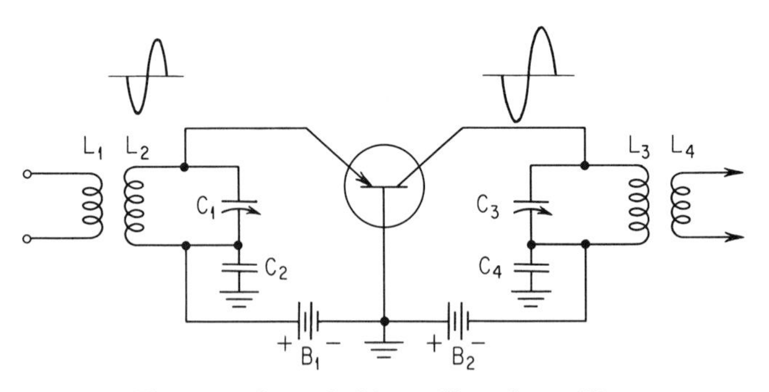

Fig. 2-11. Grounded-base Class C amplifier

vacuum-tube grounded-grid amplifier, the advantage of the grounded-base transistor amplifier is that it can be utilized for amplification of radio frequencies without the necessity for neutralization. For the grounded-base circuit shown in Fig. 2-11, conventional resonant-circuit input and output systems are employed, with L_1 and L_2 forming an input transformer, and the resonant circuit for the emitter consisting of inductance L_2 and capacitor C_1. The latter is made variable so that the emitter circuit can be tuned to resonance. On the collector side, another resonant circuit is employed, consisting of variable capacitor C_3 in conjunction with inductance L_3. The latter forms an output transformer in conjunction with inductance L_4. Capacitors C_2 and C_4 are for bypass purposes, and they place the bottom of the resonant circuit at ground (base) potential for the necessary completion of the r-f circuit through the transistor.

As with the vacuum-tube grounded-grid circuit, there is no phase reversal between the input and output sections of the amplifier. If the negative alternation appears at the input as shown, the emitter is made negative with respect to the base. This condition aids the battery potential B_1 and more current flows to the emitter side, which is directly influential in causing a current increase in the collector side. The increase in collector current causes a larger voltage drop to appear across the resonant circuit, with the consequent decline in collector voltage as shown. For a positive alternation at the input, the voltage drop across the input resonant circuit opposes that of the B_1 battery potential, and in consequence the emitter-base current declines, as does the collector current. Since the collector current decreases, there is a smaller voltage drop across the output resonant circuit and hence a rise in collector potential as shown. Because the base (which is equivalent to the grid of a vacuum tube) is at ground potential, there is excellent isolation between the input and output circuits, thus insufficient coupling exists between the input and output circuits and oscillations do not normally occur. As with all r-f amplifiers, however, some oscillations can occur if a sufficiently high frequency is employed for the type of transistor utilized. Interelectrode capacities in vacuum tubes and interelement capacities in transistors (even though small in capacitive value) will present an appreciable shunt reactance for higher frequencies. If the grounded-grid or the grounded-base amplifiers oscillate, neutralization must still be employed as with conventional triode r-f amplifiers.

The grounded-base amplifier has a low input impedance as does the grounded-emitter amplifier. For the grounded-base amplifier, however, the input impedance is somewhat lower, ranging from approximately 100 ohms to approximately 600 ohms. The output impedance is high, ranging up to 500,000 ohms for some transistors.

Current gain for the grounded-base transistor amplifier is usually less than unity, but amplification occurs because of the high impedance present in the output circuit. Hence, for a few milliamperes of current change in the input side through a low impedance, the same amount of current change in the collector side would result in considerable signal amplification because of the high impedance through which the current flows and hence the greater power which is developed ($P = I^2R$). An N-P-N transistor can be substituted for the one shown in Fig. 2-1 if the battery potentials are reversed.

GROUNDED-COLLECTOR CIRCUIT

The transistorized version of the cathode follower is the grounded-collector circuit. A typical circuit of this type is shown in Fig. 2-12. Here, the collector is placed at signal ground by virtue of the capacitor C_1. The normal forward bias is applied to the base-emitter input circuit by battery B_1, which has its positive side toward the emitter and its negative side toward the base. The reverse bias for the output circuit is provided by battery B_2, with its negative terminal toward the collector and its positive terminal toward the emitter.

The input signal is applied to the base-emitter circuit (capacitor C_2 having a bypass effect across battery B_1). The output signal is derived from across resistor R_2 in the emitter (cathode) circuit. Hence, the output signal is procured from the emitter which is comparable to the cathode of a vacuum tube. Since the polarity of the output signal "follows" the polarity of the input signal, the grounded-collector circuit is equivalent to the cathode-follower vacuum-tube type described earlier.

For a positive alternation of the input signal, terminal T_1 is positive and terminal T_2 negative. Since this polarity opposes that of battery B_1, voltage drop in current flow from battery B_2 across R_2 declines. This voltage, negative at the emitter side as shown, develops a positive potential when it becomes less negative across R_2 as shown.

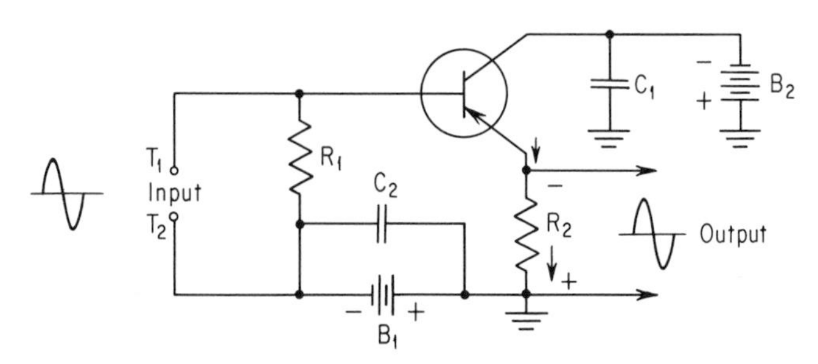

Fig. 2-12. Grounded-collector circuit

Hence, a positive signal alternation is developed across the emitter-resistor. When the second alternation of the input signal is applied, terminal T_1 becomes negative and terminal T_2 positive. With such a voltage drop appearing across the input terminals, the total voltage from base to emitter is increased, since the voltage drop across the input aids that of battery B_1. The increase in current through the input side causes a corresponding increase in current in the collector side and the voltage across R_2 rises. Such a voltage increase, however, is in the negative polarity, as shown by the polarity markings beside resistor R_2 in the drawing in Fig. 2-12. The result is the development of a signal of negative polarity across the emitter-resistor.

As with the vacuum-tube cathode follower, a grounded-collector circuit has less than unity signal-voltage gain. The input impedance is high, ranging between 200,000 and 500,000 ohms. The output impedance is low, and its actual value depends on the value of the resistor R_2 plus shunting reactances. Impedance can be between 50 and 200 ohms as needed for an equivalent step-down transformer characteristic.

THE AMPLIFIER CONTROL

Both the vacuum-tube and transistor amplifiers are useful as control devices because they can be utilized to control another amplifier, actuate a relay, or control some other device as will be subsequently detailed. When one amplifier is utilized to control another, the output from one is applied to the input of a successive stage and the latter, in turn, can be used to control another successive stage. Such an arrangement has already been shown, using a transformer for coupling one stage to another. At A of Fig. 2-13, an r-c coupled circuit is shown. Here, vacuum tube V_1 is coupled to vacuum tube V_2 by use of the coupling capacitor C_3. The use of resistors and capacitors for coupling between stages of amplifiers is an economical method and is employed extensively. It eliminates the need for the costlier transformer, although the increase in voltage amplification resulting from a step-up impedance transformer is lost. With modern vacuum tubes, however, there is sufficient gain for the purposes desired.

When the plate of one tube is coupled to the grid of the successive amplifier tube, the system is known as *cascade*. Sometimes the coupling system known as *cascode* is employed, shown at B of Fig. 2-13. With this system, the plate voltage applied to the second tube, V_2, divides across both tubes, since they are in series with the power supply. With *cascade,* the relatively lower plate impedance of a triode is coupled directly to the high impedance of a grid input (approximately 1 megohm). With *cascode,* however, the plate impedance of the first

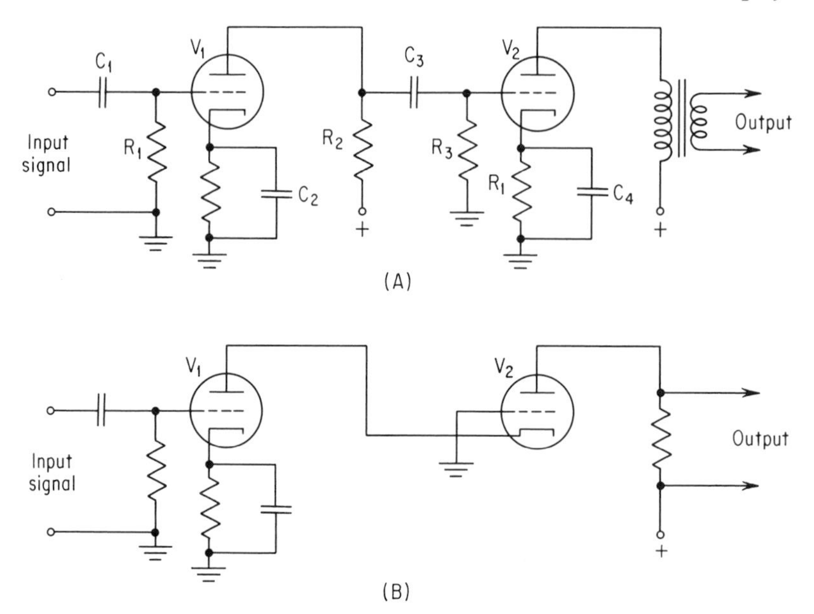

Fig. 2-13. Cascade and cascode circuits

tube is coupled to the rather low impedance of the cathode circuit. The cascode system is employed to increase the gain of an amplifier stage over that which would be obtained from a single tube. This is particularly true in r-f amplification, where the use of a pentode is to be avoided because of the additional noise created by the extra grid wires within the pentode tube. For the second tube at B of Fig. 2-13, a bias arrangement in the grid circuit is usually employed, but the grid is bypassed to ground by a capacitor in order to maintain the grid at signal ground (grounded-grid amplifier).

An amplifier can also be used to control tube circuits other than amplifiers—diode rectifier circuits, motor control tubes, and other such devices to be explained later. Also, the discussions herein which relate to the high-vacuum tubes also apply to transistors.

An amplifier can be used to control a number of other devices, some of which are illustrated in Fig. 2-14. Here, a single amplifier stage is illustrated, although if greater amplification or power is required, the circuits illustrated could be the second, third, or fourth stage of a series of cascade amplifiers to bring the signal level up to that required for operation of the device to be controlled. At A, the operation of a relay is shown. The solenoid of the relay is placed in the plate circuit of the amplifier tube, so that the plate current of the vacuum tube flows through the solenoid to actuate the relay. The relay shown is a *normally open* relay, which is closed when sufficient plate

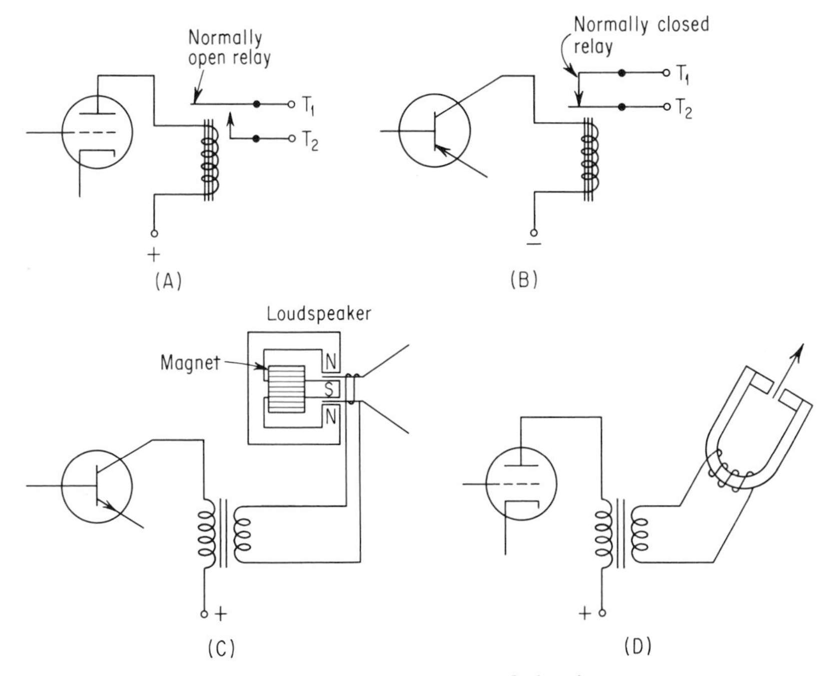

Fig. 2-14. Amplifier control circuits

current flows through the inductance of the solenoid. For operation, the amplifier stage can be a Class B amplifier where the bias is virtually at cutoff, and very little if any plate current flows. Upon the application of a positive d-c voltage at the grid, or a positive alternation or pulse, the plate-current flow through the solenoid sets up a magnetic field which in turn pulls down the flexible metal section of a relay and closes the relay. Thus, a closed circuit is present at terminals T_1 and T_2 for closing a circuit of much greater power or performing some other similar task.

The relay could also be a *normally closed* relay such as shown at B, where a transistor amplifier is shown for comparison. For this circuit, of course, a normally open relay could also be employed. The normally closed relay, as the name implies, keeps the circuit controlled by terminals T_1 and T_2 in a *closed-circuit* condition until current flows through the inductance of the solenoid to open the relay and the control circuit. Instead of the simple relays illustrated at A and B, complex relays, where many contacts are closed at one time, can be employed for performing various functions simultaneously, such as opening some circuits and closing others at a predetermined time when a signal is applied to the controlling amplifier. A typical multicontact relay is illustrated in Fig. 2-15. (See Chapter 7.)

The amplifier circuit can also control other devices—for example, a loudspeaker, shown at B of Fig. 2-14. The alternating-current signal-power variations in the secondary of the output transformer are applied to the voice coil of the loudspeaker. The fields set up in the latter by the signal power aid and oppose the magnetic field established by the loudspeaker magnet and pole pieces, and the flexible cone of the loudspeaker is made to move in and out at a rapid rate, thus displacing air for the production of sound. The loudspeaker is then, in essense, a *transducer,* because it converts electric energy into acoustic energy.

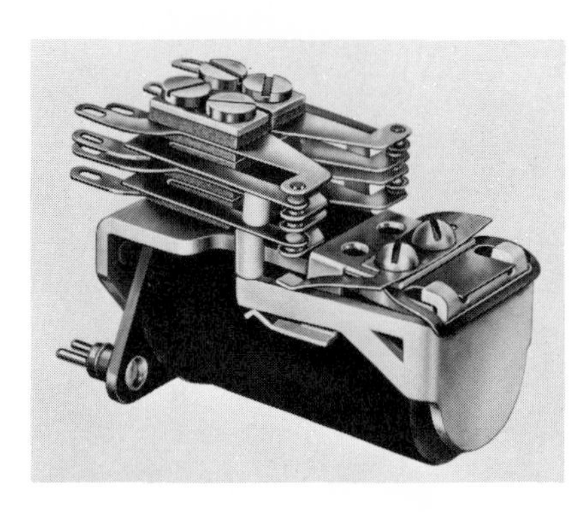

Fig. 2-15. Multi-contact relay (Courtesy Allied Control Co., Inc.)

Another illustration of amplifier control is shown at D, where the secondary of the output transformer is connected to another type of transducer device, one in which a permanent magnet has attached to it two pole pieces, at the center of which is an armature rod as illustrated. This is a basic illustration of several devices which can be actuated by the amplified power produced in the vacuum-tube stage or transistor stage. One process is that of a disk recording, as for phonograph records, where the armature acts as a vibrating stylus. In another use, the armature rod can be employed as a writing stylus, so that the signal variations which occur in the amplifier can be converted to mechanical vibrations to be recorded on a moving sheet of paper. Hence, such a device finds numerous applications for the recording of various signals, more fully illustrated subsequently. If the moving paper (usually in the form of a roll) has graph lines on it, a graph can be plotted by use of such a vibrating reed.

Many indicating devices can also be controlled by an amplifier, as illustrated in Fig. 2-16. At A, the transformer secondary is attached to a thermo-device. The latter could be a light bulb, and the audio or other amplified power developed would then be visible in terms of light of a certain intensity, related to the intensity of an amplified power which is developed. Instead of a light bulb, the thermal device might be a resistance strip which heats up to a certain degree, again depending on the amount of power developed in the amplifier. The thermal device can then be used to indicate the amount of heat developed, by coupling to it a device which reads heat variations.

At B of Fig. 2-16 is shown the control of meters, and hence of needle deflection. A d-c ammeter or milliammeter can be placed in series with

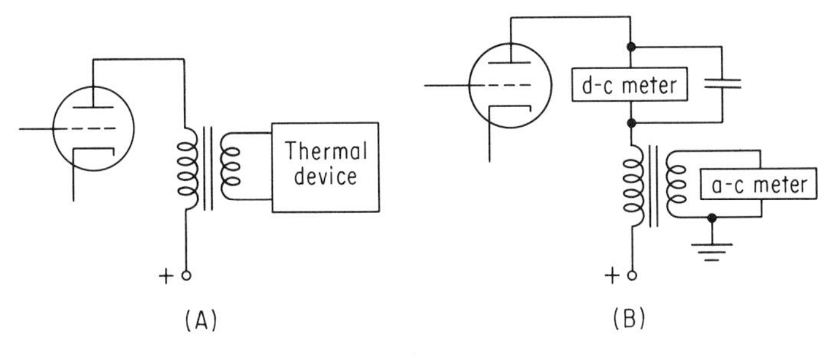

Fig. 2-16. Amplifier control of indicators

the plate-current flow as shown to read the amount of direct current in the circuit. Again, if a Class B amplifier is employed, the bias can be adjusted so that no current flows in the absence of a signal at the grid. For a certain degree of positive signal amplitude at the grid, however, a specific amount of plate current would flow, which would then be indicated on the ammeter or milliammeter in the plate circuit. If an a-c type of signal is applied to the grid of the amplifier, such a-c current variations would also be present in the anode circuit, hence the d-c meter is bypassed with a capacitor to prevent the a-c signal from passing through the meter. An a-c meter, or a wattmeter, can be employed in the secondary of the output transformer as shown. Here, the output a-c power can be measured directly.

THE DIRECT-COUPLED AMPLIFIER

When it is necessary to use control signals of a very low frequency, or when the control signals must be of such a slow rate of amplitude change as to constitute d-c which varies slightly over a long time interval, neither the r-c coupled amplifier nor the transformer-coupled amplifier is suitable. In the transformer-coupled amplifier, the frequency response suffers to some extent at both high and low frequency as mentioned previously. For the r-c coupled amplifiers, there is attenuation of the lower frequencies by virtue of the high reactance present in the coupling capacitor. Even though extensive measures are taken to increase the frequency response of such devices, a slow rate of change will not be passed through the amplifier because of the limitations on d-c imposed by both transformers and coupling capacitors. Where direct-current changes are to be amplified and sensed, the direct-coupled amplifier is employed. Such an amplifier is known as a *d-c amplifier* because its low-frequency signal handling range extends down to the d-c level, and also because it uses direct coupling.

The vacuum-tube version of the d-c amplifier is shown at A of Fig. 2-17. Here, the plate of the first tube, V_1, is coupled directly to the

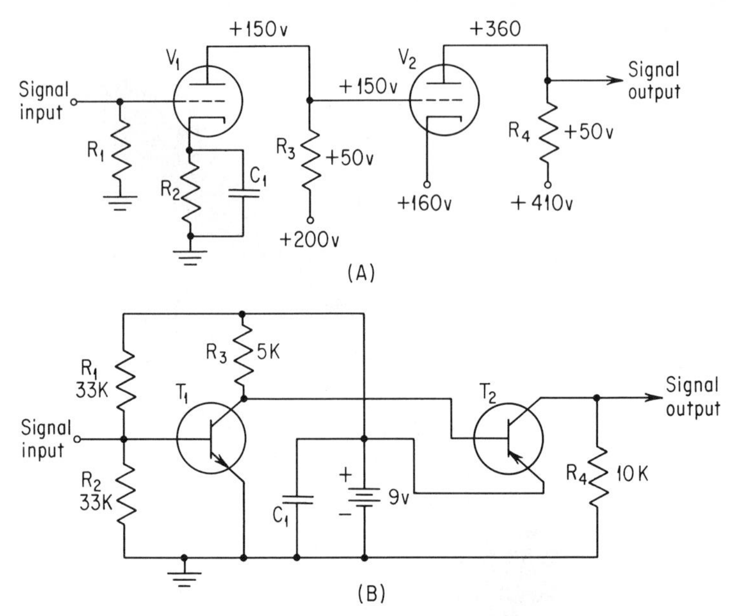

Fig. 2-17. Direct-coupled amplifiers

grid of the second tube, V_2. When this is done, however, the positive plate voltage at the anode of V_1 also appears at the grid of V_2 and could damage the tube if the design were not such that the grid of V_2 is still negative with respect to the cathode. Thus, in the vacuum-tube version of the d-c amplifiers, the design must be such that proper voltages appear at the various places as required. The manner in which this is done is illustrated at A. If, for instance, there is a 50-volt drop across the plate load resistor R_3, and 150 volts is required at the plate, a positive voltage of 200 would be applied at the terminal beneath R_3 as shown. The positive 150 volts then appears at the grid of V_2 also. If, however, this tube requires a negative 10 volts of bias, then 160 volts is applied to the cathode, so that the latter will be positive with respect to the grid by 10 volts. Thus, the 160 volts on the cathode and the 150 volts on the grid make the grid negative with respect to the cathode and satisfy the negative-bias requirement for the grid. Now, if the anode of V_2 is to be 200 volts positive, and again 50 volts drops across the anode's load resistor (R_4), then 410 volts must be applied to the terminal beneath resistor R_4. With 50 volts dropping across R_4, 360 volts appears at the plate of V_2. Because the cathode is positive by 160 volts, however, the potential difference between plate and cathode is only 200 volts.

Although the vacuum-tube d-c amplifier shown at Fig. 2-17 functions satisfactorily, the design is such that the power supply requirements are severe. Hence, for more than two stages impractical voltage requirements are encountered, since each successive stage would require correspondingly higher and higher anode voltages. In consequence, direct-coupled stages in excess of two cascade units are seldom encountered.

In transistors, the fact that an N-P-N and a P-N-P type can be utilized makes for a *complementing* factor which is useful in direct-coupled applications. A typical direct-coupled transistor amplifier is shown at B of Fig. 2-17. Here, an N-P-N transistor, T_1, is employed for the first stage. The collector of this transistor is connected directly to the base of the second transistor, T_2, a P-N-P type. For transistor T_1, the N-P-N type, the forward-bias requirements are such that the emitter should be negative with respect to the base. This condition is satisfied, because the emitter is connected to the ground lead, which is negative since the negative terminal of the battery potential is connected to ground. The positive terminal of the battery is connected to the top of resistor R_1, and the latter in conjunction with resistor R_2 acts as a voltage divider. Because both resistors are equal in value, a positive potential of 4.5 volts appears at the base of T_1 with respect to the emitter. The collector of T_1 is positive with respect to the emitter, since the emitter is applied to the negative potential of the battery and the collector to the positive potential through resistor R_3.

For the P-N-P transistor T_2, the forward-bias requirements are such that the emitter should be positive with respect to the base. This condition is satisfied, since the emitter is connected to the positive terminal of the battery. It would appear, however, that the base of T_2 is also positive because it is connected to the positive terminal of the battery through resistor R_3. However, resistor R_3, in conjunction with the impedance of the transistor T_1, also shunts the battery and thus forms a voltage divider. Therefore, the junction of R_3 with the collector of T_1 is negative with respect to the positive terminal of the battery. Hence, the base of transistor T_2 is negative to a small degree with respect to the positive emitter. For the collector of T_2, a negative potential must be applied to satisfy the reverse-bias requirement. This condition is satisfied since the collector is connected to the minus battery terminal through resistor R_4.

Because of the complementing factor which can be utilized with N-P-N and P-N-P transistors, successive stages of amplification can be employed using the direct-coupled principle without an increase in the battery potentials to the proportions necessary for vacuum-tube direct-coupled amplifiers. The only increase in potential required with transistor d-c amplifiers is that necessary to satisfy the additional power handling which must be accomplished by the final stages of amplification. For the d-c amplifiers using transistors, each successive transistor is of a type opposite to the preceding one. Thus, for the circuit shown at B of Fig. 2-17, a third transistor stage would be an N-P-N type again, and a fourth stage would consist of a P-N-P type. If the same circuit arrangement is used as shown at B, the base of each succeeding transistor stage would have the proper polarity and potential applied to it for function in the required forward-bias arrangement.

CONTROL AMPLIFIER

The amplifier is, of course, also a control device, since it requires some signal input to create the amplification process. Thus, the second stage of a two-stage amplifier is controlled by the output signals from the first stage. The first stage, in turn, is under the control of whatever input device is utilized, for it is the latter which furnishes the type and amplitude of signal which regulates the output.

Figure 2-18 illustrates some input devices. At A is shown a magnetic-type transducer (see Chapter 6) which could consist of a magnetic phonograph cartridge, a sensing device for surface roughness, or any other unit which converts mechanical vibrations into electric energy. With a low-impedance transducer, a step-up transformer is required to step up the low impedance of the transducer to the high input impedance of the vacuum tube. A crystal transducer, shown at B, can be connected directly to the grid circuit, because the

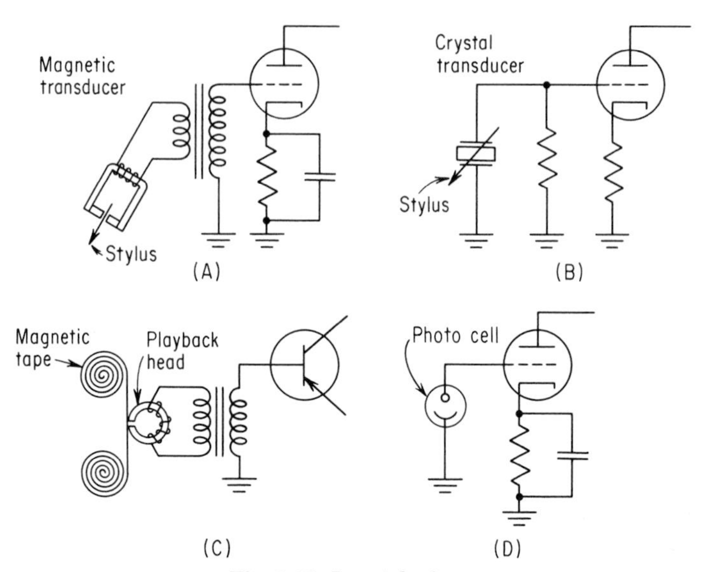

Fig. 2-18. Input devices

crystal (and ceramic) units have a high impedance. If the stylus is replaced with a diaphragm, either device shown would then represent a microphone. The latter is also a transducer, since it converts acoustical energy to electric energy.

The amplifier can also be controlled by the magnetic field densities which exist on recorded magnetic tape, as shown at C of Fig. 2-18. By use of a tape-playing head, magnetic variations are converted to electric signals. The amplifier can also be controlled by visible light or invisible infrared rays by use of appropriate photocell devices as basically illustrated at C and more fully described in a later section. Thus, virtually any type of existing energy—mechanical, visual, thermal, or electrical—can be employed to control an amplifier circuit.

TUNNEL-DIODE AMPLIFIER

The tunnel diode functions as an amplifier because of its negative-resistance characteristics, mentioned in Chapter 1. The negative-resistance phenomenon is not new, in fact it occurs in an ordinary tetrode tube. This is illustrated at A in Fig. 2-19 which shows a tetrode characteristic curve for a variation of plate current (I_p) with an increase of plate voltage (E_p). The negative-resistance characteristic occurs because of the secondary emission which prevails in a tetrode when the screen-grid voltage is higher than the plate voltage. The higher screen-grid potential increases the electron velocity from cathode to plate, and the electrons strike the plate with sufficient force to dislodge other electrons. The disloged electrons are attracted to the screen grid and, in consequence, plate current decreases. A decrease in plate current results in a decrease in the internal resistance of the tube. Since this occurs for a rise in plate potential, the decreased resistance is known as *negative resistance*.

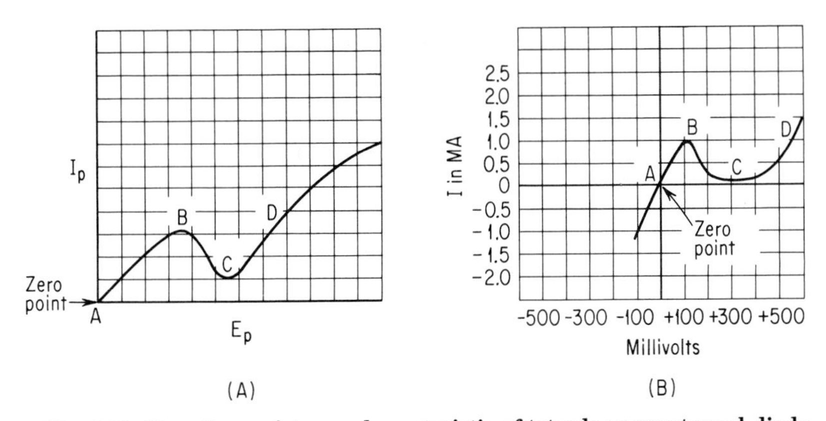

Fig. 2-19. Negative resistance characteristic of tetrode versus tunnel-diode

As shown at A, if the voltage on the plate is gradually increased, plate current rises from its zero value at A on the graph to point B. (It is assumed that the control-grid and screen-grid voltages are held constant.) When the plate voltage is increased an additional amount, the electrons increase in velocity and the secondary emission causes the screen-grid current to increase because the latter absorbs the electrons which are knocked off the plate. This point occurs between B and C on the graph. After the plate voltage reaches a value equal to or in excess of the screen-grid voltage, the secondary emission decreases rapidly and hence the negative-resistance effect also decreases. Hence, at point D on the graph, the plate voltage has a sufficiently higher potential than the screen to attract the secondary-emission electrons.

The tunnel diode also exhibits such negative-resistance characteristics, but is essentially a two-element solid-state device as opposed to the four-element vacuum-tube tetrode. As shown at B, a reverse bias will cause an increase in current at a steeper rate than is the case with the silicon diode, the graph of which was illustrated in Chapter 1. With the application of forward bias, the current rises from its zero value at A to an increasingly higher level with a peak at B. An additional increase in voltage will now cause the current to drop from the level at B to C as shown on the graph. This, again, represents a negative-resistance characteristic because the internal resistance decreases with a rise in the applied voltage. An additional increase of voltage will cause a rise in the level from C to D as was the case with the tetrode characteristic curve shown at A of Fig. 2-19. If a forward-bias potential is applied so that it has a value which falls midway between the current level from B to C, amplification will occur upon the application of a signal to the input. If one alternation of the input signal opposes the fixed forward bias, there will be a reduction in the applied forward bias, and current flow will increase toward the level shown at B on the graph. For a signal alternation which coincides in polarity to the forward bias, there will be an increase in the resultant forward bias and the current will drop to a low level in the C region on the graph. Thus, a low-energy signal input causes a comparatively high signal-current charge to occur in the circuit, with the result that amplification occurs. As with transistors, the tunnel diode acts as a power amplifier since voltage gain is unity.

Two typical basic circuits are shown in Fig. 2-20. At A is the series-type circuit, where the tunnel diode (TD) is in series with the output resistor R_2. The forward bias is supplied by a battery in series with the input resistor R_1. The battery or power source is shunted by a bypass capacitor to minimize signal-voltage variations across the

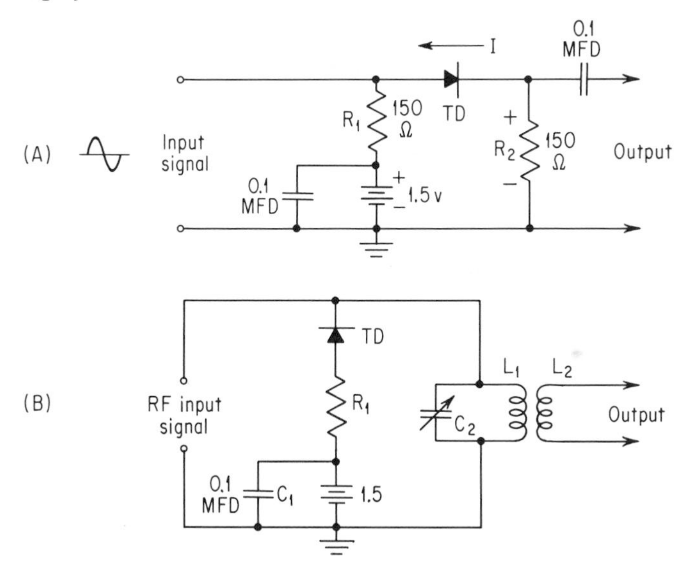

Fig. 2-20. Tunnel-diode amplifiers

battery. If the first alternation of the input signal is positive as shown, it will aid the forward potential of the battery with the result that the total forward-bias voltage is increased and the plate current decreases, resulting in a decrease in the voltage drop across resistor R_2. The result is the production of a negative output alternation. For the second alternation applied to the input, the negative voltage of the signal opposes the positive forward potential of the battery and total forward bias decreases. The result is a rise in current flow and the production of a positive output alternation signal. The circuit shown at A is for low-frequency operation.

At B of Fig. 2-20 is shown an r-f tunnel-diode amplifier. For contrast, a parallel-type tunnel-diode circuit is shown. Here, the tunnel diode shunts the output impedance consisting of the parallel resonance circuit composed of variable capacitor C_2 and inductor L_1. The output is derived via inductance L_2 which, in conjunction with L_1, creates a transformer. Its basic function is similar to the circuit previously described. The forward-bias battery, in conjunction with resistor R_1, sets the bias on the slope of the curve between B and C on the graph to take advantage of the amplifying characteristics of the negative resistance. Again, the signal input alternation aids or opposes the forward-bias potential and varies the negative-resistance characteristics to cause a change in current for the production of the amplified signal energy.

Review Questions for Chapter 2

1. What is the primary factor which determines the classification of an amplifier as Class A, B, etc.?
2. What are the essential differences between a voltage amplifier and a power amplifier?
3. How is cutoff bias procured in a Class C amplifier?
4. What are the essential differences between the grounded-cathode and the grounded-grid amplifiers?
5. Briefly explain the characteristics of the cathode-follower type of circuit. What is its main purpose?
6. To what type of vacuum-tube amplifier does the grounded-emitter transistor amplifier compare?
7. Show by simple drawings the circuit for forward bias and the circuit for reverse bias.
8. In a grounded-emitter transistor amplifier, what circuit changes must be made when an N-P-N transistor is substituted for the P-N-P type? (Assume each transistor has the same basic characteristics.)
9. Briefly explain how cutoff bias is procured in a transistorized Class B amplifier.
10. Show by a simple drawing the basic grounded-base transistor amplifier. To what vacuum-tube amplifier does this compare?
11. Compare the grounded-collector transistor circuit with its vacuum-tube counterpart.
12. Define the terms *cascade amplifier* and *cascode amplifier.*
13. Using simple schematic drawings, show at least two methods by which an amplifier is used as a control device.
14. Briefly explain the characteristics of a direct-coupled amplifier. What is the disadvantage of the vacuum-tube type?
15. What are the advantages of using transistors in direct-coupled amplifiers as compared to the vacuum-tube direct-coupled amplifiers?
16. Briefly explain how an amplifier can be controlled as well as being used as a control device.
17. Describe the general characteristics of the tunnel diode.
18. Describe how a tunnel diode can be used in an amplification circuit to produce results similar to those obtained from triode tubes.

3

Oscillators

INTRODUCTION

Oscillators are used in all branches of electronics to generate signals. Some oscillators generate signals in the audio-frequency range and other oscillators produce signals in the radio-frequency or microwave spectrum. Some oscillators furnish square-wave type signals and others generate sinewaves. Basic oscillator circuits are of two types: the so-called *relaxation* oscillators and the *resonant-circuit* types, both of which are discussed in this chapter.

THE PLATE-COUPLED MULTIVIBRATOR

One form of the relaxation oscillator is the so-called *multivibrator* illustrated in Fig. 3-1. A multivibrator utilizes two tubes, usually contained in one envelope as a dual-triode type. The multivibrator does not, of course, vibrate physically; the term applies only to the electrical rapid-rate oscillations.

As shown in Fig. 3-1, a symmetrical circuit is employed, where both plate resistors, R_1 and R_2, are identical in value. Coupling capacitors C_1 and C_2 are also of identical value, as are the grid leaks R_3 and R_4. As shown, the output signal developed at the plate of V_1 is coupled to the grid of V_2, and the output signal developed at the plate of V_2 is coupled back to the grid of V_1.

Despite the symmetrical circuit, some minor unbalance always exists; hence when power is applied to the circuit, one tube will draw

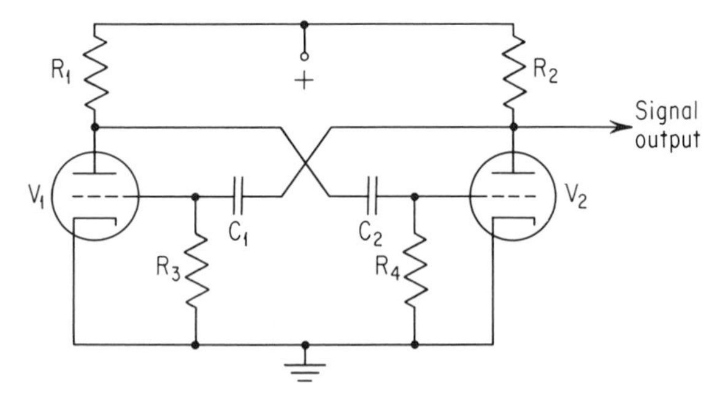

Fig. 3-1. The plate-coupled multivibrator

more current than the other. Assume, for instance, that the current flow for V_1 rises more rapidly than that in V_2. The current through V_1 also flows through resistor R_1, causing a decline in the plate signal voltage of V_1. This is indicated at the left-hand side of the top drawing in Fig. 3-2. The change in voltage at the plate of V_1 is also felt across capacitor C_2, charging the latter with a negative potential at the grid of V_2. Hence, as the voltage at the plate of V_1 declines, the capacitor C_2 establishes an increasing negative potential at the grid of V_2, also shown in the waveform drawing of Fig. 3-2. As the bias on V_2 is made more negative, less current flows through V_2 and in consequence the voltage drop across R_2 declines and the plate voltage for V_2 rises as shown in the third drawing of Fig. 3-2. The rising potential at the plate of V_2 is also felt at the grid of V_1, since capacitor C_1 becomes positively

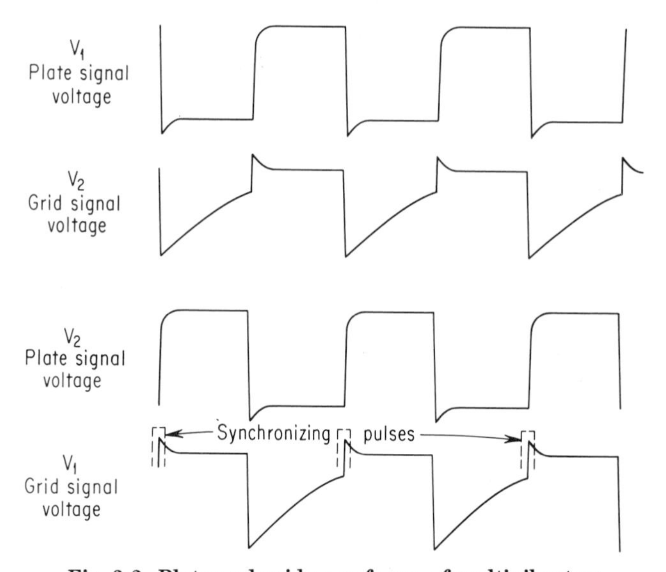

Fig. 3-2. Plate and grid waveforms of multivibrators

charged toward the grid of V_1. The rising positive potential at the grid of V_1 causes an additional increase in current through V_1. The process continues until V_1 has reached saturation, where maximum current flows and V_2 is at cutoff, with zero current flow. At this time there is no longer any *change* of current through either tube.

Capacitor C_2 will now discharge across resistor R_4, thus gradually reducing the high bias value at the grid of V_2. This is shown in the second waveform drawing of Fig. 3-2, where the grid signal voltage is rising. When the charge across C_2 has declined sufficiently to permit V_2 to conduct, the current flow through the latter tube causes an increase in the voltage drop across R_2, hence a decline in the plate voltage for V_2. The voltage decline is felt at the grid of V_1 and again the process continues until V_1 is at cutoff and V_2 is at saturation. Now, capacitor C_1 has been charged to a negative value at the grid of V_1 and to a positive value toward the plate of V_2. Thus, capacitor C_1 holds V_1 at cutoff until C_1 has discharged sufficiently across resistor R_3 to permit vacuum tube V_1 to conduct again. When the latter occurs, the process starts all over again.

As can be seen from Fig. 3-2, the continuous conduction-nonconduction cycles of V_1 and V_2 produce a squarewave voltage at the plate of V_1 as well as at the plate of V_2. Hence, either V_1 anode or V_2 anode can be employed for obtaining the output-signal waveform.

The usefulness of the multivibrator, as well as other relaxation oscillators of this type, is enhanced to a considerable extent because it can be locked in to maintain a frequency which coincides with that of another oscillator. If a series of pulses is applied to the grid of V_1 in Fig. 3-1, such pulses will lock in the multivibrator, provided that the synchronizing pulses occur near the free-running frequency of the multivibrator. As shown in the bottom waveform of Fig. 3-2, the synchronizing pulses can be set slightly ahead of the positive portions of the grid signal voltage of V_1 so that they will cause conduction of V_1 at predetermined intervals.

The multivibrator has been used extensively in television receivers for generating sweep signals the frequencies of which are controlled by synchronizing pulses sent out by the television transmitter. The multivibrator also finds applications in computers, radar, and other industrial devices where squarewave pulses are desired and where synchronization is required. By the use of suitable clipper circuits, single-polarity pulses can be obtained instead of squarewave signals.

CATHODE-COUPLED MULTIVIBRATOR

Another multivibrator circuit in common use is the cathode-coupled type illustrated in Fig. 3-3. Here, the anode of V_1 is coupled

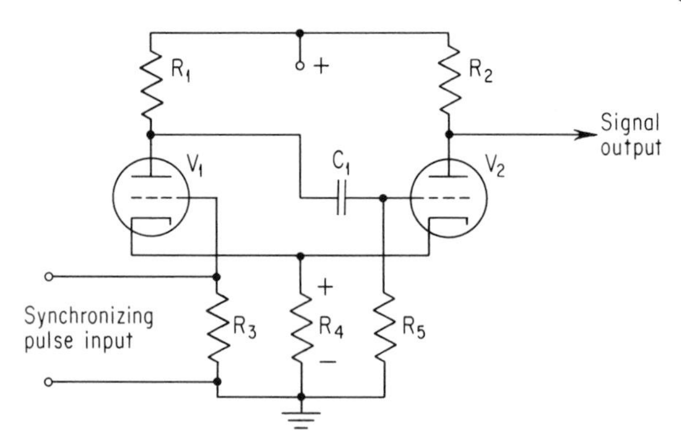

Fig. 3-3. Cathode-coupled multivibrator

to the grid of V_2 using capacitor C_1 in a fashion similar to the plate-coupled type. In the cathode-coupled multivibrator, however, the anode of V_2 is not coupled to the grid of V_1. Instead, common cathode coupling is employed by virtue of resistor R_4 as shown in Fig. 3-3. As with the plate-coupled multivibrator, when power is first applied, one tube initially will conduct more than the other. Assume that current through V_1 rises more rapidly at first. The current flow through R_1 reduces the anode voltage at V_1 and capacitor C_1 is charged with a negative potential toward the grid of V_2 and a positive potential toward the plate of V_1. In consequence, V_2 is driven to cutoff, while V_1 reaches saturation. The voltage drop across resistor R_4 also creates a potential difference with a polarity as shown, which also applies a negative potential to the grid of V_2 with respect to the cathode.

When V_1 is conducting full current at saturation and V_2 is at cutoff, capacitor C_1 discharges across R_5, lowering the bias at the grid of V_2. Eventually, V_2 conducts and reaches saturation, while V_1 is held at cutoff because of the voltage drop across R_4. As with the plate-coupled multivibrator, the process repeats itself and the waveforms are similar to those shown earlier in Fig. 3-2.

TRANSISTOR MULTIVIBRATOR

A typical multivibrator using P-N-P junction transistors is shown in Fig. 3-4. This circuit resembles the plate-coupled multivibrator discussed earlier. As shown, the signal voltage at the collector of T_1 is coupled to the base of transistor T_2 via coupling capacitor C_1. The signal voltage at the collector of T_2 is coupled to the base of T_1 by capacitor C_2.

If transistor T_1 conducts, the voltage drop across collector resistor

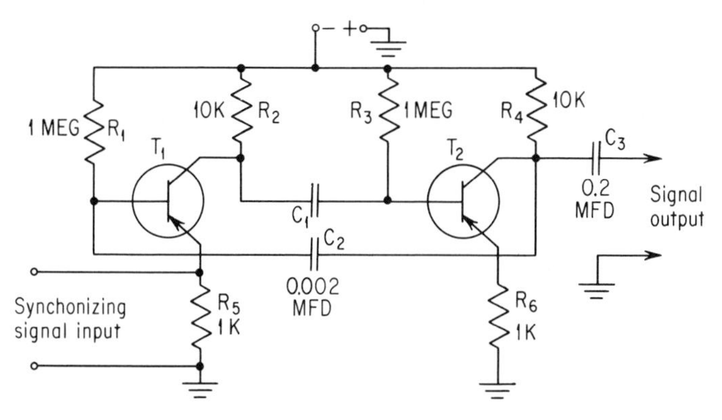

Fig. 3-4. Transistor multivibrator

R_2 will charge capacitor C_1 with a positive polarity at the base of T_2 and a negative polarity at the collector of T_1. The rising positive potential at the base of T_2 reduces conduction through the latter, because the forward bias is being reduced. The reduced conduction through T_2 causes an increase in the negative potential at the collector of T_2, which is coupled by capacitor C_2 to the base of T_1. The increase in the forward-bias potential at the base of T_1 causes an increase in conduction through T_1 until eventually saturation is reached. When T_1 is at saturation, transistor T_2 is at cutoff and no change in conduction occurs. Capacitor C_1 will now discharge, and eventually the point is reached where T_2 conducts. When the latter occurs, there is a decrease in the collector potential and this charges C_2 with a positive polarity at the base of T_1, thus reducing the forward bias of the latter and causing a decrease in conduction. The process continues until T_1 is at cutoff and T_2 at saturation. The waveforms produced at the base of each transistor conform to the grid waveforms shown in Fig. 3-2. Also, the collector waveforms conform to the plate waveforms shown in Fig. 3-2.

BLOCKING OSCILLATOR

The blocking oscillator is another often-used type of relaxation oscillator. The basic circuit is shown at A of Fig. 3-5, and the plate-voltage and grid-voltage waveforms are shown at B.

Initially, assume that the device is turned on and current flow through the tube rises. This changing current also flows through inductance L_1 and a voltage is induced into the secondary winding L_2. The transformer windings are so arranged that the voltage induced across L_2 is positive at the grid and negative at ground. The positive potential change which appears at the grid of the vacuum tube causes

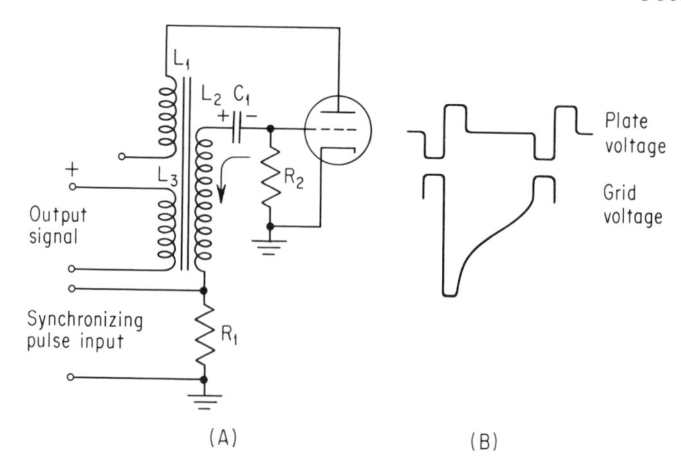

Fig. 3-5. Blocking oscillator and signal waveforms

grid current to flow in the direction shown by the arrow, charging capacitor C_1 with a polarity which is negative toward the grid and positive toward transformer winding L_2. When current flow has reached the saturation level, there is no longer a *change of current,* hence the current flow through L_1 is constant. With constant current through L_1, there is no induced voltage applied to the secondary winding L_2 and the charging of capacitor C_1 ceases. Capacitor C_1 now has a sufficiently high charge to hold the tube at cutoff. The capacitor, however, discharges across the grid leak R_2 so that the cutoff bias gradually declines. During the time the tube is cut off, there is a steady-state plate voltage.

When capacitor C_1 has discharged sufficiently to permit the tube to conduct, the process starts over again. As shown at B, a square-wave signal is obtained at the output and, as with all relaxation oscillators, the frequency of the output signal is determined by the resistance-capacitance constants of the circuit. If capacitor C_1 is made larger, it will take longer to charge it to its peak value and it will also take longer for it to discharge, hence decreasing the frequency of the signal generated. A lower-frequency signal is also obtained by increasing the value of resistor R_2, because it will take longer for the capacitor to discharge. On the other hand, a higher frequency can be produced by decreasing the value of either C_1, R_2, or both. As shown, a three-winding transformer can be employed so that the output signal can be obtained from one of the windings. The resistor R_1, placed in series with inductance L_2, can be utilized for the application of a synchronizing signal so that the free-running frequency of the blocking oscillator can be locked in synchronization with a control signal.

TRANSISTOR BLOCKING OSCILLATOR

A blocking oscillator using a P-N-P transistor is shown in Fig. 3-6. Operation of this oscillator is similar to that of the vacuum-tube type previously discussed. When the transistor conducts, current flows through the emitter-collector side and through the primary winding *P*. As the current rises through the transistor, a voltage is induced into the secondary which causes capacitor C_1 to become charged with a positive polarity toward the transistor base. Since this applies reverse bias to the base-emitter circuit, current flow through the transistor declines. Eventually, capacitor C_1 becomes sufficiently charged to cut off the transistor, hence a steady-state condition occurs. Since there

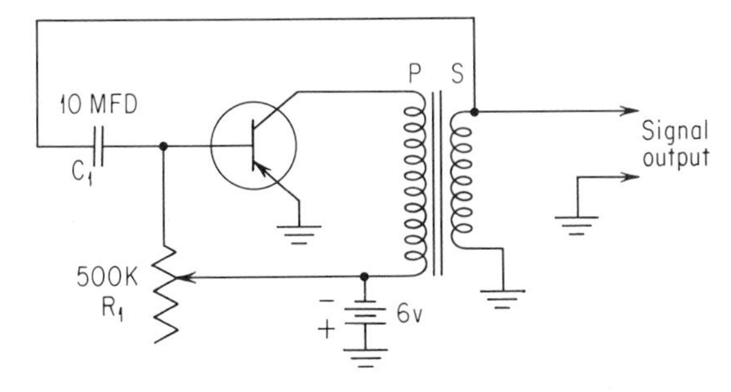

Fig. 3-6. Transistor blocking oscillator

is no change in current through the primary winding, no voltage is induced into the secondary and the charging of capacitor C_1 stops. The capacitor will now discharge across resistor R_1 until the normal forward bias established by the battery prevails and the transistor again conducts. The output waveform is similar to that shown for the vacuum-tube blocking oscillator. The frequency can be altered by varying the ohmic value of R_1 or the capacity value of C_1. Since the transformer contributes to the over-all impedance of the circuit, it also influences the frequency of the blocking oscillator.

FLIP-FLOP CIRCUIT

The Eccles-Jordan flip-flop circuit, named after its originators, is shown in Fig. 3-7. Although this circuit is not strictly an oscillator, its resemblance to the multivibrator and its widespread use in industrial electronics warrant its inclusion here. The flip-flop circuit is extremely useful as a counting device as well as for providing signals for actuating relays or for gating other electronic circuits.

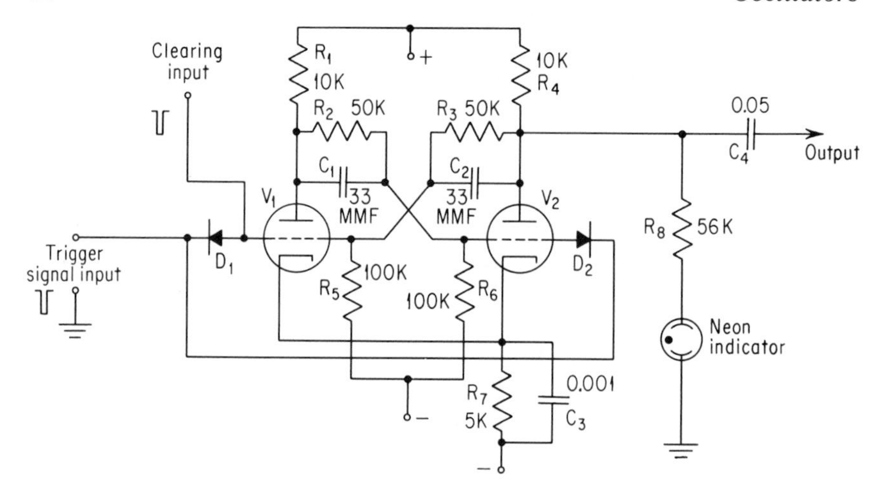

Fig. 3-7. Eccles-Jordan flip-flop circuit

As shown in Fig. 3-7, two tubes are used in a symmetrical circuit which closely resembles the plate-coupled multivibrator. In the flip-flop circuit, however, there is no oscillation and no output waveform is developed, unless an input signal is applied to the circuit. This circuit has two stable states and is often known as a *bistable* circuit. Because of its characteristics it is extensively used in digital computers and can act as a storage device as well as an adder and counter.

One of its two stable states is designated as the *zero* state and the other as the *one* state. When in the zero state, vacuum tube V_1 is nonconducting, and vacuum tube V_2 is conducting. When the device is first turned on, however, either tube could go into conduction before the other, so to make sure that V_1 is nonconducting, a negative pulse is applied initially to its grid. Such a negative pulse is sometimes known as a *clearing pulse* or a *reset pulse.*

In contrast to the plate-coupled multivibrator discussed earlier, note that a negative potential is applied to each grid, via resistors R_5 and R_6. The cathode of each tube also has a negative potential applied to it. With V_1 at cutoff, there is no current flow through resistor R_1, hence the anode voltage at V_1 is at a high level. This potential is also applied to the grid of V_2 through resistor R_2, and this positive potential is sufficiently high to overcome the negative potential normally applied to the grid through R_6. Hence, a positive potential appears at the grid of V_2 which causes the latter to conduct fully at saturation. The current flow through V_2 also flows through the plate resistor R_4, causing a large voltage drop to appear across the latter. Consequently, the plate voltage for V_2 is low. The plate voltage for V_2 is also coupled to the grid of V_1 through resistor R_3.

Because the plate voltage for V_2 is low, however, it is insufficient in value to overcome the negative potential appearing at the grid of V_1 and the latter tube is held at cutoff. Also, the low anode potential of V_2 is coupled to the neon-light indicator through resistor R_8, but the voltage is not high enough to cause the neon indicator to glow. This stable state thus indicates the *zero* condition of the flip-flop.

When a negative pulse is applied to the trigger-signal input terminals, such a pulse will appear at the grid of V_1 and also at the grid of V_2. A negative potential at V_1 grid, however, has no effect on this tube because it is already cut off. A negative polarity applied to the grid of V_2, on the other hand, will drive this tube from its maximum conduction level to the cutoff point. When V_2 current flow ceases, there will no longer be a voltage drop across resistor R_4, hence anode voltage is high. This high anode voltage also appears at the grid of V_1 and overcomes the negative potential, causing this tube to conduct heavily. The high current flow through R_1 sets up a voltage drop across the latter and reduces the anode potential of V_1. The reduced voltage, appearing at the grid of V_2, is insufficient to overcome the negative potential applied through R_6, and V_2 remains at cutoff. The second stable state has now been achieved. The high anode voltage of V_2 will now cause the neon indicator to light; the flip-flop is in the *one* state. Because the anode voltage of V_2 rose from a low steady-state value to a high steady-state value, a positive pulse is developed at the output terminals beyond capacitor C_4. If the flip-flop shown in Fig. 3-7 is followed by a number of other flip-flop stages, only negative pulses will be effective, because of the grid diodes D_1 and D_2. Hence, all subsequent stages of the flip-flop circuits will be in their zero state. (Capacitors C_1 and C_2, because of their voltage-delay characteristics, assure accurate triggering. A trigger pulse, since it appears at both grids, would not only cause one tube to go into nonconduction, but would also hold the other tube at cutoff. The capacitors provide sufficient voltage delay to eliminate this condition.)

Upon the application of another negative signal to the trigger input terminals, V_1 is cut off and V_2 conducts. Thus, the anode voltage of V_2 drops from a high steady-state value to a low steady-state value and develops a negative pulse at the output which is effective in causing the second flip-flop stage to change to its *one* state. The decline of anode voltage at V_2 will cause the neon indicator to go out. The fact that the second flip-flop stage neon indicator is lit indicates that two pulses (each representing a digit) have been entered into the trigger-signal input of the flip-flop stages. In digital computers many stages of flip-flops are used to perform arithmetic operations, as mentioned earlier. Positive pulses can also be employed, by reversing the grid diodes and taking the output from the anode of V_1.

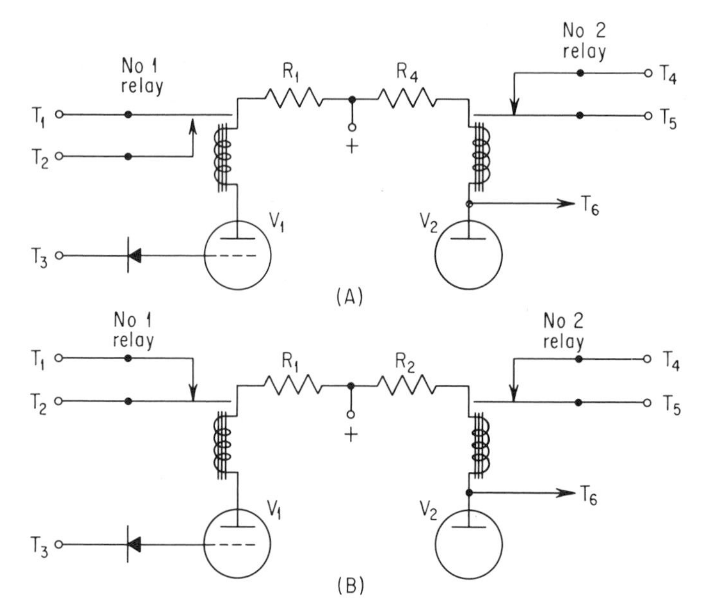

Fig. 3-8. Relay triggering with flip-flop circuits

Because the anode voltages change from low values to high and vice versa during the operation of the flip-flop circuit, the latter can also be utilized to actuate relays or to fire ignitrons and thyratrons as shown in Fig. 3-8. Successive pulse entry into the trigger-signal input of the flip-flop will actuate the devices connected to the anode circuits as shown. The relays can be either the normally open or the normally closed type, depending on the function required, or both types can be used simultaneously, as shown.

For the circuit shown at A of Fig. 3-8, a normally open relay is in the anode circuit of V_1 and a normally closed relay is in the anode circuit of V_2. This is a partial schematic of the complete flip-flop circuit shown earlier in Fig. 3-7. When the flip-flop is in its zero state, V_1 is cut off, and V_2 is operating with a high value of plate current. In consequence, relay no. 1 remains in its normally open condition, but relay no. 2, normally closed, will open because of the current circulating in the solenoid of the relay. If a pulse is now applied to terminal T_3, the trigger-pulse input, V_1 will change from cutoff to saturation, and relay no. 1 closes. The second relay will also close, because V_2 goes into cutoff and the current decline causes the relay to assume its normally closed condition.

From the foregoing, it is evident that if dissimilar relays are used as shown at A of Fig. 3-8, both will perform the same function. Successive pulses applied to the flip-flop alternately open or close circuit terminals, T_1, T_2, and T_4, T_5. If the relays are to perform alternate functions—that is, one provides an open circuit during the time the other closes a circuit—then the arrangement shown at B of Fig. 3-8 can be used. Here, both relays are the normally closed type, although the normally open type could be substituted for reversing the function of the individual relays. When the flip-flop is in its zero state, the cutoff condition of V_1 will not actuate relay no. 1 and the latter remains closed. For relay no. 2 in the anode circuit of V_2, however, the high current circulating in the solenoid will open the relay. Now when a pulse is applied to terminal T_3, high current will flow in the anode circuit of V_1 and relay no. 1 opens. At the same time, V_2 reaches cutoff, and relay no. 2 then assumes its normally closed condition.

Plate-sensitive relays, that is, relays sensitive to small changes of current or low current values, are employed and these in turn can be utilized to open or close larger relays where higher power is to be handled. Output terminal T_6 can be applied to a succeeding flip-flop stage, or the changes of voltage which occur at this terminal during operation can be employed for triggering thyratrons or other devices as required. (See Chapter 6.)

As described earlier in the operational discussion of the flip-flop circuit, there will be one negative pulse output for every two negative pulses applied to the trigger input. Because of the grid diodes, only negative pulses are instrumental in triggering; hence the positive pulse which develops at the output of a flip-flop when the latter is triggered from its *zero* to its *one* state has no effect on a second-stage flip-flop. When the second pulse is applied to a flip-flop, it will trigger the latter into the *zero* state again, but at the same time a negative output pulse is developed which, in turn, will trigger the second flip-flop circuit into its *one* state. Assume, for instance, that four stages of flip-flop are connected in cascade as shown in Fig. 3-9. If two pulses are entered in flip-flop no. 1, the output negative pulse will trigger flip-flop no. 2 into its *one* state. The latter stage will then develop a positive output pulse, but this polarity pulse has no effect on flip-flop no. 3 because of the grid diodes. When a third pulse is entered into the first flip-flop, it will again trigger into its *one* state, but the positive pulse output has no effect on the second flip-flop. When a fourth

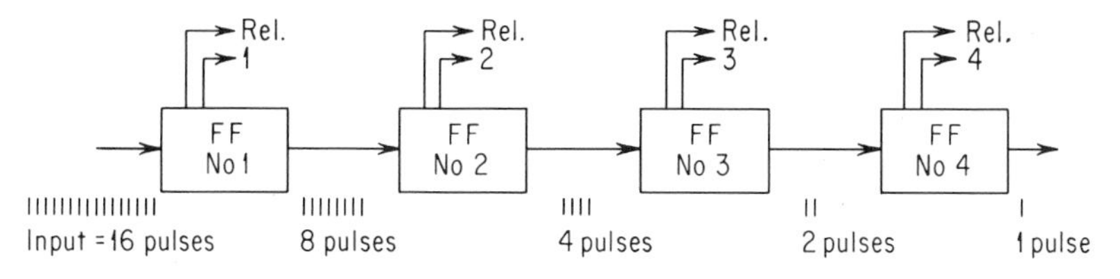

Fig. 3-9. Scaling control relays with cascade flip-flop circuits

pulse is entered into flip-flop no. 1, however, it triggers into its *zero* state and sends a negative pulse to flip-flop no. 2. Since the latter is in its *one* state, it is flipped over to its *zero* state and sends a negative pulse to flip-flop no. 3, which is then triggered into the *one* state.

The step-by-step procedure just detailed indicates that each individual flip-flop produces one negative output pulse for every two entered. Hence, for every four entered, there will be two produced at the output, and for every eight entered, four will be developed at the output. For this reason, a series of flip-flop stages has the ability to *count down,* or *scale.* As shown in Fig. 3-9, if 16 pulses are entered into flip-flop no. 1, there will be eight produced at the output and applied to flip-flop no. 2. From the latter, four pulses are produced and applied to flip-flop no. 3. In turn, flip-flop no. 3 sends two pulses into flip-flop no. 4 and one pulse output is produced from the latter.

The scaling characteristic of a series of flip-flop stages means that relays placed in the anode circuits of the various stages will also perform count-down functions for industrial control applications. The input pulses to the first flip-flop stage can be procured from a photoelectric cell or other sensing devices described elsewhere herein. The photoelectric cell, with a suitable light-beam source, will generate a series of pulse signals as the beam is periodically interrupted. The pulse signals, entering the cascade flip-flop system, then act as the control to perform various functions in counting, fabrication, sorting, or other processes.

As an illustrative example of the application of bistable circuits to the fabrication of metal, note the typical arrangement shown in Fig. 3-10. Here, a continuous metal strip is progressing down an assembly (fabrication) line. The metal strip already has sections bent at right angles as shown, and these upright sections are conveniently employed for breaking the light beam to the protoelectric sensing cell. Hence, as each of the bent sections interrupts the light beam, a pulse is generated. The latter is then amplified, and perhaps shaped or changed in polarity, to suit the triggering requirements of the bistable circuits.

A particular fabrication process for such a metal strip may require that circular holes be punched at each place marked *A,* and square holes punched at each place marked *B.* Also, after each second square section, it may be necessary to cut out a slot marked *C* in the illustration. It may also be required to bend or crimp the metal sheet at various places, separated by a number of the *B* sections.

As the metal sheet moves from left to right, the first upright angle intercepts the light beam and a single pulse output is obtained from the pulse amplifier. This pulse is then used to fire the ignitron or thyratron tube to furnish power to the punch press which will cut

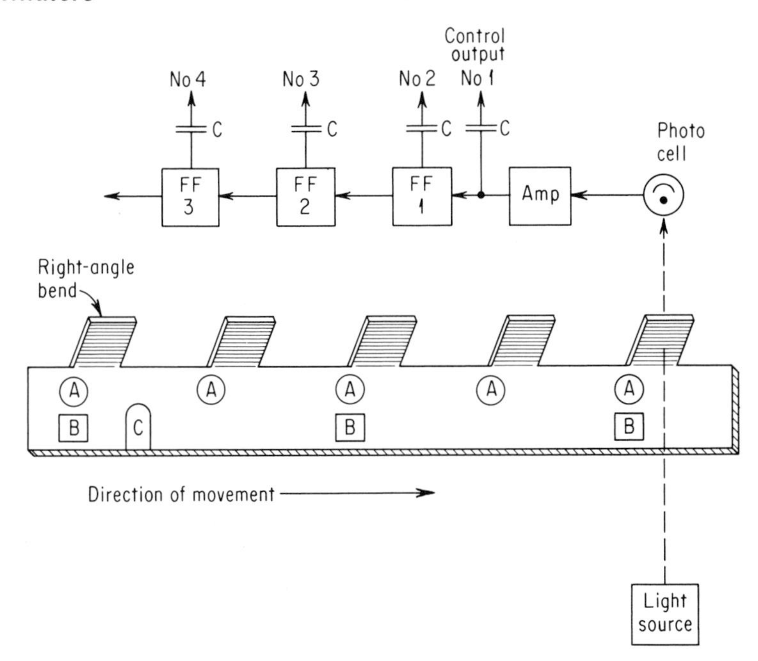

Fig. 3-10. Fabrication control using bistable circuits

the circular holes marked *A,* because for every pulse generated by the breaking of the light beam there is a direct electrical connection from control output no. 1 to the circular-hole press. The pulses also enter the first flip-flop circuit, wherein a single relay is connected in one of the anode circuits. The relay closes and a pulse appears at output no. 2. This pulse controls the punch press for fabricating the square holes marked *B,* and in consequence a square hole is punched below the first round one. The square hole *B,* if necessary, could be punched between the *A* sections, or at any other place desired, by proper placement of the punch press cutting the square hole.

When the interval between the bent sections occurs, the relay in the first flip-flop is still closed, but this represents a steady-state voltage and no additional pulse output occurs from control output no. 2, because the capacitors only transfer a pulse when a voltage change occurs. The opening of the relay would also generate a pulse, but of opposite polarity to that obtained when the relay is closed. The circuits which are triggered, however, will be actuated only for the polarity of pulses obtained when the relay *closes.* (Relative triggering polarities are discussed later.)

When the second bent section interrupts the light beam, another pulse is obtained from the photocell and again a circular hole is punched. The second pulse enters the first flip-flop and causes the relay to open. Consequently, no square hole is punched at this time. The entry of a second pulse into the first flip-flop produces a triggering pulse which closes the relay in the second flip-flop and produces an output at no. 3 terminal. This could be used to perform some function such as crimping, bending, or punching around the area of the second circular hole from the right, but is not employed in this instance.

When the third bent section produces a pulse from the photocell, the third circular hole is punched, and at the same time the relay in the first flip-flop is actuated, producing the signal to cut the second square hole. At the fourth bent section, the pulse produced again causes a circular hole to be cut, but the relay in the first flip-flop is opened and no signal of correct polarity is sent to the square-hole cutting circuitry. As the fourth pulse triggers the first flip-flop, the latter sends a pulse to the second flip-flop, causing the latter to revert back to its original state. Hence, the relay in the second flip-flop opens, and when a flip-flop is triggered to its *zero* state, a triggering pulse is sent to the next stage. Consequently, flip-flop no. 3 is triggered on and its relay closes, sending a control pulse through ouput no. 4 to the punch-press circuitry for cutting out the elongated circular section marked *C*. As the metal sheet moves along, successive circular *A* holes are cut in progression, and alternate square *B* holes are cut as shown. After each *fourth* bent strip, the section marked *C* is cut.

The entire process just described in detail could be duplicated by mechanical means, but the electronic control system can operate at much higher speeds, is more compact, and provides more flexibility with specification changes in the particular fabrication process.

When it is not feasible to employ the photocell (for instance, when perfectly flat sheets move down the line), the sensing device can be one that takes advantage of rotation as shown in Fig. 3-11. A plastic disk is connected to a shaft, and the latter has a roller at one end. The roller is rotated by the moving sheet of metal or material to be fabricated. Instead of the sheet's moving directly across the roller,

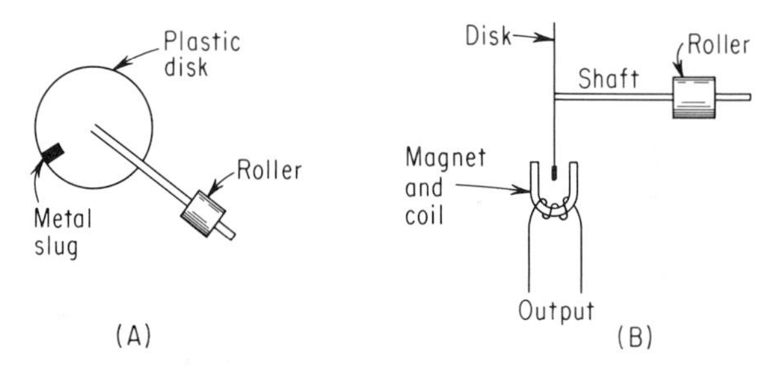

Fig. 3-11. Electric sensing device

the shaft of the sensing device can be rotated by the same mechanical means used to move the sheet metal along the line. In the plastic disk is imbedded at one section an iron slug, as shown at A. The side view is given at B, and the pickup device is also shown. The latter consists of a horseshoe-type magnet with a coil. As the plastic disk rotates, the metal slug moves through the magnetic fields of the sensing device, and the process of cutting the lines of force of the magnet induces a voltage across the coil, with a resultant current flow. Hence, each time the slug moves through the fields, a pulse is generated for use in controlling the electronic circuits which will actuate the fabricating processes.

The number of pulses produced during a given time interval can be regulated by the speed of the disk rotation, which in turn depends on the roller size and the speed at which the metal sheet moves along the fabrication line. The diameter of the plastic disk also regulates the number of pulses produced for a given time interval. An increase in the number of pulses per minute (or fraction thereof) can also be accomplished by placing more metal slugs along the circumference of the plastic disk. (Additional sensing devices are described in Chapter 6.)

TRANSISTOR FLIP-FLOP

A flip-flop circuit using two P-N-P transistors is shown in Fig. 3-12. The operation of this circuit is similar to that of the vacuum-tube type previously discussed. If transistor T_1 is conducting, there will be a voltage drop across resistor R_1, and a low voltage appears at the base of transistor T_2. The reduction of forward bias on the latter stops current flow. Collector voltage for T_2 increases and this is felt

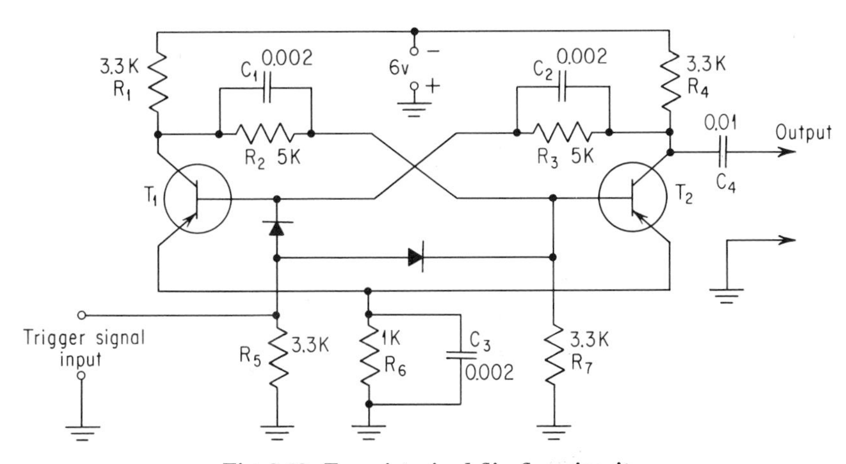

Fig. 3-12. Transistorized flip-flop circuit

at the base of T_1, where the increase in negative potential raises the forward bias and increases conduction. Eventually the state is reached where T_1 conducts at saturation and T_2 is cut off. Upon the application of a positive triggering pulse to R_5, a positive voltage appears at both base circuits. Transistor T_2, however, is already cut off and the reverse bias appearing at the base has no effect. For T_1, however, the positive potential at the base applies sufficient reverse bias to cut current flow through this transistor to zero. When current flow stops, collector voltage for T_1 rises to a high *negative* value and applies forward bias to T_2, permitting the latter to conduct. When the latter conducts, a large voltage drop occurs across R_4 and the voltage at the base of T_1 becomes less negative; as the process continues, in a fraction of a second T_1 is at cutoff and T_2 at saturation. The application of another positive pulse to the base circuits will flip the circuit over and again it will revert to its original state. The output can be obtained from either collector circuit as required, depending on which bistable state is designated as the *zero* state and which the *one* state.

HARTLEY OSCILLATOR

The oscillator shown in Fig. 3-13, known as the *Hartley oscillator* after its inventor, generates a signal, the frequency of which is regulated by adjustments of the variable capacitor C_1. Feedback is accomplished by coupling the anode circuit to the grid circuit by a single coil which is tapped to form two sections (L_2 and L_3) as shown. Resonance is achieved by the inductance formed by L_2 and L_3 in conjunction with the capacitor C_1. The interchange of energy between the capacitor and the inductance (known as flywheel effect) establishes the frequency of the sinewave produced. The r-f (or audio) output is obtained by a transformer arrangement whereby coil section L_3 acts as a primary for the inductance L_1.

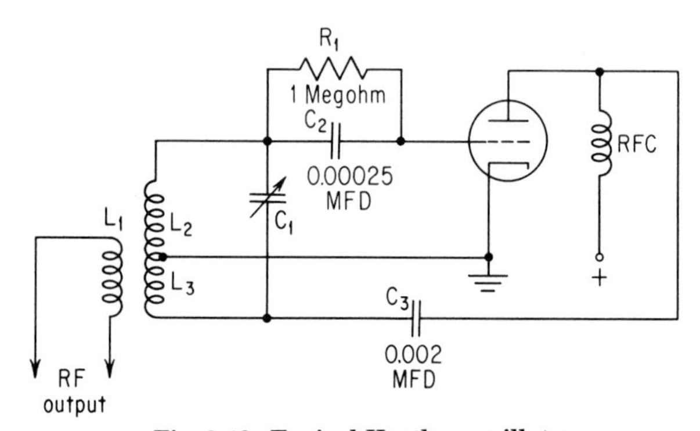

Fig. 3-13. Typical Hartley oscillator

There is no applied bias to this tube, but bias is developed because the grid signal goes positive for every other alternation. When the grid goes positive, it charges capacitor C_2 so that it is negative at the grid side and positive at the inductor side. When the signal which is circulating across the resonance circuit swings in the negative direction, capacitor C_2 discharges across resistance R_1 and thus maintains a bias substantially beyond the cutoff point. Since the grid signal is sufficiently high in amplitude to drive the grid positive periodically, plate current flows in spurts. Such periodic bursts of plate current flow through inductance L_3 and supply energy to the resonance circuit at intervals corresponding to the cyclic interchange of energy between the tuning capacitor and the inductance. Capacitor C_3 isolates the d-c from the cathode circuit and prevents it from being grounded. The time constant (RC) of R_1 and C_1 must be of the proper value for circuit efficiency. The inductance in series with the positive anode voltage source is to isolate the radio-frequency energy from the power supply and prevent losses which would otherwise occur when this oscillator is used to generate r-f. This inductance is referred to as a *radio-frequency choke* (r-f-c).

Oscillators of this type may drift from the desired frequency because of temperature effects, variations in power-supply voltages, and changes in component-part values. When greater stability is required, the electron-coupled and crystal oscillators discussed subsequently must be employed.

TRANSISTOR HARTLEY OSCILLATOR

A transistorized Hartley-type oscillator employing an N-P-N transistor is shown in Fig. 3-14. Circuit operation for this oscillator is similar to the vacuum-tube Hartley previously discussed. The grid leak-capacitor combination consists of C_2 and R_1. Capacitor C_3 is for

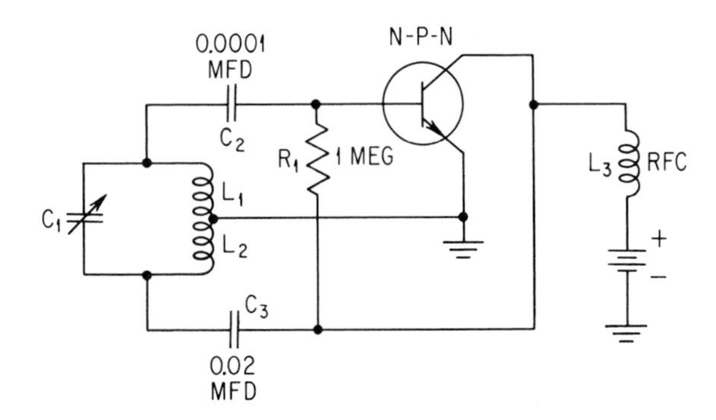

Fig. 3-14. Transistor Hartley oscillator

isolation purposes, to prevent the shorting of the negative voltage at ground potential to the positive potential applied to the base and collector. As with other transistor circuits discussed herein, a P-N-P type can be employed provided that its characteristics are such that it will operate efficiently at the signal frequency which is to be procured. However, when a P-N-P transistor is used, the battery potentials must be reversed.

ELECTRON-COUPLED OSCILLATOR

A typical electron-coupled oscillator is shown in Fig. 3-15. This oscillator incorporates an electronic coupling between the primary oscillator section and the output, and at the same time provides isolation with respect to loading effects so that the stability of the oscillator is considerably greater than that of the ordinary Hartley.

The electron-coupled oscillator utilizes the Hartley principle except that the screen grid of the tube is utilized as the *anode of the oscillator.* (Because the screen grid is positive, it can act as an anode; the only restriction is that it cannot handle as much power as an actual plate.) Thus, the Hartley-oscillator section of the electron-coupled oscillator functions the same way as the Hartley oscillator previously described. Inductance L_2 is the anode inductance (screen grid) while L_1 is the control-grid inductance section. Signal-current variations occur between cathode and screen grid, but because current also flows to the plate of the electron-coupled oscillator tube, the signal-voltage variations are also present in the latter circuit. Thus, the electron stream is used to couple the signal-current variations which occur for the Hartley-oscillator section to the output resonant circuit composed of C_3 and L_3. Variations in the load imposed on the output circuit usually affect the stability of an oscillator, but in the electron-coupled oscillator the r-f signal output which is applied to the load is not taken from the oscillator inductances L_1 and L_2 but

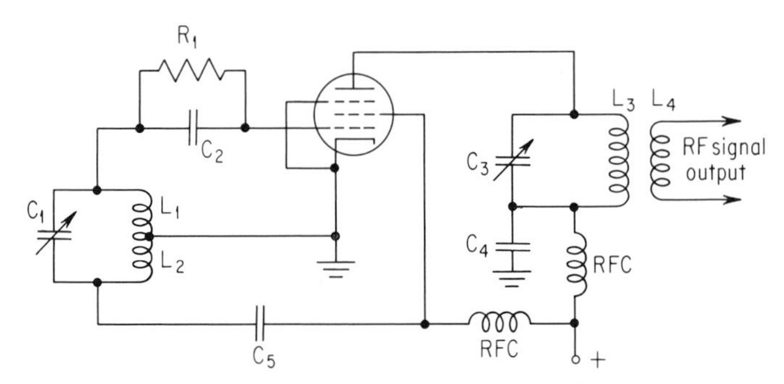

Fig. 3-15. The electron-coupled oscillator

instead from a separate inductance L_3. Thus, variations in the load circuit have little effect on the actual oscillator section, hence the stability of the electron-coupled oscillator is much superior to that of the ordinary Hartley oscillator described earlier.

THE CRYSTAL OSCILLATOR

Where the highest order of oscillator stability is desired, a piezo-quartz crystal is utilized as shown in Fig. 3-16. The piezo-quartz will vibrate at a given frequency when subjected to electric energy. The frequency of oscillation depends on the thickness of the crystal and the manner in which it is cut from the original crystal. The thinner the slab of crystal, the higher the resonant frequency. As shown, the crystal is placed in the grid circuit of the oscillator, and because of its vibrations it generates the fundamental frequency of the oscillator. In the anode section the resonant circuit is composed of C_2 and L_1. The latter inductance forms the output transformer in conjunction with inductance L_2. Resistor R_2 in shunt with capacitor C_1 is a form of protective bias which will prevent tube damage in case the crystal fails to oscillate.

The crystal slab is held between two flat plates, one of which is attached to ground and the other to the grid as shown in Fig. 3-16. The two plates form a capacitance and, in combination with R_1, achieve cutoff bias as with the Hartley oscillator previously described. Capacitor C_3 places the bottom of the resonant circuit at ground potential, while inductance L_3 is a radio-frequency choke which isolates the signal energy from the power supply. For extreme stability the crystal is placed in an enclosure known as a *crystal oven* and a heating element within the oven keeps the crystal chamber at a constant temperature. Thus, the slight drift in frequency which might occur because of temperature changes is minimized. Coupling between the amplified output-signal energy and the grid section occurs by virtue of the interelectrode capacities of the tube. When a pentode

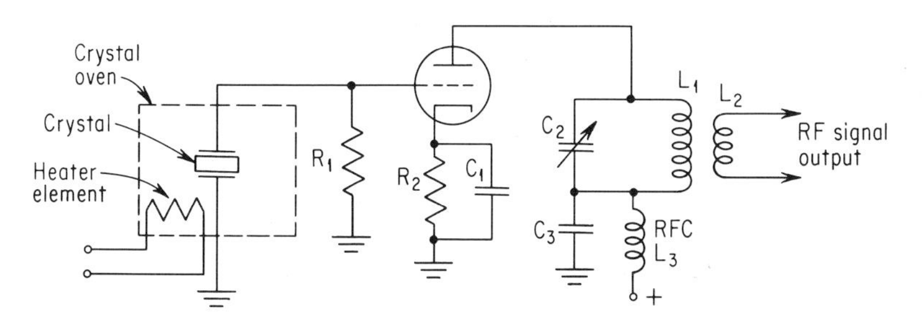

Fig. 3-16. The crystal oscillator

tube is employed, it may be necessary to place an external capacitor between the anode and the grid to maintain oscillations.

TRANSISTOR CRYSTAL OSCILLATOR

A transistorized version of the crystal oscillator is shown in Fig. 3-17, where a grounded-base circuit is employed. As mentioned earlier, there is no phase reversal between the input and output of a grounded-base circuit, hence the crystal can be placed between the

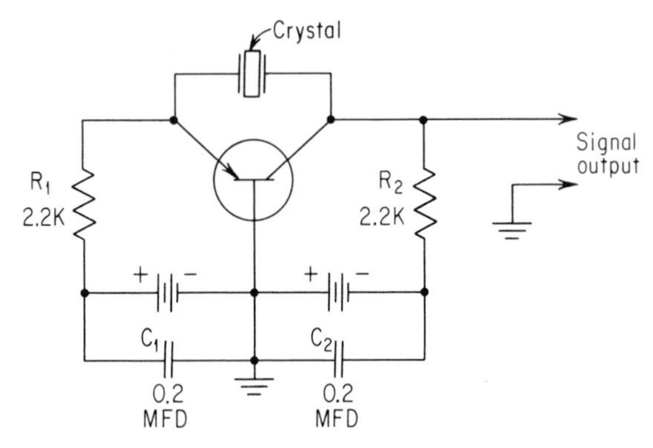

Fig. 3-17. Transistor crystal oscillator

emitter and collector as shown to provide a coupling path to sustain oscillations. The oscillations produced are the result of the crystal's acting as a resonant circuit. Capacitors C_1 and C_2 have a bypass effect across the batteries, hence they provide a direct return to the base circuit for the signal energy in the emitter and collector sections. The output-signal energy is procured from across resistor R_2 placed between collector and ground as shown.

ADDITIONAL OSCILLATORS

Two additional r-f oscillators, used less frequently in industrial electronics, are shown in Fig. 3-18. The one at A is known as the *tuned-plate tuned-grid* oscillator because of an independent tuned resonant circuit in both the grid and plate sections. As with the crystal oscillator previously described, coupling between the output and input circuits is provided by the capacities existing within the tube elements. If a pentode is employed, it may be necessary to connect a capacitor between the anode and grid of the tube to sustain oscillations. Cutoff bias is procured in a fashion similar to that described for the previously discussed oscillators. Typical component values for broadcast-band frequency generation are shown.

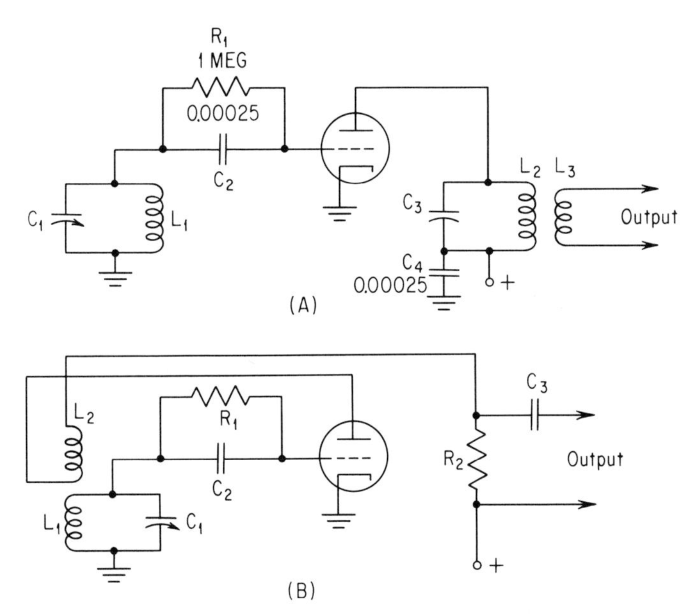

Fig. 3-18. TPTG and feedback oscillators

The oscillator illustrated schematically at B is a feedback type, the latter function accomplished by inductance L_2 (commonly referred to as a *tickler* coil). By use of this coil, a portion of the anode r-f energy is inductively coupled to the grid inductance L_1 to sustain oscillations. The degree of coupling is regulated by spacing between L_1 and L_2 as well as by the number of turns of coil L_2. The connecting leads to inductance L_2 must be transposed to bring the signals into phase if the circuit fails to oscillate. The output r-f energy is obtained from across the output resistor R_2 and capacity-coupled to a Class C amplifier or other circuit via C_3.

SAWTOOTH GENERATOR

In addition to the sinewave and pulse waveforms required in industrial electronics, it is often necessary to generate a sawtooth-type waveform for use in the sweep circuits of oscilloscopes or in other devices where a gradually rising waveform with an abrupt decline is required. A sawtooth generating circuit is sometimes known as a *discharge* circuit because the charging and discharging characteristics of a capacitor are utilized for forming the sawtooth waveform.

A basic discharge circuit is shown in Fig. 3-19. At A, a negative voltage is applied to the grid of the tube which has sufficient amplitude to bias the tube to cutoff. With the tube at cutoff, it has an

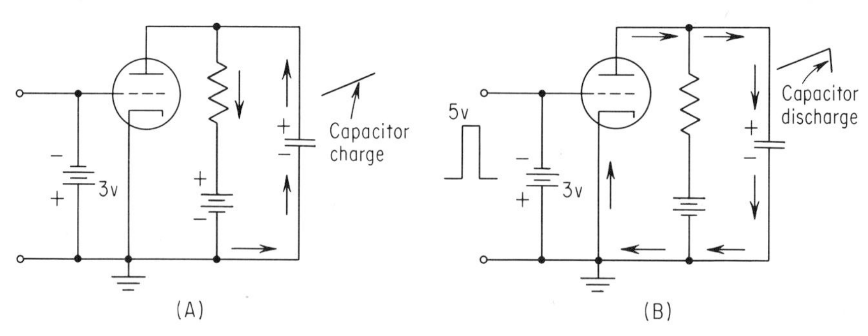

Fig. 3-19. Basic discharge circuit

extremely high resistance and represents an open circuit. Under the conditions just outlined, the circuit shown at A of Fig. 3-19 will start to charge the capacitor as soon as the switch is closed and power applied. The capacitor charges in the direction shown by the arrows, current flowing from the negative side of the battery to the bottom of the capacitor, and current flowing away from the top side of the capacitor and through the resistor to the positive terminal of the battery. The capacitor will start to charge, with the voltage rising at a fairly linear rate initially, although it would curve in an exponential manner if the capacitor were permitted to approach the full charge. With a large capacitor, and a series limiting resistor, advantage is taken of the linear rise portion and the voltage builds up across the capacitor as shown.

If a positive signal voltage is now applied between grid and cathode of the circuit as shown at B, the positive signal voltage will overcome the negative voltage of the bias battery and the tube will conduct suddenly. When the tube is conducting, its internal resistance is low and such a low resistance now shunts the sawtooth-forming circuit. Consequently, the low impedance path provided by the tube permits the capacitor to discharge suddenly in the direction shown by the arrows. The sudden discharge causes a decline in the voltage across the capacitor and a single sawtooth waveform is thus produced. When the incoming signal declines to zero, the bias battery again cuts off the tube, and current flow through the latter ceases. Consequently, the tube again presents a high impedance to the sawtooth-forming circuit, and the battery again starts to charge the capacitor to form the gradual incline of the sawtooth waveform. Upon the arrival of the second signal at the input of the circuit, the capacitor again discharges through the tube to form the second sawtooth. Repetitions of the process form successive sawteeth.

For the basic circuit shown in Fig. 3-19, the frequency of the sawtooth waveform will depend on the frequency of the incoming pulses at the grid, since the latter will determine the discharge rates of the sawtooth signals. If the pulses arrive at more frequent intervals, the sawtooth waveform will not reach as high an amplitude before its decline portion. If the incoming pulses are at a lower repetitive rate, the amplitude of the sawtooth will build up to a higher level before discharging. The amplitude of the sawtooth waveform can also be adjusted by a variable resistor used in place of the fixed resistor shown in Fig. 3-19. Thus, when an input pulse train of a different repetition rate is employed, the variable resistor can be used to maintain the output sawtooth amplitude at the level previously established.

For synchronization of the sawtooth signal frequency, a relaxation-type oscillator such as a multivibrator or blocking oscillator is usually employed. A typical blocking oscillator and discharge circuit is shown in Fig. 3-20. As described previously, the grid of the blocking oscillator is cut off periodically, and as the capacitor C_1 discharges, a short interval of conduction occurs to produce the waveform shown. If the grid of the blocking-oscillator tube V_1 is now connected to the grid of the discharge tube V_2, the waveform developed at the grid of V_1 will also be applied to the grid of V_2. Thus, while the blocking-oscillator grid is at cutoff, the negative voltage also appears at the grid of V_2 and holds the latter at cutoff. During this time the power supply or battery of the discharge circuit charges capacitor C_2 and the initial rising voltage of the sawtooth waveform is developed.

When capacitor C_1 of the blocking oscillator has discharged across R_2 sufficiently to permit tube conduction, both V_1 and V_2 go into full conduction suddenly. During conduction, capacitor C_2 of the discharge circuit will discharge through the low impedance of the conducting tube V_2 and the decline portion of the sawtooth waveform is developed across the sawtooth-forming capacitor C_2. The blocking oscillator, after conduction, is driven to the cutoff region again as shown by the

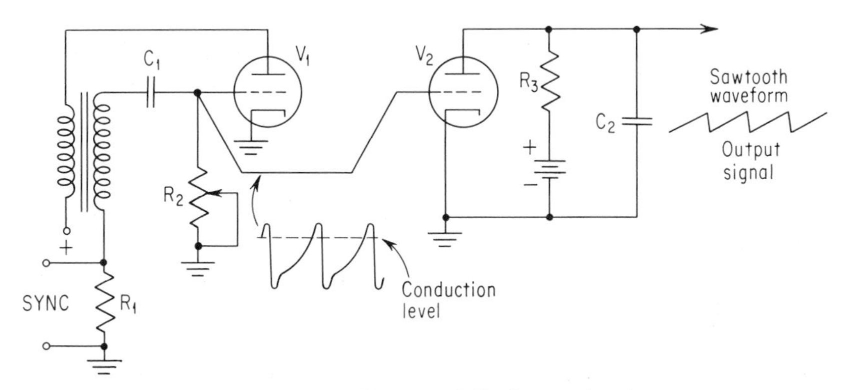

Fig. 3-20. Oscillator and discharge circuits

grid waveform. Since the grids of V_1 and V_2 are common, V_2 also is cut off and the discharge circuit starts to charge capacitor C_2 again. Repetitions of the previously described process form the sawtooth signal train illustrated in Fig. 3-20.

The gradual incline of voltage of the sawtooth makes the waveform useful for sweep purposes in oscilloscopes, television cameras, television picture tubes, and other devices. When the sawtooth waveform is applied to the horizontal deflection plates of an oscilloscope tube, for instance, as shown in Fig. 3-21, the gradual incline of voltage makes the plate at the right more positive as the plate at the left becomes more negative. Hence, the electron beam traveling between these plates is influenced by the electrostatic fields set up by the voltage applied to the plates. The negative potential on the left plate repels the electrons in the electron beam, while the positive potential on the right-hand plate attracts the electrons. Consequently, the beam's position will be altered and the beam will move to the right. As the voltage on the plates gradually increases, the beam is pulled from left to right, leaving a glowing, visible trace on the phosphor screen.

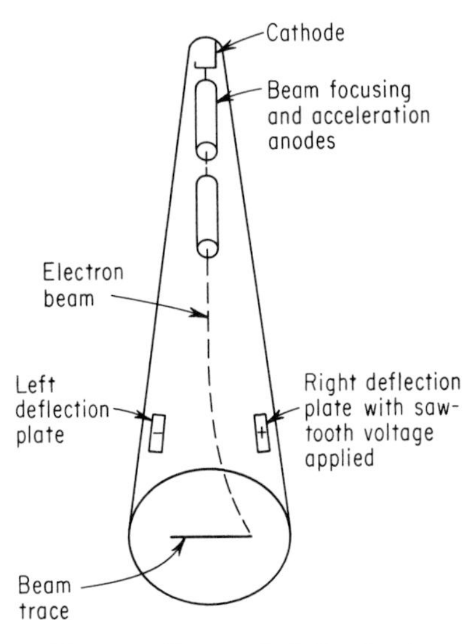

Fig. 3-21. Sawtooth deflection in oscilloscope tube

In industrial closed-circuit television the beam deflection in the cameras is controlled by deflection coils rather than by deflection plates. Deflection coils are also used in industrial television receivers, as well as in receivers designed for private use. A magnetic field deflects an electron beam at right angles, as mentioned for the Hall effect in Chapter 1, hence the vertical deflection coils are at the right and left of the tube neck, whereas the horizontal coils are at top and bottom as shown in Fig. 3-22. For magnetic deflection it is necessary to use a sawtooth of current in the coils, and to produce this, it is necessary to use a modified sawtooth waveform for the reasons given below.

If a small inductance has a large value of resistance in series with it or the coil itself has a high d-c resistance, a sawtooth of signal voltage will produce a sawtooth of current through the inductance as shown at A of Fig. 3-23. If the resistor has a ohmic value which is ten or more times the ohmic value of the inductive reactance, the prop-

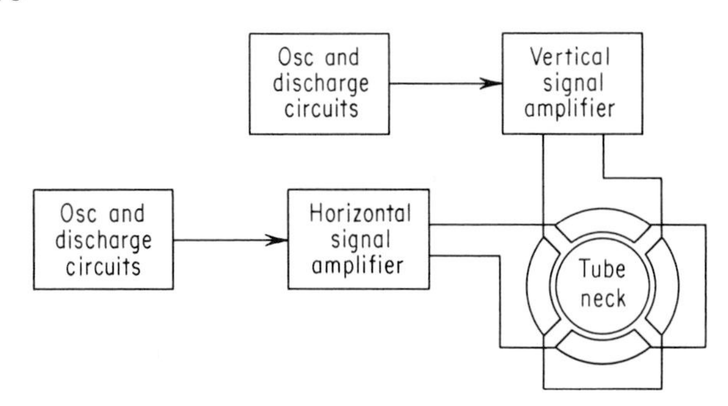

Fig. 3-22. Principle of magnetic deflection

erties of the inductance which tend to oppose a current change will have little effect, since the circuit is primarily resistive. If, however, a large value of inductance is employed and there is very little resistance in the circuit, the conditions prevail as shown at B of Fig. 3-23. Here the resistance indicated would be the *total* resistance of a circuit, including any series resistors plus the internal resistance of the inductance. In this instance, the ohmic value of the inductive reactance is substantially greater than the ohmic value of the resistance so that the circuit is primarily inductive. In such an instance, it is necessary to employ an input-signal waveform voltage which is substantially a

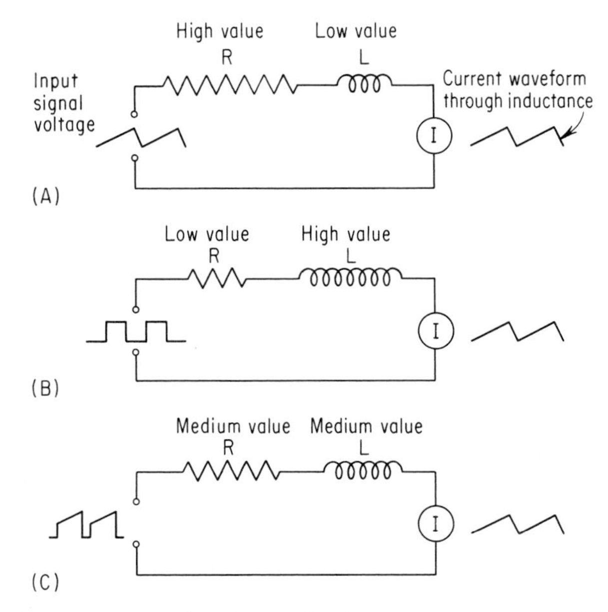

Fig. 3-23. Input signals required to produce a sawtooth of current

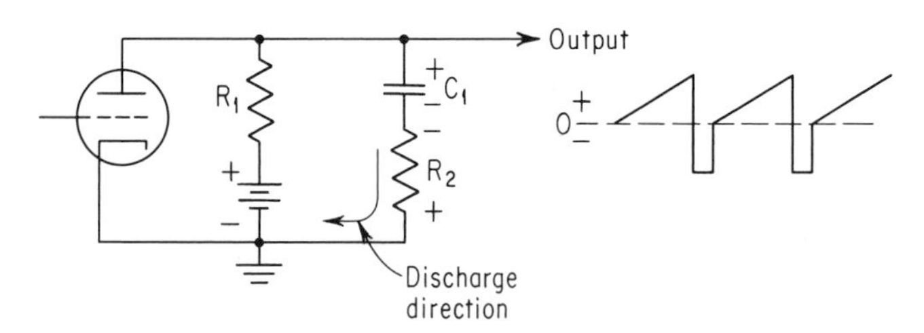

Fig. 3-24. Circuit for sawtooth modification

squarewave such as shown. Here, the voltage rises from a low value to a maximum and levels off, maintaining such a maximum for a definite time interval. During this time, the current through the inductance rises gradually. Before the current rise can curve exponentially because of the time-constant factor, the squarewave of voltage drops suddenly and the collapsing fields of the coil produce the discharge portion of the sawtooth of current. Thus, successive squarewaves at the input will produce a series of sawteeth of current as shown at B.

When both the resistance and inductive reactance values are of a medium value (or both are of like value, either high or low) a modified type of squarewave must be employed in order to obtain a sawtooth of current as shown at C of Fig. 3-23. Since the resistive component of the circuit prevents the inductance from having a full 90-degree current-lag characteristic, the modified waveform will compensate for the dual influence of the resistance and capacitance and will produce the current sawtooth shown.

The modified signal shown at the input of C is sometimes known as a *modified squarewave,* since it can be considered as a squarewave with a sloping top section rather than a horizontal top section. However, the waveform is also referred to as *modified sawtooth,* because it resembles a sawtooth waveform with a negative pulse incorporated in its decline section. Such a modified waveform can be produced by placing a resistor in series with the discharge capacitor of the sawtooth-forming circuit as shown in Fig. 3-24. The additional resistance incorporated into the circuit by adding the waveform-modifying resistor can be compensated for by readjustment of R_1 in series with the power supply, to obtain the same time constant as heretofore. Thus, the waveform-modifying resistor R_2 has little effect on the charging cycle of the sawtooth-forming capacitor C_1 during the time the tube is nonconducting. When the tube conducts, capacitor C_1 discharges through the tube in the direction shown by the arrow. Of necessity, the discharge current must flow through resistor R_2, and in consequence the capacitor not only discharges to its zero level but in so doing it establishes a voltage drop across resistor R_2 in the nature of a squarewave of negative polarity. Since the capacitor discharges suddenly, there will be current flow through the resistor only during the time the capactior is discharging; consequently, a short-duration rectangular pulse of negative polarity is added to the discharge section of the sawtooth waveform as shown. When the resulting modified waveform is now applied to an inductance wherein is also present a medium value of resistance as compared to the inductance, the modified waveform will produce a sawtooth of current in the inductance.

OTHER SOLID-STATE OSCILLATORS

In addition to the transistor oscillators previously discussed, the Unijunction transistor and the tunnel diode also lend themselves to the design of signal generators. The basic principles of the tunnel diode, plus amplifier circuitry, have already been covered in previous chapters. The GE Unijunction transistor, like the tunnel diode and the vacuum-tube tetrode, has negative-resistance characteristics which make it advantageous in switching and generating circuits. It also exhibits thyratron characteristics (see Chapter 5).

As shown at A of Fig. 3-25 the Unijunction transistor is formed from a bar of N-type silicon to which is chemically joined another element (such as indium) to form a P-N junction. As shown, there are two base leads and one emitter lead. The basic circuit is shown at B, with voltage polarities applied as indicated.

If zero (or reverse) voltage is at the emitter, the bar acts as a conventional resistor. Because the emitter taps the bar, a voltage difference exists between the emitter and ground. When a forward bias is now applied (above that present at the emitter) transistor action occurs and the resistance of the bar between the emitter and base 1 decreases, with a resultant current increase. The emitter voltage can now be decreased with a consequent current increase (negative-resistance characteristic). Because a reduction of emitter voltage no

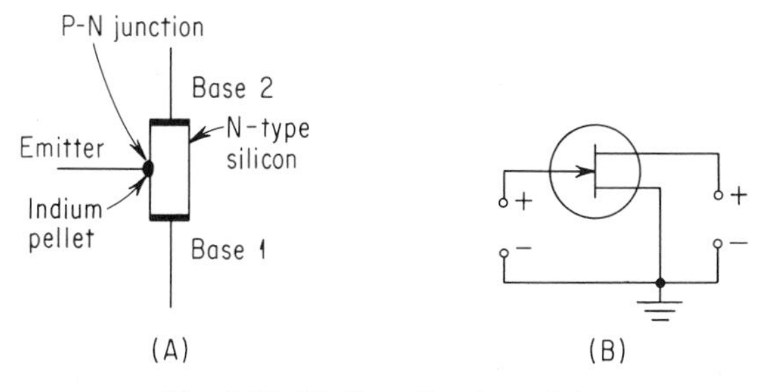

Fig. 3-25. Unijunction transistor

longer decreases base current, a thyratron action prevails. These qualities make a single Unijunction transistor sufficient for producing relaxation oscillators or bistable circuits.

Unijunction Oscillator

A basic circuit of a Unijunction oscillator is shown in Fig. 3-26. As the positive voltage builds up across capacitor C_1 it finally reaches a level above the emitter potential and the transistor is triggered into the high-conduction state. With the lowering of impedance between

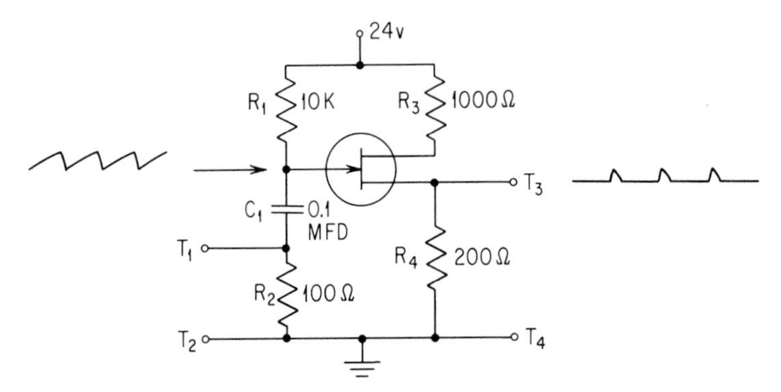

Fig. 3-26. Unijunction oscillator

the emitter and base 1, the capacitor discharges and drops the emitter potential into the reverse-bias region and the cycle starts over again. Thus, this circuit is basically a relaxation-type oscillator. The frequency of the signal output can be altered by changing the values of R_1 and C_1. Terminals T_1 and T_2 are for synchronizing purposes as with the relaxation oscillators previously described. The output is obtained from terminal T_3, although if a sawtooth type of waveform were desired, it could be obtained from a terminal connected to the emitter.

If resistor R_1 is increased to a value above 1 megohm, the transistor oscillator shuts off. By proper selection of resistor and voltage values the circuit will operate as a bistable flip-flop unit, with terminal T_1 acting as a positive trigger input or terminal T_3 acting as a negative trigger input for obtaining the conduction state. A reverse polarity signal at either terminal will revert the circuit back to a nonconducting state.

Tunnel-diode Oscillator

Because of the negative-resistance characteristics of the tunnel diode, it can also be used in relaxation oscillators or bistable circuits.

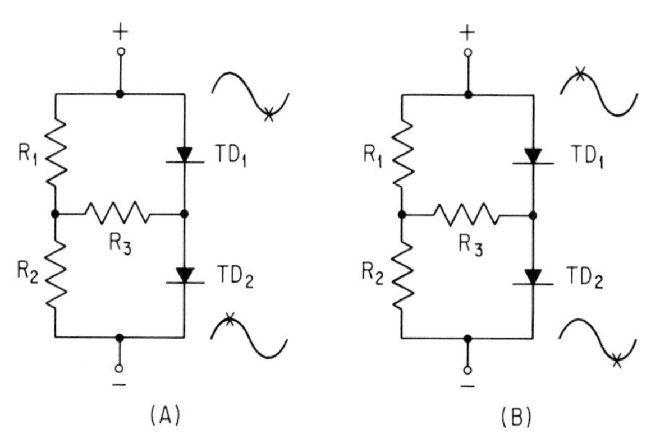

Fig. 3-27. Tunnel-diode bistable states

Consider, for instance, the circuit shown at A of Fig. 3-27 which represents one state. Here, diode TD_2 has a relatively high current compared to TD_1. This high current through TD_2 presents a low impedance and virtually applies the negative d-c supply potential to the bottom of TD_1, thus assuring the latter of high voltage. Since the voltage on TD_1 is sufficiently high, it brings the latter to the low-current (high-resistance) point of the graph, as shown. Thus, TD_1 has a high impedance, and current flow for TD_2 takes the lower-resistance path through R_1 and R_3. The resultant low voltage on TD_2 keeps the operation at the high-current point of the graph as shown.

For the second state, assume that TD_1 has a low voltage on it and operates at the current peak of the graph as shown at B of Fig. 3-27. Thus, TD_1 has a low resistance and virtually places the positive potential of the d-c supply to the top of TD_2, driving the latter to the low-current point of operation as shown. This represents a high resistance for TD_2, hence current flow for TD_1 (from the negative terminal) is via resistors R_2 and R_3, keeping the voltage on TD_1 at a low value.

Shown at A of Fig. 3-28 is the type of basic multivibrator developed by General Electric engineers for high-frequency signal output. Inductance L_1, by virtue of the back emf produced by collapsing fields during current changes, keeps the circuit in continuous operation and triggers it from one state to another. As the current through one diode reaches a value as determined by the voltage applied, a current change no longer is felt through the inductance and the collapsing field causes the voltage to rise in the other diode with a consequent reversal of the state. Resistors R_1 and R_2 isolate the low impedance of the battery from across resistors R_3 and R_4.

A basic flip-flop circuit is shown at B of Fig. 3-28. Here the circuit values and voltages are chosen to keep the diodes in one stable state

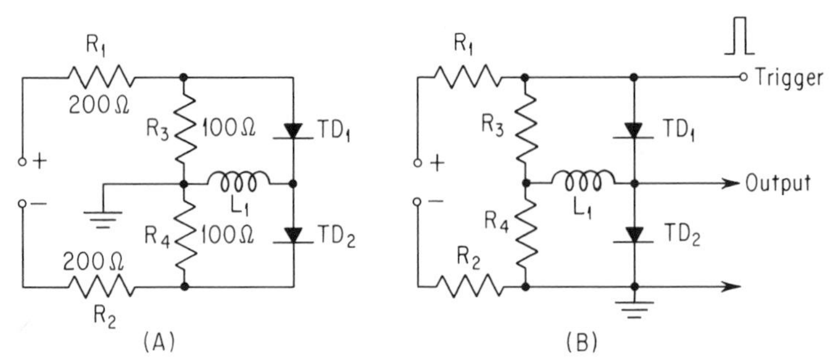

Fig. 3-28. Tunnel-diode multivibrator and flip-flop circuits

until a triggering pulse is applied. If TD_1 is at a current peak, its low resistance would provide sufficient potential to keep TD_2 at the low-current, high-resistance point. A positive pulse raises the voltage on TD_1, driving it to the low-current, high-resistance state (the negative-resistance region). The change of voltage across L_1 is now present at the output, and at the same time drives TD_2 to the high-current low-resistance condition, thus changing the state of the bistable circuit.

With TD_1 at a low-current, high-resistance value, a positive pulse would result in a voltage increase and the diode would be driven out of the negative-resistance current valley. Current rises to a value determined by the pulse amplitude, and levels off. The inductor again flips over the circuit, and after the pulse has left diode TD_1, voltage drops to the value where the current again is high (below the negative-resistance section).

Review Questions for Chapter 3

1. Why are relaxation oscillators of particular importance in electronic systems?
2. What are the essential circuit differences between the plate-coupled and cathode-coupled multivibrator?
3. What circuit components are used in the blocking oscillator but not used in the multivibrator?
4. Briefly explain how the operation of a flip-flop circuit differs from that of a multivibrator?
5. Briefly explain how flip-flop circuits in cascade may be used for industrial control purposes.
6. Define the term *flywheel effect* and explain how it functions in a resonant-circuit oscillator.
7. How does the circuit of a Hartley oscillator differ from that of the electron-coupled type?

8. List the special considerations which apply to the crystal unit in a crystal oscillator for obtaining stable operational characteristics.
9. Explain briefly how the production of a sawtooth signal may be precisely synchronized by another signal.
10. Briefly explain why a modified sawtooth signal must be employed when an inductance is used for sweep purposes.
11. Summarize the circuit factors which relate to the generation of a modified sawtooth.
12. Explain briefly the basic characteristics of the Unijunction transistor.
13. Briefly explain what is meant by a *negative-resistive characteristic* such as displayed by the tunnel diode.
14. Briefly explain how a tunnel diode can represent two states in a bistable circuit.

Coils and Reactors

INTRODUCTION

Coils and transformers with metallic cores are extensively employed in various branches of industrial electronics. Sizes vary from very small units weighing only a few pounds to huge devices weighing tons. Some have generally fixed characteristics, other have variable characteristics to fit specific needs for the control of manufacturing processes. Individual coils or solenoids find application in relays and sensing devices, or where an inductance is required to counteract the effect of capacity in circuitry. They are used to present a high value of reactance in series with one or more other devices, for example as a filter choke in power supplies as more fully described later. As in other branches of electronics, transformers are used to increase or decrease line voltage or to furnish a given amount of signal voltage amplitude in circuitry. Coils and transformers are also used as control devices in such applications as magnetic amplifiers and other devices subsequently detailed. For a clearer comprehension of the part such devices play in industrial electronics, it is important to understand thoroughly the characteristics of the inductances and their cores. For this purpose, the principles of magnetism will be summarized and coils, cores, and transformers will be analyzed in this chapter.

SUMMARY OF MAGNETISM UNITS

The number of magnetic lines of force existing in a given area of magnetism (in air or within a core) is called *magnetic flux*. The Greek letter phi (ϕ) is used as a symbol for flux. The unit of magnetic flux is a *maxwell,* named after James Maxwell, the nineteenth century's great theoretical physicist (1831–1879), who contributed much to our knowledge of magnetism by his experiments and his publication of several important documents explaining his findings. The maxwell represents one line of force of the total magnetic flux. (See Fig. 4-1.)

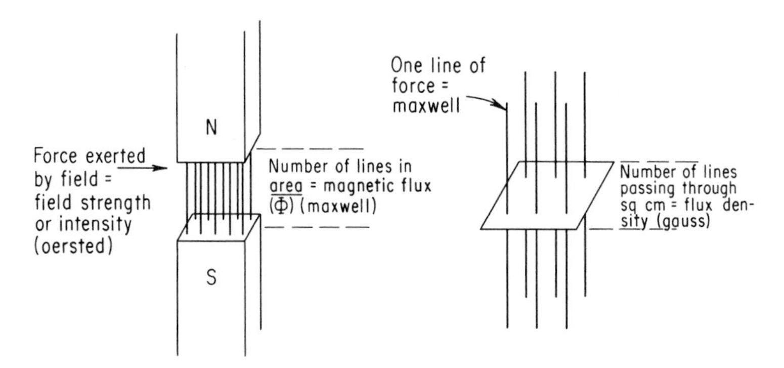

Fig. 4-1. Illustration of terms in magnetism

Another term applied to magnetic flux is *flux density,* which relates to the number of lines of force that pass perpendicularly through a square centimeter of area. The flux density has for its symbol the capital letter *B*. The unit of flux density is a *gauss,* which derives its name from Karl Gauss, the German mathematician (1777–1855).

The strength of the magnetic field (*field strength* or *field intensity*) relate to the force which is exerted by the magnetic field. The unit of magnetic field strength is the *oersted,* after Hans Oersted, the Danish physicist (1777–1851). Oersted was the first to show the connection between electricity and magnetism. The unit *oersted* represents the intensity of the magnetic field at a distance of 1 centimeter from the unit magnetic pole (a unit pole defines the strength which is exerted to create a force of 1 dyne upon an equal pole in air or vacuum). The *dyne* is a unit of force in the centimeter-gram-second (CGS) system equal to the force required to produce an acceleration of 1 centimeter per second in a mass weighing 1 gram for every second that the force exists.This unit of force, the dyne, is very small since 980 dynes equal only a single gram of force. The oersted is symbolized by the italic capital letter *H*.

MAGNETIC CHARACTERISTICS OF CORES

The term applied to the measure of conductivity of magnetic flux lines through core material is known as *permeability*. The latter has for its symbol the Greek letter mu (μ). Permeability, therefore, is the ratio of the amount of magnetic flux present when a particular core material is used to the amount of magnetic flux which exists when the core is removed, leaving only air as a core. Hence, the permeability of air is used to represent unity (1), and all other materials have a higher permeability rating. The permeability of core materials used in coils and transformers varies considerably. Soft iron has a permeability of approximately 2000, whereas certain alloys have a permeability of over 50,000. Thus, the type of core material can be chosen with respect to its conductivity for magnetic lines of force, and in consequence its influence on the coil will be in proportion to its permeability rating.

Reluctance and retentivity are also terms applied to magnetic core materials. *Reluctance* refers to the opposition offered by a core to the magnetic flux lines; it can be compared to the resistance of current flow in electric circuits. The symbol for reluctance is the italic capital letter R. The *retentivity* of a core is a measure of how well the core retains magnetism after removal of the external magnetizing influence. Iron, for instance, has very little ability to retain magnetism compared to steel; the latter has higher retentivity.

The various metallic cores used in coils and transformers are known as *ferromagnetic* materials to distinguish them from the *diamagnetic* materials such as copper, silver, gold, etc., and the *paramagnetic* materials such as aluminum, chromium, platinum, etc. The ferromagnetics have high permeability and become strongly magnetized by a field which is weak in comparison with the magnetic fields required to magnetize the other two materials. Paramagnetic and diamagnetic materials become only weakly magnetized, even by an extremely strong magnetic field.

The magnetic characteristics of diamagnetic and paramagnetic materials differ with respect to the direction in which they become magnetized. The diamagnetic materials, when magnetized, become so in a direction opposite to the magnetizing force. The paramagnetic materials, on the other hand, become magnetized in the same direction as the magnetizing field, just as is the case with the ferromagnetic materials. Compared to the ferromagnetic materials, the diamagnetic and paramagnetic can be considered as almost non-magnetic.

The insertion of a core into a coil through which current is flowing alters the over-all characteristics of the coil. Without a core, current

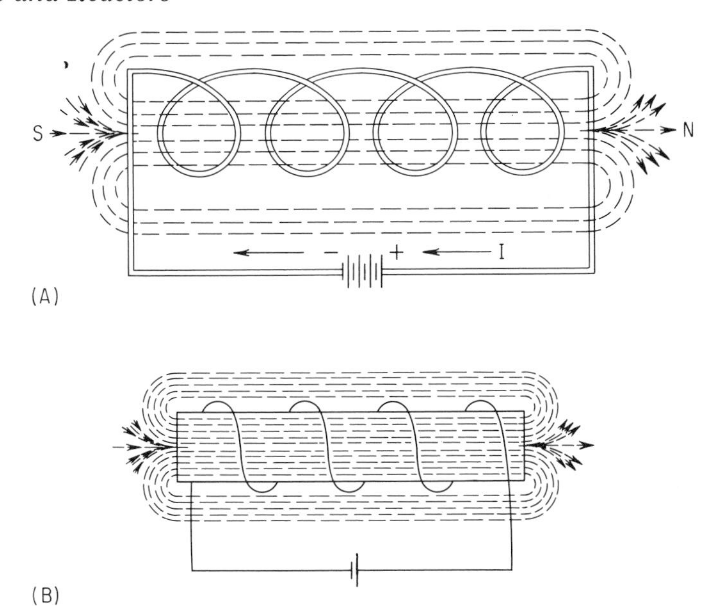

Fig. 4-2. Air core and metal core coils

flowing through the coil sets up magnetic lines of force around the coil as shown at A of Fig. 4-2. When a metallic core is inserted, the core material also becomes magnetized since it is under the influence of the magnetic lines of force of the coil, hence the core itself produces a field. Because the core furnishes increased conductivity of the magnetic flux, more definite north and south magnetic pole areas are created at each end of the coil, as shown at B. Also, the magnetic lines of force making up the total magnetic field are greatly increased, because of the additional magnetic lines of the core material.

With a soft iron core, the removal of current through the coil causes the magnetic lines of force to collapse. Because the iron has little retentivity, it also becomes demagnetized. Thus, since the magnetic fields exist only while current is flowing, and current flows because of the applied voltage, electric power is required to create the magnetic fields of force. The force required to create magnetic fields is known as *magnetomotive force.* Whether it is produced by current flow through the coil, or by the force exerted by an external device such as a permanent magnet or electromagnet, the unit of magnetomotive force is known as the *gilbert,* after William Gilbert (1540–1603), the English researcher and scientist who undertook extensive experiments in magnetism. The gilbert represents the magnetomotive force required to produce a magnetic flux of 1 maxwell in a magnetic circuit which has 1 unit of reluctance.

COILS IN CONTROL DEVICES

Coils with cores are used extensively in all branches of industrial electronics; some basic applications are shown in Fig. 4-3. At A is the basic relay mentioned earlier, a *normally open* relay. The spring metal constitutes the moveable arm of the relay attached to one terminal as shown. The other terminal is connected to the point which makes contact with the metal spring. When d-c flows through the coil, an electromagnet is formed and the magnetism pulls the spring metal toward the core of the coil, thus closing the relay. Normally closed relays and multicircuit relays are also employed, as more fully described in Chapter 8.

At B, the coil and core is shown as a sensing device. When metallic objects on an assembly line reach a position directly over the coil, a signal is produced for counting or control purposes which will be more fully described later.

At C, the coil is used to actuate a switch. As with the relay, when

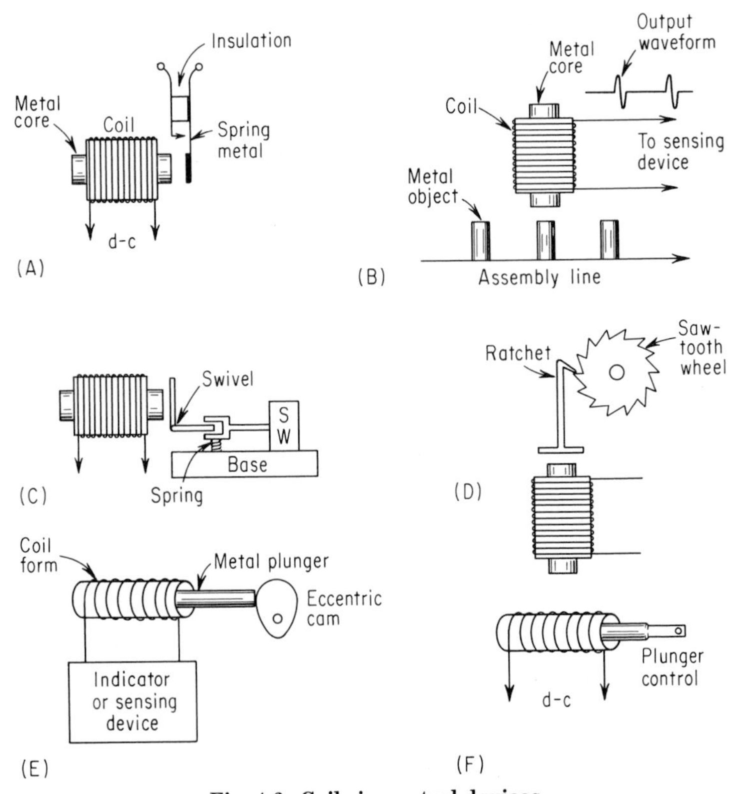

Fig. 4-3. Coils in control devices

the coil is energized by the application of d-c, the L-shaped section pulls in toward the coil core which raises the switch arm. The switch can be wired to either close or open a circuit when the coil is energized.

At D, a ratchet and sawtooth wheel arrangement is illustrated. When the coil is energized, the metallic fields pull down the ratchet, and consequently the sawtooth wheel turns slightly. Successive applications of energy to the coil rotate the wheel in successive steps.

At E, a moveable metal plunger is shown which, by spring arrangement, rests against an eccentric cam. As the cam rotates, it alternately moves the metal plunger core in and out of the coil form, thus generating an a-c signal which will have a frequency related to the rotation of the cam. Thus, this device can sense the number of revolutions per minute.

At F, the plunger core arrangement is again shown. In this instance, however, a lever arm is attached to the plunger. When the coil is energized, the magnetic field will draw the plunger within the coil. By spring arrangement, the removal of the field can force the plunger out of the coil. By this design a pistonlike action is secured for control of some mechanical devices.

THE HYSTERESIS LOOP

Two important characteristics of core material are the retentivity of the material after the magnetizing force has been removed and the amount of flux density which is created for a given magnetomotive force. These inherent characteristics of a core material are of particular significance with such devices as swinging chokes, magnetic amplifiers, and other devices more fully described later.

The retentivity of a core material such as soft iron, for instance, is such that after the magnetizing force is removed, a little magnetism is still retained by the iron. The magnetism which remains is called *residual magnetism.* Once such a material has been magnetized, the residual magnetism remains and the material no longer exhibits zero magnetism even though magnetized in the reverse direction. Also, all core materials can be magnetized to such a degree that an increase in the magnetizing force will no longer increase the field intensity. When this is done, the condition known as *saturation* has been reached, since the core is considered to be so saturated with magnetism that it has reached its peak.

The characteristics of a core material can be plotted and graphed in order to give an immediate indication of the varying levels of field intensity for a given magnetizing force of a certain polarity. The apparatus for setting up a graphing procedure consists of a coil with a core as shown in Fig. 4-4, a battery or other source of d-c voltage, a variable resistance, and instrument for indicating the field intensity established in the core material.

The sensing device can be a magnetoresistive unit as described in Chapter 1 using the Hall effect. An alternate method for sensing the variations in field intensity is to sample the current changes flowing to the coil and compare these with the flux density produced. These two variables are then applied to an automatic plotter instrument such as described in Chapter 12.

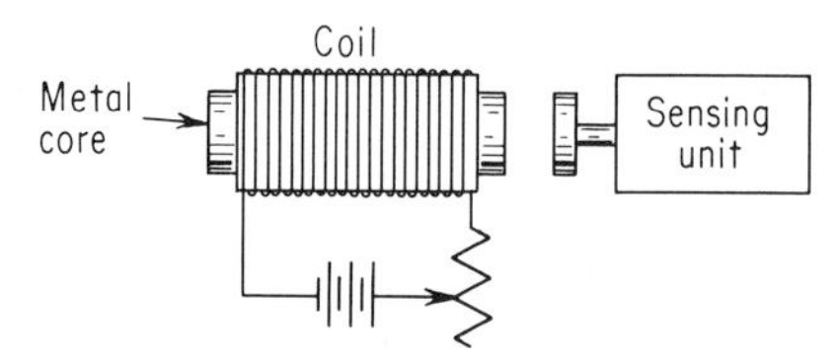

Fig. 4-4. Method of varying flux density

The variable resistor in Fig. 4-4 permits changing the magnetizing force—hence the flux density—because the voltage impressed across the coil can be increased from zero to a high value in one polarity direction and then reversed, by reversing the battery terminal connections. As the voltage is increased, starting from zero, current flow through the coil also increases and the magnetizing force (H) which is applied to the core material can then be graphed along a horizontal axis as shown in Fig. 4-5. As the flux density (B) within the core material increases, it is graphed along the vertical axis as shown. Initially, assume that the core material is completely unmagnetized. With zero magnetizing force, and zero flux density, the point of origin on the graph would be at the intersection of the vertical and horizontal lines as shown in Fig. 4-5.

When current starts to flow through the coil, the magnetizing force which is applied to the core is plotted to either the left or the right of the vertical axis, depending on the polarity of the voltage applied. Assume, for instance, that the polarity is positive. As the positive magnetizing force is increased along the horizontal axis, it is plotted to the right of the zero intersection as shown. This causes a rise in the flux density of the core material, starting at *a,* and curving upward to the right to *b*. At *b,* a leveling off occurs which indicates that the flux density no longer increases even though the magnetizing force is increased. This is the saturation level of the core material.

If the magnetizing force is decreased, by varying the resistance value of the resistor to decrease current flow, the flux density declines, but fails to retrace along the original line *a* to *b*. Instead the flux-density line retraces from *b* toward *c* which it reaches when the magnetizing force has been reduced to zero. Thus, the reduction to zero of the magnetizing force has failed to bring the flux density back to zero, but instead, a fairly high level of flux density remains for the material graphed in Fig. 4-5. In order to bring the flux density to zero,

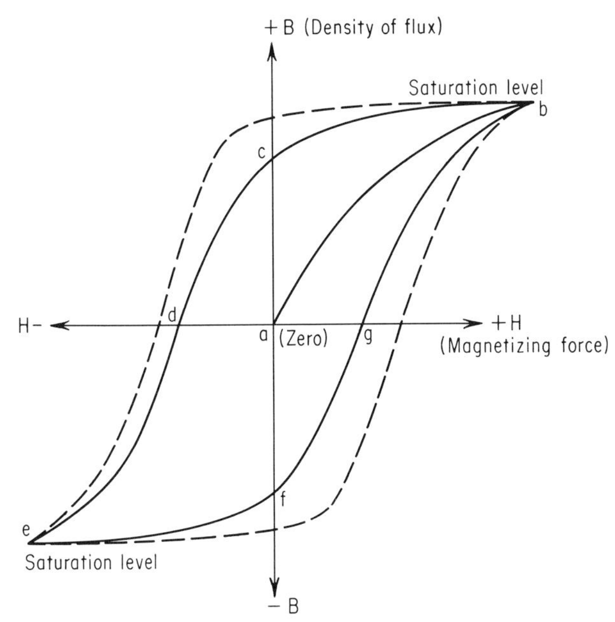

Fig. 4-5. Hysteresis loop (B-H curve)

a magnetizing force of opposite polarity must be applied as shown. (For the circuit shown in Fig. 4-4, this means a reversal of the battery terminals and an application of current to the coil, starting again at zero voltage.)

As the negative magnetizing force is increased, the density of flux in the core material again increases (opposite to the initial direction) until point *e* is reached, which indicates the saturation level of opposite polarity to that reached originally. Again, if the magnetizing force is reduced to zero, a high degree of flux density remains, because the flux density retraces from *e* to *f* and remains at that level with a zero magnetizing force. If the battery were again reversed to apply a positive magnetizing force, the curve would trace upward from *f* to *g*, and again reach saturation at *b*. When this is done, the ferromagnetic core has undergone a complete magnetic cycle. Again, removal of the magnetizing force would result in the flux density's reaching point *c* on the graph. Point *a* could not be reached, since zero flux density can be maintained only at points *d* and *g* by a specific magnetizing force level.

It will be noted from the graph that the flux density always lags behind the magnetizing force, and this lag is referred to as *hysteresis,* from the Greek word *hysterein* which means "to lag, to be behind." A graph such as shown in Fig. 4-5 is known as a *hysteresis curve* or a *hysteresis loop.* On occasion, it is also referred to as a *B-H curve.* The magnetizing force necessary to bring (and hold) the flux density at either of the zero points *d* and *g* is known as *coercive force.* The only way the core can be brought to its original zero-state magnetism is by use of an alternating-current field. In some small devices such as certain transducers, tape recording and erase heads, etc., demagnetizing procedures are employed because residual magnetism should be avoided for best results. In industrial coils and transformers, however, the residual magnetism is of no consequence, although the characteristics of varying flux densities with changes in magnetomotive force are of considerable importance. Coils used to demagnetize cores are known as *degaussing coils.*

The shape of the hysteresis loop which is graphed depends on the type of material. With a core material having a high permeability, the graph would be much narrower with respect to its height than with a material of lower permeability. Ferrite materials used for cores of radio antennas or memory devices in computers produce almost rectangular hysteresis loops, as shown by the dotted outline in Fig. 4-5. Such cores have very high permeability and lend themselves to certain switching and gating applications whereas materials with a more inclined slope are useful for saturable reactors and other devices.

CORE LOSSES

Metallic cores, in either single inductors or transformers having two or more windings, increase the over-all inductance because the magnetic lines of force which make up the total field are considerably greater in number than they would be without the metallic core. The core material, however, introduces both hysteresis losses and eddy-current losses. The hysteresis losses are established by virtue of the successive magnetization and demagnetization of the core occurring when a-c power is applied to the inductance. With 60 cps, for instance, the fields build up in one direction for one alternation of the a-c signal and then the fields collapse as the alternation drops to zero. During the second alternation, the fields must be built up again but in reverse. This means that the magnetizing force is changing rapidly, as is the case for the hysteresis loop shown in Fig. 4-5, where magnetizing force is changed rapidly from a plus polarity to a negative polarity and back again. This means that the field intensity also changes from negative to positive and repeats itself to conform to the change of polarity of the magnetizing force. The constant and rapid change of the magnetic state of the core material creates losses in the form of generated heat. Hysteresis losses cannot be eliminated entirely, but they can be kept to an acceptable value if high-quality core materials are used. In industrial applications the cost of higher-quality core material is also a factor, and if material of poor quality is employed, provision must be made to keep the generated heat at a minimum so as not to damage the inductor or transformer. Heat dissipation can be achieved by placing the unit in an area with adequate ventilation and also by designing the core and housing in such a manner that the heat is more readily radiated away from the unit.

Metallic cores have a high degree of conductivity for the magnetic lines of force. Eddy-current losses occur because of the current circulating within the core. The lines of force cut across the core material in such a direction that they create an induced voltage across the core material and set up circulating currents. These do not flow along any well-defined path, and for this reason they are termed *eddy* currents. Eddy-current losses may be kept at a minimum by breaking up the solid core structure into thin sheets known as *laminations*. Laminations are stamped from metal sheets, in a pattern permitting them to be assembled to form a core area which extends through and around the coil. Some typical laminations are shown in Fig. 4-6.

Several other shapes are also employed for core laminations, one of which is L-shaped, as shown at A in Fig. 4-7. The laminations, when stacked, are placed together to form a square pattern as shown at the right. (One leg of the L lamination could be longer than the other, to form a rectangular assembly.) The coil wraps around one core leg as shown later.

Fig. 4-6. Core laminations

Another type of stamped lamination is shown at B, where an inverted U type is used in conjunction with a straight bar. The assembly again forms a rectangular or square unit. The third method is to use the E-type laminations in conjunction with a straight bar as shown at C. This type of assembly finds many applications and has a number of advantages over the other types illustrated. The E-shaped assembly permits the placement of the coil at the center, hence the coil not only has a core through its center, but also has a core at each side as well as at the top and bottom. This reduces reluctance and increases permeability to a considerable extent. This arrangement also permits a core to be used at each center leg for the construction of a saturable reactor as more fully described later.

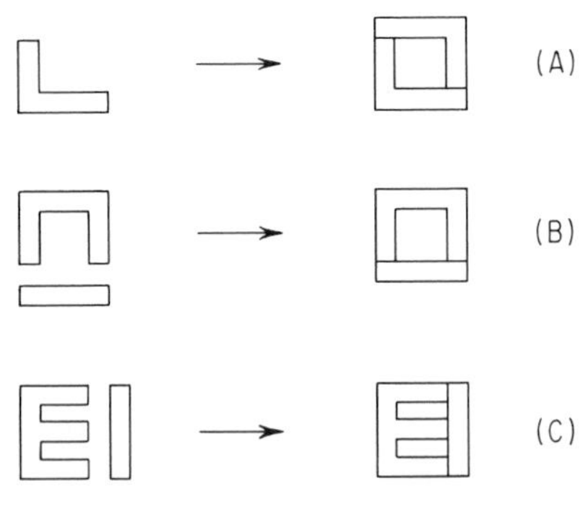

Fig. 4-7. Core assemblies

The individual laminations, after they are stamped out during the manufacturing process, are often heated to produce oxidization. When oxidized, the laminations acquire some insulating properties and hence provide better break-up of the core material structure in terms of the isolation of one lamination with respect to another. On occasion, a special varnish is also applied to the laminations to provide increased insulation. Although eddy-current losses may be reduced materially by the use of laminated cores, the latter have no effect on hysteresis losses.

For industrial applications, core material is composed of either soft iron or silicon steel for coils and transformers operating at the normal power-main a-c frequency of 60 cps. In general electronic applications, such core material is also used for other low-frequency signals such as audio, pulses, or other special waveforms. For the r-f frequencies involved in radio, f-m, and television broadcasting and reception, powdered metal cores (pressed into a solid rod) or cores made of high-permeability ferrite, as mentioned earlier, are often used. The latter is a very brittle and hard material composed of spinel crystals. Ferrite is formed from a mixture of magnetic metals including nickel, zinc, and manganese. Ferrite is also useful in computer systems where it is employed for the storage of information in the form of magnetized areas. The ferrite is formed into extremely small (less than $\frac{1}{4}$-inch diameter) rings which are magnetized in one direction to represent zero, or in the other direction to represent the digit one.

AIR GAPS

There are many instances in industrial electronics where core material with a rectangular hysteresis is desirable. The rectangular hysteresis loop lends itself more readily to switching devices, utlization of cores which saturate quickly, and in other applications subsequently described. There are occasions, however, when it is desirable that the core not saturate as readily, such as with amplifier transformers and certain filter reactors in power supplies.

The saturation characteristics of the core can be altered by including in the core of a reactor or transformer an air gap, such as illustrated at A of Fig. 4-8. The effect of an air gap is shown at B, where the hysteresis graph for the core without the gap is shown by the dotted outline. When the air gap is included, the hysteresis curve takes the form shown by the solid pattern. Without the air gap, the flux density reaches the saturation level quite early for an increase in the magnetizing force (*e* along the horizontal graph line). With the air gap, however, the saturation level is not reached until the magnetizing force has been increased to point *f* along the horizontal (*X*) axis.

An additional air gap can be included beneath the coil opposite to the air gap (shown at A of Fig. 4–8). The gap, although known as an air gap need not necessarily be of air. Any nonmetallic material—paper, mica, plastic, or even brass and gold—can be employed. Gold, because it is malleable and can be formed into extremely thin sheets, is often used to form the air gap in tape-recorder heads, where the narrowness of the gap is important for high-frequency signal sensitivity.

In reactors and transformers the presence or absence of an air gap

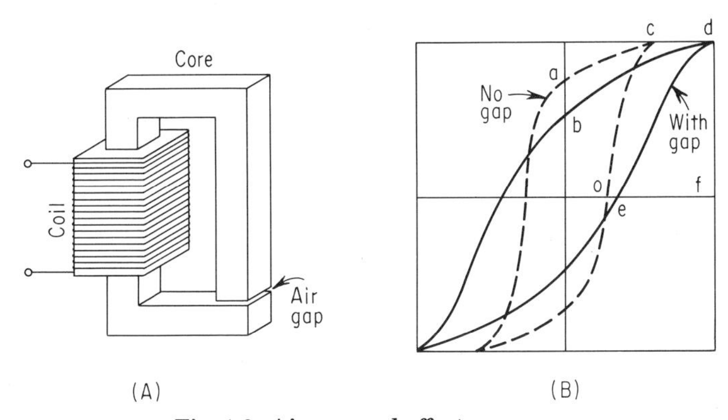

Fig. 4-8. Air gap and effect on curve

is a matter of design and requirements. In many devices, however, the air gap is unavoidable. With motors, generators, meters, and other similar devices, the necessity for a moveable section automatically forms an air gap between the latter and the stationary core material.

TOROIDS

Ferrites and other core material can be formed into a circle and the coil wound around it as shown at A in Fig. 4-9. This forms what is known as a *toroid,* and the toroidial winding of the coil provides for a highly effective device. The reluctance is decreased and the magnetic flux lines find a continuous path through the coil section. The circular cores and coils are used in various applications of industrial electronics. Extremely tiny toroids are utilized as storage devices in computers and also in some bistable devices as described in Chapter 15. Large units weighing hundreds of pounds are employed as transformers and reactors in high-power work. Shown at B of Fig. 4–9

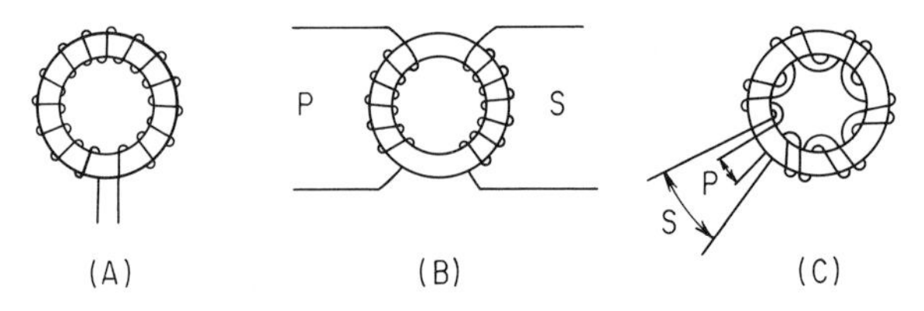

Fig. 4-9. Toroidal windings

is a transformer arrangement where the primary is wound on the opposite part of the ring from the secondary. The primary and secondary windings can also be wound in what is known as a *bifalar winding,* as shown at C. Here, the primary and secondary wires are laid side by side and wound around the toroid.

TRANSFORMERS

The transformer, which has been mentioned earlier and illustrated schematically, has a number of applications, including step-up or step-down, impedance matching, and control.

When the transformer is used as a voltage step-up device, the number of turns in the secondary winding is increased over the number in the primary winding to the proportion required. Thus, if it is necessary to increase 110 volts to 330 volts as shown at A of Fig. 4-10, the secondary winding would have three times as many turns as the primary. The actual number of turns is related to the efficiency of the transformer as well as to the quantity and quality of its core material.

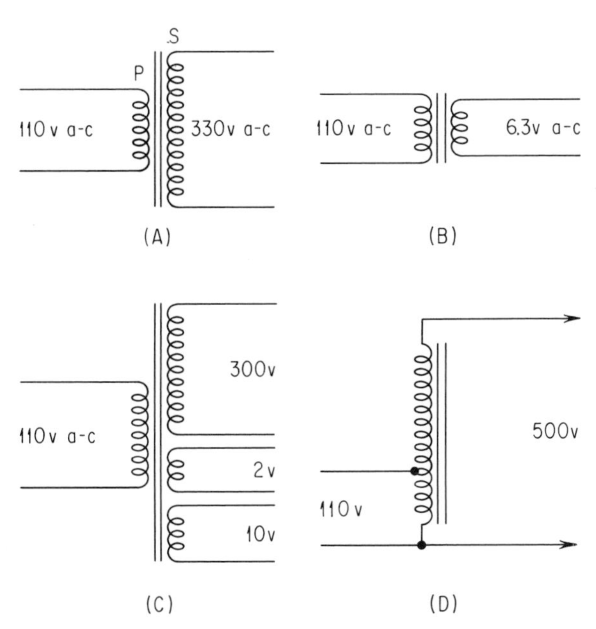

Fig. 4-10. Voltage transformations

With a good core material of sufficient quantity, the number of turns in the primary and secondary could be much less than with insufficient and poor-quality core material. A sufficient number of turns must be present to provide good linkage of the electromagnetic lines of force between primary and secondary. A well-designed transformer has an efficiency of over 95 per cent, which means that little energy is lost within the transformer when it transfers energy from primary to secondary.

The transformer, of course, can also be used as a step-down device as shown at B, where 110 volts is stepped down to 6.3 volts for application to vacuum-tube filaments. There can be a number of secondary windings as shown at C, where various voltage levels are required. Transformers can also be of the single-coil variety, as shown at D, where the primary consists of tapping in on the coil form as shown and obtaining the output from the end terminals of the total winding. This is known as an *auto-transformer.*

If a voltage is applied to either the secondary or primary, and the voltage measured in the other winding, the turns ratio of a transformer can be ascertained. Such a measurement will not, of course, determine the power-handling capability of the transformer. This depends on the size of wire used and generally is obtained from the specifications of the manufacturer.

When voltage is stepped up as shown at A of Fig. 4-10, there is

Fig. 4-11. Industrial filament transformer (Courtesy Nothelfer Winding Labs., Inc.)

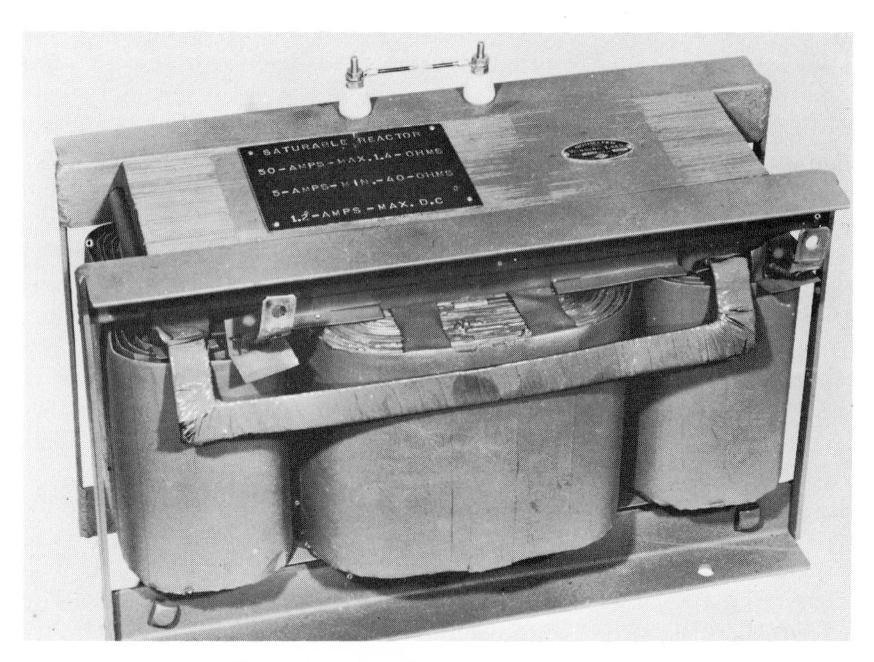

Fig. 4-12. Saturable reactor (Courtesy Nothelfer Winding Labs., Inc.)

no gain in over-all power since the higher voltage results in a reduction in current available. Similarly, when the voltage is stepped down as shown at B, the same amount of power could be obtained in the secondary as is present in the primary, because the current available will be higher in the secondary (assuming, of course, that the wire of the secondary is large enough to carry the current required for such power). In power transformers, the primary and secondary windings are usually wound one over the other to provide a maximum degree of coupling.

A typical industrial filament transformer, illustrated in Fig. 4-11, has a number of primary and secondary taps to meet varying conditions. Units such as these are available to handle fractional powers as well as thousands of watts. Figure 4-12 shows a commercial saturable reactor transformer manufactured by the Nothelfer Winding Laboratories, Inc. The center coil is the d-c winding and the outer coils are the a-c windings. These reactors are used in magnetic amplifiers as described in Chapter 11, are capable of controlling considerable amounts of a-c power by relatively small d-c values, and are available from 500 watts to 50 kilowatts.

Impedance Matching

A transformer is not a load; that is, it is not intended to use up electric energy. It can, however, be advantageously employed for matching dissimilar impedances. Ordinarily, if the device furnishing the source of energy has an impedance identical to the load which uses up the energy, a transformer having a one-to-one turns ratio is employed as shown at A of Fig. 4-13. Assume, however, that the generator has an impedance of 10,000 ohms and the load is only 10 ohms as shown at B. In such an instance, the load impedance can be matched to the generator impedance by utilizing a step-down transformer with the proper turns ratio so the impedances are matched. This cannot be done simply by making the primary turns equal to the generator impedance and the secondary turns equal to the load impedance. Such a simple expedient does not function because of the cross-action

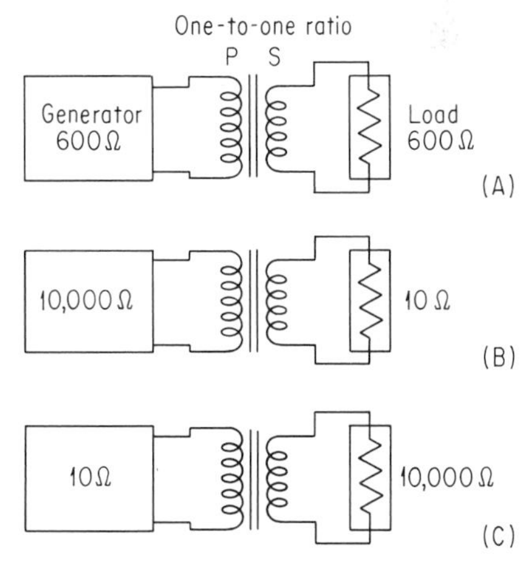

Fig. 4-13. Generator and load impedances

of the transformer which transfers the low impedance to the primary and the high impedance to the secondary. Instead, the turns ratio is calculated by using the formula:

$$\text{turns ratio} = \sqrt{\frac{Z_1}{Z_2}}$$

Thus, if the generator impedance (Z_1) is 10,000 ohms and the load (Z_2) is 10 ohms, the ratio would be

$$\sqrt{\frac{10{,}000}{10}} = \sqrt{1000} = 32 \text{ (approx.)}$$

Thus, the matching transformer should have a turns ratio of 32 to 1. Hence, the primary could have 96 turns and the secondary 3 turns, or the primary could have 320 turns and the secondary 10 turns. The number of turns depends on transformer design and can be any number as long as the calculated turns ratio is maintained.

The transformer can, of course, be used as an impedance step-up device as shown at C where the generator is 10 ohms and the load is 10,000 ohms. Here, the same transformer can be used that was employed for B simply by reversing connections. When using the formula, the larger impedance is placed over the smaller, regardless of which represents the primary or secondary.

VARIABLE TRANSFORMERS

The toroid-type core lends itself to construction of a voltage-variable transformer. As shown in Fig. 4-14, a sliding contact arm is mounted above the toroid, and the individual wires over which the contact arm slides have had the insulation removed for direct contact. The sliding arm can contact one winding only in auto-transformer style as shown at A in Fig. 4-15, or can be of the primary-secondary arrangement as shown at B.

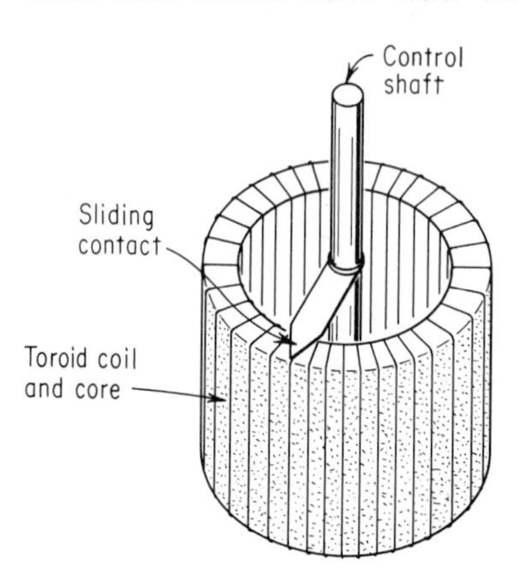

Fig. 4-14. Variable transformer construction

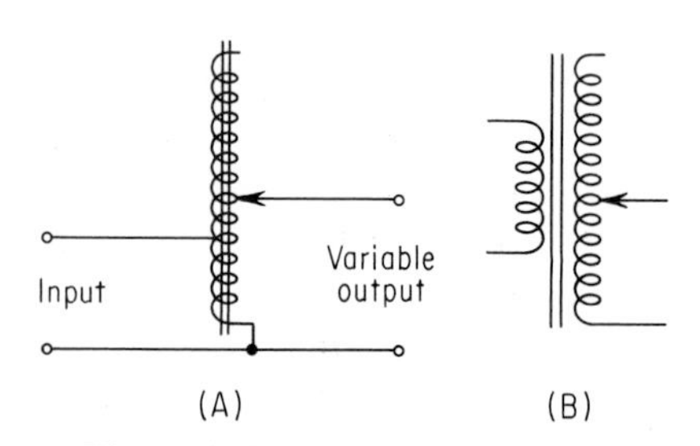

Fig. 4-15. Variable transformers

These devices are quite useful for varying the power applied to various industrial units for control purposes.

A typical variable transformer of this type is shown in Fig. 4-16, which illustrates the Varicell manufactured by The Superior Electric Company. The Varicell has a manual control knob at the top; the output voltages available are either a-c or d-c. The wire diagrams for this transformer are shown in Fig. 4-17. As shown, this model V4050-3 consists of a three-phase, low-voltage variable transformer combined with a d-c power supply. Silicon rectifier cells are connected for full-wave, three-phase operation. (See Chapter 6.)

Instead of manual operation, remote-control operation of the variable transformer can be accomplished by a motor which controls the rotation of

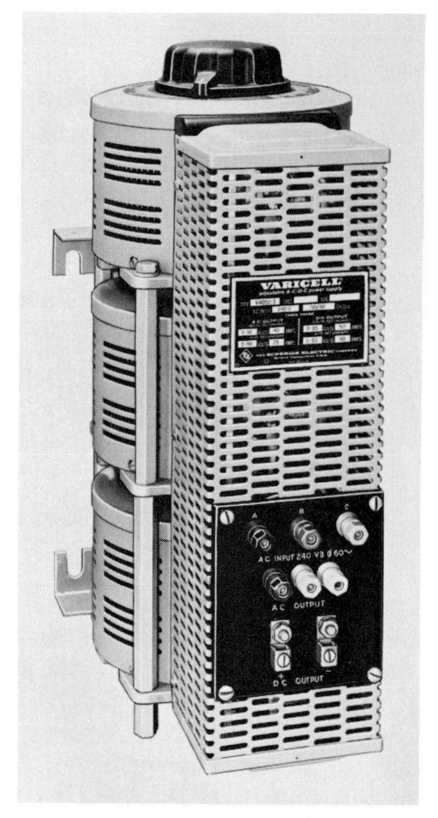

Fig. 4-16. Variable transformer (Courtesy Superior Electric Co.)

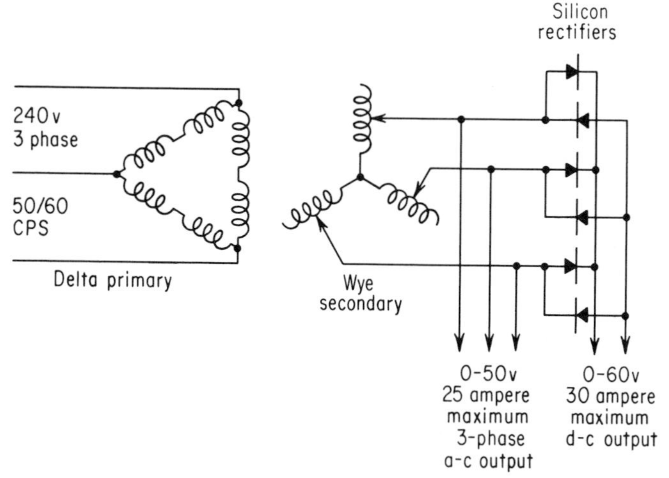

Fig. 4-17. Varicell circuit

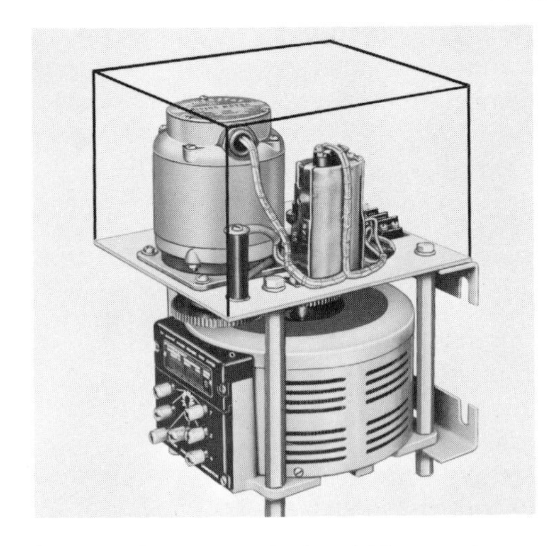

Fig. 4-18. Motor control of variable transformer (Courtesy Superior Electric Co.)

the variable-transformer arm. The motor rotation is actuated at any distance for remote-control purposes. A transformer of this type is shown in Fig. 4-18, where the motor is a special synchronous unit with two windings and an externally mounted capacitor and resistor. (See Chapter 9.) These motor-driven devices are available in speeds of 5, 15, 30, and 60 seconds for full-range travel from zero to maximum output voltage. In the units with a 5-second speed the motor directly drives the variable arm shaft. For the slower speeds, a planetary gear reduction unit is furnished on the motor shaft.

A cutaway of an auto-transformer variable unit is shown in Fig. 4-19, the Variac manufactured by General Radio Company, Model W5. As shown, a single winding is wound on a toroidal iron core. A carbon brush contact is employed, which is always in contact with the winding. The voltage changes available are always less than the voltage between winding turns because the brush has a width sufficient to span more than one turn, giving a virtually continuous voltage variation as the dial is turned. (The voltage between turns of the larger models is less than 1 volt, and in the smallest model is only approximately 0.3 volt.)

As mentioned earlier, the insulation must be removed from that portion of the windings over which the contact brush slides. In the Variac the brush track surface is coated with a uniform silver alloy to prevent oxidation and also deterioration of the contact surface. The Variac is available in a variety of models and sizes, including motor control of shaft rotation. It is also furnished in models for use in 400- to 1200-cycle service.

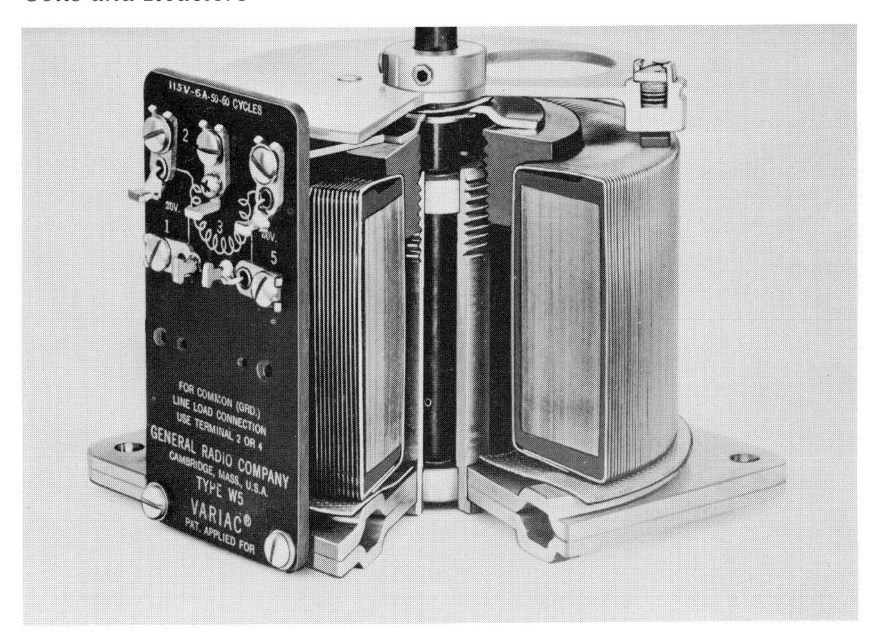

Fig. 4-19. Cutaway of the Variac (Courtesy of General Radio Co.)

Review Questions for Chapter 4

1. Give brief definitions of the following terms: *magnetic flux, flux density,* and *permeability.*
2. What are the advantages of using a metallic core in a reactor?
3. Define the terms *reluctance* and *retentivity.*
4. Briefly explain what characteristics are displayed by a graph of the hysteresis curve.
5. How are eddy-current and hysteresis losses minimized?
6. Describe three uses in industrial electronics for coils with cores.
7. Describe two types of core material.
8. Explain what effect an air gap has on the characteristics of a coil and transformer.
9. Briefly describe what is meant by a *toroid.*
10. Briefly describe how a transformer is made to have a variable output voltage.

5

Generators

INTRODUCTION

Generators are used in industry as a source of d-c or a-c power; hence the generator can be considered as a device which converts mechanical energy to electric energy. This is accomplished by rotating an armature within magnetic fields. In contrast, the motor (discussed in Chapter 9) can be considered as a device for converting electric energy into mechanical energy, because the application of electric power to the motor will cause a shaft rotation with considerable potential physical energy. The oscillators described in Chapter 3 are sometimes also called "generators," because they generate electric signals. The specific reference must be ascertained when the word *generator* is used.

Devices which combine the function of both the generator and motor are also employed. One such unit is the *dynamo,* used as either a generator or a motor, as required. Sometimes a separate motor is used to run a generator, and both devices can be housed in a single unit, with the motor shaft common with the generator shaft. As shown in Fig. 5-1, no external shafts are present, since both the input and output energy is in the form of electric power. This combination of the motor and generator is known as a *dynamotor.* (Special motor and generator types such as the *sylsyn units* and *amplidynes* are discussed in subsequent chapters.)

A dynamotor is sometimes called an *inverter* where one form of electric energy is changed to another (*a-c* used to power the motor,

Fig. 5-1. Dynamotor

and *d-c* produced from the generator). (The oscillators previously described can also be called inverters, because they employ *d-c* and produce an "inverted" output power, such as sinewave or squarewave *a-c* signals.)

THE BASIC GENERATOR

Generators work on the principle of inducing voltage and current flow in a wire by having the latter cut magnetic lines of force. The basic components which make up a generator are shown in Fig. 5-2.

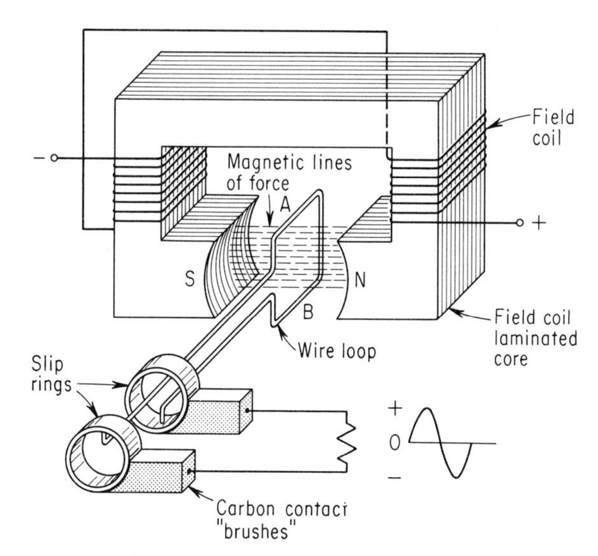

Fig. 5-2. Basic parts of a-c generator

For production of the magnetic field, permanent magnets can be employed, or an electromagnet can be employed as shown in the illustration.

The electromagnetic principle is the one commonly found in generators. The inductance which is wound around the laminated core is known as the *field coil.* The extensions of the field-coil core which set up the north and south magnetic poles are known as the *poles* or *pole pieces.* Between the two poles is a high degree of magnetic flux concentration as shown. To summarize the basic characteristics of a generator, a single wire loop is illustrated. When this wire loop makes a half turn in the magnetic field, it will generate one alternation of a-c. Two slip rings are employed on the shaft which holds the wire loop, and as the slip rings rotate, carbon contact brushes slide over the slip rings and thus pick up the electric energy produced by the generator. When the wire loop coil makes a half turn to generate one alternation of a-c, assume that the portion of the wire loop marked A moves downward, and the part marked B moves upward, with the wire loop thus going in a clockwise direction. As the wire loop continues to turn, at the second half turn the section marked A will move up through the lines of force and the section marked B will move down through the lines of force. In consequence, the emf produced will be opposite in polarity to that which was generated for the initial half turn. Thus, a second alternation of a-c is produced as shown beside the resistor connected to the carbon contact brushes in Fig. 5-2. As the wire loop keeps turning, successive cycles of a-c are produced at the generator output. Thus, for the mechanical energy which was required to turn the wire loop within the magnetic lines of force, power having a-c characteristics is produced.

In the practical a-c generator, the wire loop is replaced by a number of turns of wire wound around a core material. Also, a more efficient core area is utilized, and often more than two pole pieces are employed.

Shown in Fig. 5-3 is a d-c generator, produced by employing a single split ring instead of the two slip rings shown in Fig. 5-2. Here, the single split ring is known as a *commutator.* If the wire loop portions A and B are in a vertical plane and start to rotate in a clockwise direction, the carbon brush, B_1, will slide along the commutator segment S_1 as the latter starts to rotate. Also, the commutator segment S_2 rotates, hence carbon brush B_2 slides along the latter. Thus, a voltage is built up across the resistor as shown, arising from a zero value to a peak value as the loop makes a quarter turn and dropping to a zero value again when the loop has made a one-half turn. When the loop continues to make the second half turn, sections A and B of the loop now have induced in them a voltage with a polarity opposite

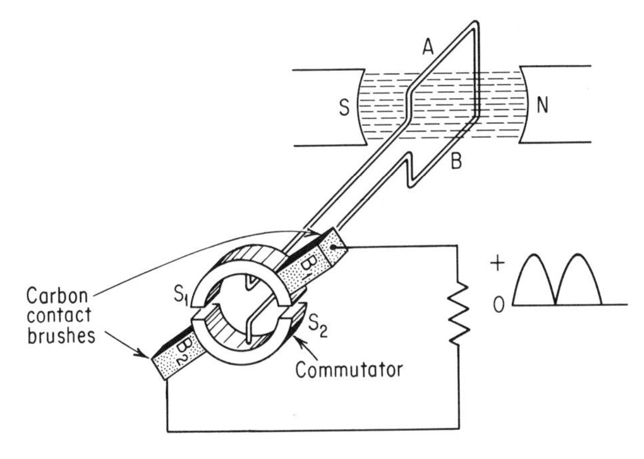

Fig. 5-3. Basic parts of d-c generator

to the initial polarity. Now, however, brush B_1 makes contact with the commutator segment S_2, and brush B_2 makes contact with commutator segment S_1. In consequence, the output is again an alternation which starts from zero, reaches a maximum value, and drops to zero again—but this second alternation *has the same polarity as the first.* Thus, *direct current* is produced by use of the commutator instead of the slip rings. For the d-c generator in practical applications, there are again many turns of the coil as with the a-c practical generator, and the coils are wound on a core material. Also, as shown later for both the a-c and d-c generators, multisegment commutators and poles are employed.

THE d-c GENERATOR

The basic d-c generator previously discussed produces pulsating d-c instead of smooth d-c. Also, a single-turn coil is inefficient because of the small voltage it produces. In order to increase the output from the generator while at the same time producing fairly smooth, ripple-free d-c, a number of coils are employed. These are wound around a central core, and in combination this central core is known as the *armature.* Instead of a two-section commutator, a multisection commutator is employed; each section is known as a commutator *segment.* There are as many segments used as there are coils, and each coil has connections to two segments as shown in Fig. 5-4. Thus, the coils are all connected electrically in series, with the carbon brushes dividing the coils into two sections as was the case with the A and B sections illustrated earlier for the basic generator. The carbon brushes are placed vertically with respect to the pole pieces as shown, so that the brushes are in the neutral magnetic plane representing zero voltage.

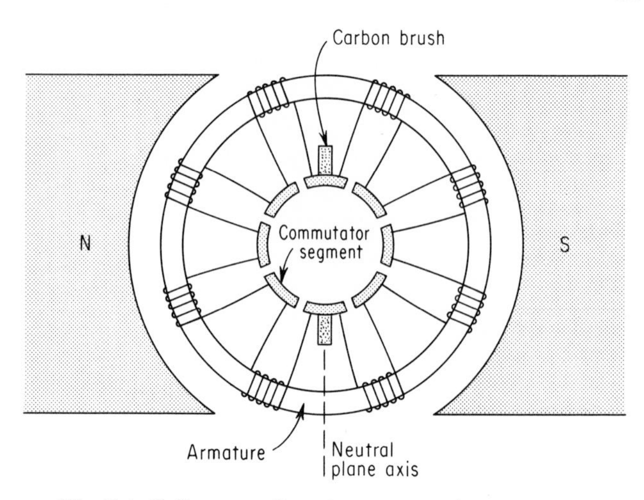

Fig. 5-4. Coil connections to commutation segments

In a practical generator, the coils are not wound around the armature frame in the manner shown in Fig. 5-4, but are actually wound into slots in the armature as shown in greater detail in the cross-sectional view of a two-pole generator in Fig. 5-5. As shown, the field

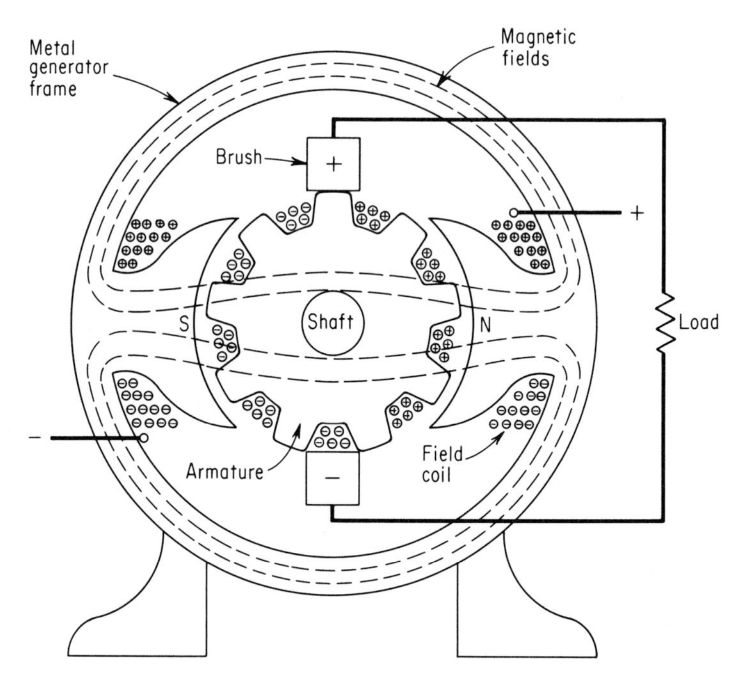

Fig. 5-5. Two-pole generator

coils are wound around the pole pieces at left and right, and the d-c current flowing through the field coil sets up a high degree of magnetic density between the pole pieces. The armature coils are wound around the slots as shown, and the energy produced by the rotation of the armature is picked up by the brushes and applied across the load represented by a resistor in Fig. 5-5. As shown, the motor generator frame carries the fields around and through the pole pieces across the armature area as indicated by the dotted lines.

In the drum-shaped armature core, with the windings laid in slots, most of the wire area of the armature coil cuts the magnetic lines of force, hence the drum-type armature is more efficient. Because a number of coils are used, the d-c which results is smoother than the pulsating d-c shown earlier. As more and more coils are employed, a smooth low-ripple d-c results. The pulsating d-c from the individual coils combines as shown in Fig. 5-6 to produce the resultant d-c. As the peak d-c from one coil starts to decline, the d-c is increased to a peak value again by the next coil. Each coil, in succession, keeps the peak d-c at nearly the same level. The d-c which results has fewer ripple components because a greater number of coils in the armature results in a smoother d-c output. (This is covered more fully in the next chapter.)

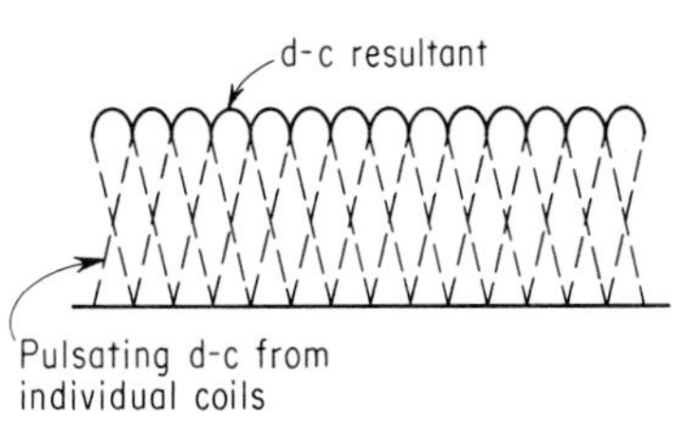

Fig. 5-6. Voltage of multi-coil d-c generator

As with transformers, core material for generators as well as motors is usually composed of laminated metals to reduce eddy currents. High-permeability materials are also employed for reduction of hysteresis losses. (The factors relating to eddy currents and hysteresis were detailed in the discussion on saturable reactors in the preceding chapter.)

Because the magnetic intensity is established by the current flowing through the field coils, the amount of magnetic density can be regulated by varying this current flow. Since current flow depends on the amplitude of the applied voltage, the field strength can be regulated by adjustment of the voltage applied to the field coils. Thus, the output from the generator can be regulated by varying the amount of field excitation. This regulation of output is useful in industrial applications as precise control can be established for the generator output without altering the speed of the armature rotation. Normally, the armature would be driven at a constant speed and a fixed output power would be obtained with a fixed amplitude of field voltage. By using a variable input d-c to the field, however, the output power from the generator can be controlled.

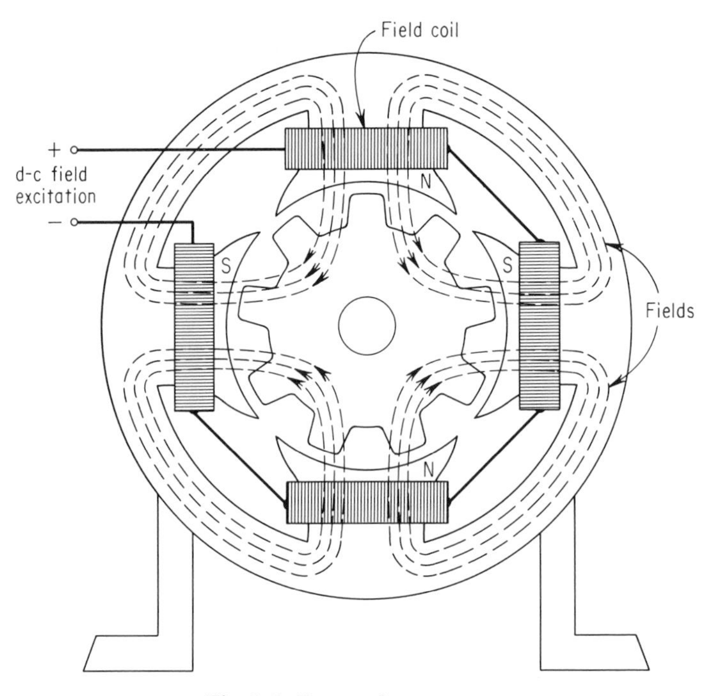

Fig. 5-7. Four-pole generator

If the number of poles around a generator armature is increased, the magnetic field which is produced can be made more uniform around the periphery of the armature. Figure 5-7 shows a four-pole d-c generator, and the dotted lines show the fields which exist in this device. Note that the opposite poles now have the same polarity, and the magnetic lines of force are distributed more evenly and surround the armature more fully. For simplicity, the carbon brushes and the armature coils are not shown in this drawing. In most instances, however, there are as many brushes employed in the generator as there are poles. Usually each brush is located halfway between two poles. Since half of the total number of brushes employed pick up a positive potential, these are all connected together to form a common positive output terminal. Also, the half of the total number of brushes which pick up the negative potential are tied together to form the negative output terminal. The four-pole generator has a lower internal resistance than the two-pole generator and is generally more efficient.

A generator having four poles can be operated at one-half the rotation speed of the two-pole generator and still produce the same output voltage—because the amount of voltage generated is dependent on the *rate* at which the armature coils cut through the lines of force. With a four-pole generator, each individual wire of the armature coil cuts across four sets of lines of force for each complete revolution, instead of two sets as with the two-pole generator. Since the increase in the number of poles in the generator makes for reduced speeds, many practical generators use four, eight, ten, twelve, or more poles.

d-c Field Excitation

As mentioned earlier, permanent magnets could be used to generate the magnetic fields for use in the generator and motor devices. However, the production of electromagnetism by use of a d-c field excitation for coils is preferred because the magnetic fields produced can thus be controlled, hence the applications of the generator and motor become more diversified.

The d-c for the field coil can be procured from an external source, such as another d-c generator, or the generator itself can supply its own field excitation. When the latter is the case, the unit is known as a *self-excited generator.* Because magnetic lines of force are necessary so that the armature coil can cut such lines of force to produce voltage, it would seem that the self-excited generator cannot produce any voltage for its fields initially, because it must have a magnetic field and this is not present in the absence of d-c excitation. Such is not the case, however, because the core material of field coil retains some slight magnetism (residual magnetism). Hence, when the armature is rotated initially, the small amount of residual magnetism present in the core structure is sufficient to generate a small amount of voltage. The latter is then applied to the field coil, and in turn increases the magnetic fields slightly above the level of residual magnetism. The increase in magnetism produces a still greater voltage which is applied to the field—the process is cumulative and occurs within a very short time after the generator armature starts to turn. Hence, normal output voltage is reached very quickly.

The manner in which the field coil is wired with respect to the armature coil to form a circuit determines the type of self-excited generator which is produced. There are three basic circuit hookups for the field—the *series-wound,* the *shunt-wound,* and the *compound-wound.* Their circuits are shown in Fig. 5-8.

At A, the series-wound generator circuit is shown. Here, the armature coil and the field coil are wound in series, hence the same amount of load current flows through both coils. Therefore, such a generator must use coils having low internal d-c resistance, and for this reason, much heavier wire is employed than with the shunt-wound generator. The series-wound generator produces very little output voltage when there is no load on the circuit. (A "no-load" circuit condition would appear as an open circuit when there is very high resistance at the load

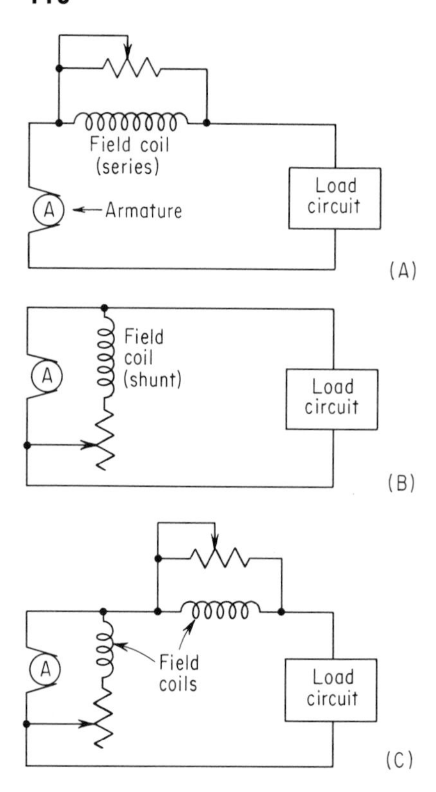

Fig. 5-8. Basic types of generators

terminals. Under this condition, very little current could flow through the armature and field coils because they are in series with the load circuit.) When the load circuit only permits a small current to flow in the field and armature coils, the magnetic lines of force produced are correspondingly small and not much voltage is induced into the rotating armature. When the load increases, it is equivalent to having a lower resistance since it will draw more current. The greater current flow through the armature and field coil sets up a greater magnetic field in the field-coil core, hence a larger voltage is induced in the armature coil winding. Thus, the voltage output from the generator becomes higher and as the load on the generator is increased an additional amount, the generator voltage rises proportionately. If the load on the generator is made too high, the electromagnetism produced by the field coils and field core reaches saturation and an additional increase in current through the field coil will no longer increase the magnetic fields. When the magnetism cannot be increased, there will be no increase in output voltage for a given rotation of the armature. At saturation, the voltage output from the generator could actually decrease because of the large voltage drops which occur across the armature coils.

Because the voltage output from this generator varies as the load varies, it is not used as frequently as the other generators.

In the shunt-wound generator, at B of Fig. 5-8, the field coil shunts the armature and the load circuit as shown. In this generator the field coils consist of a high-resistance winding, using a number of turns of thinner wire as compared to the armature. The voltage output is steadier than for the series-wound type for slight variations of the load. For no-load conditions, however, output voltage is at a maximum and the voltage decreases in proportion to the load. With excessive currents drawn by the load, generator breakdown can occur. Under normal load conditions, however, the output voltage remains at approximately 70 to 80 per cent of the voltage obtained under the zero-load condition.

The compound-wound generator circuit, a combination of the series-wound and the shunt-wound generator circuits, is shown at C of Fig. 5-8. Instead of a single field-coil winding, the two-coil field winding is employed. Compound-wound generators have better voltage regulation than either the series- or shunt-wound types and tend to keep the output voltage at a constant level automatically because of the combined features of both the other generators. Usually, the compound-wound generator is of the cumulative type wherein the series and shunt coils are wound in series-aiding, that is, the field of each coil aids the other. In some instances the *differential*-compound type is utilized, where the two field coils are wound so that their magnetic fields are opposing. Thus, as the load on the generator increases, the magnetic field strength of the series field increases because it is wound in a direction opposite to the shunt field. The result is that the total field strength is decreased and the output voltage will decrease. The differential-compound d-c generator is often used to furnish power to welding equipment where of necessity high power is periodically shorted. The differential-compound generator thus has built-in protection against the momentary shorts which occur during the welding process. For the cumulative-compound generator, an increase in the load causes the armature voltage to decrease and the voltage applied to the shunt field coil decreases. The increased load current which flows through the series field increases the magnetic field of the latter, hence compensation is procured with respect to keeping the output voltage at a fairly constant level and with good regulation. Hence, where good voltage regulation for considerable variations in load circuit is required, the cumulative-compound generator is recommended.

THE a-c GENERATOR

As mentioned earlier, the basic a-c generator is similar to the basic d-c type. However, because the a-c generator has a magnetic field which follows the alternating current cycle, self-excitation cannot be employed. Hence, the excitation for the a-c generator must be from an external source such as a low-power d-c generator, which is often coupled to the same shaft as the a-c generator.

In the generators previously discussed and illustrated, the armature was the rotating element and the field coils were placed around it. Actually, according to alternating-current principles, it would make very little difference with respect to the generation of voltage if the armature coils were kept stationary and the field coils rotated. In

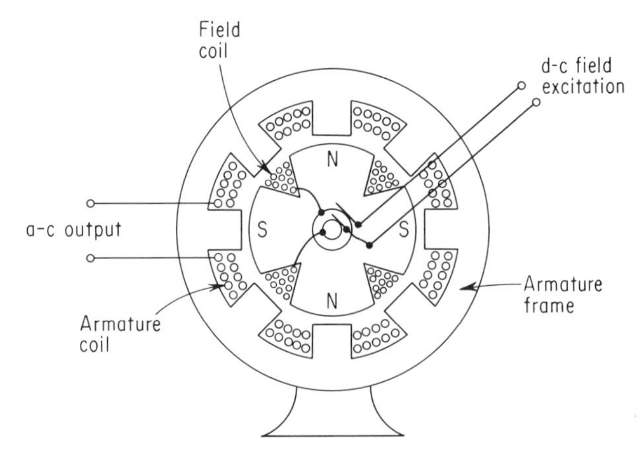

Fig. 5-9. a-c Generator with rotating field

practical applications the a-c generators mostly use rotating fields because such design offers more simple construction and also the slip rings no longer need to carry the high amount of current which the generator must furnish. The basic principle of the a-c generator with a rotating field is shown in Fig. 5-9. Here, the center cylindrical section is in the form of a laminated metal drum with appropriate slots for accommodating the field coils. The center field section has four poles. The field coils are in series and the two terminals are connected to two slip rings as shown. The d-c field excitation is applied to these two collector rings by carbon brushes which slide over the collector ring as the field-coil section rotates. Thus, the power handled by the slip rings and brushes is much lower than would be the case if they were required to handle a high amount of power generated in the armature output winding.

For the generator shown in Fig. 5-9, the individual coils of the armatures are all in series and provide an a-c output from the terminals as shown. Such a generator is a single-phase type, and it produces a single-phase a-c output.

In practical work, the three-phase generator is of considerable importance and widely used. In this generator the armature coils are divided into three sections. That is, the armature coils, regardless of the number, are grouped into sets which are so arranged that the device picks up a voltage from each set of coils which differs from the other coils by a third of a cycle (120 degrees). When this is done, the generator is known as a *polyphase* type, indicating that it has more than one phase. With three sets of coils, a three-phase generator is produced and the output voltage will be three-phase.

With the armature coils divided into three sets, six terminals are produced, as shown at A of Fig. 5-10. If the generator were of the rotat-

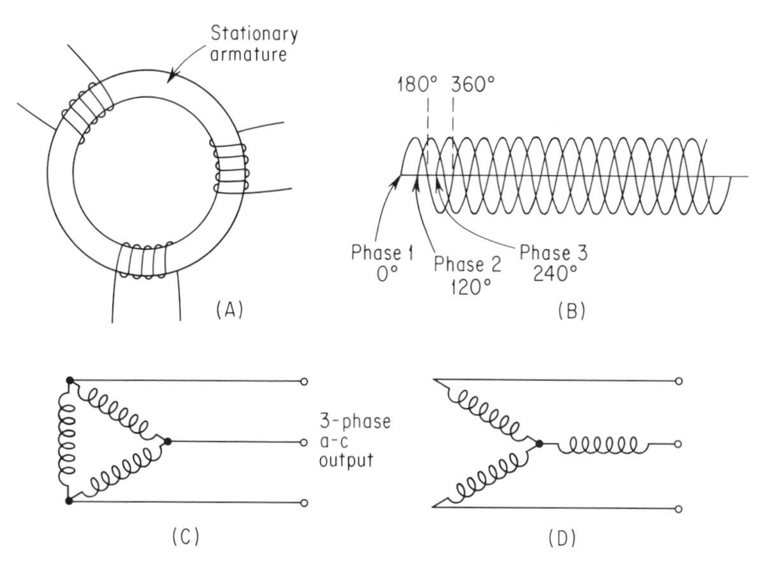

Fig. 5-10. Production of 3-phase a-c

ing-armature type, it would mean an increase in the number of slip rings and brushes over the amount required for the single-phase generator. With the rotating field and the stationary armature, however, the output is derived from the fixed-position armature. Therefore no slip rings are necessary. With three coils, the three-phase voltage produced is as shown at B of Fig. 5-10. Since one complete cycle (two alternations) of a-c takes in 360 degrees, one alternation takes 180 degrees, as shown. For the three-phase a-c, phase 2 is displaced with respect to phase 1 by 120 degrees (one-third cycle), and phase 3 is displaced by 240 degrees with respect to phase 1 and by 120 degrees with respect to phase 2.

To avoid the six output connections as shown at A, the connections shown at C or D are employed for the armature-coil windings. At C, the *delta* connections are shown for the armature coils. With this circuit, only three output wires are necessary instead of the six as shown at A. At D, the *star* or *Y* connection is shown. This is an often-used connection, which also produces a three-wire output from the armature coils instead of six. In the three-phase system, current at any instant is flowing out from one wire and returning through the other two. At another instant, the current flowing from the generator goes through two of these three wires and returns through one. Single-phase a-c can be obtained from the three-phase system by taking the voltage from across two of the three wires, leaving one wire unused as a terminal.

Obviously, since the three-phase system employs three terminals for the a-c output, the load circuit equipment must be such that it can take advantage of the three-phase voltage which is produced. Hence, the load circuit must be a balanced type with three input terminals rated for the particular voltage and frequency of power furnished by the a-c generated. In power distribution to industrial plants a neutral (ground) wire is often used. Such a wire is connected to the junction of the three inductances shown at *D*. This arrangement then constitutes a four-wire, three-phase system.

The standard frequency for power produced by the huge generators in the United States is 60 cycles. In some localities 25-cycle currents have been employed, but the lower frequency has several disadvantages. Larger transformer and generator cores are necessary, and the ripple frequency is noticeable in incandescent-light applications. With 60 cycles, it is also easier to filter the ripple component which results when this frequency is rectified, because the higher the ripple frequency, the less rigid the filter-circuit requirements, as more fully discussed in the next chapter.

Review Questions for Chapter 5

1. Briefly define *generator, dynamo,* and *dynamotor.*
2. What is the purpose of the field coil in a d-c generator?
3. Explain the essential differences between an a-c generator and a d-c generator.
4. Briefly explain how a d-c generator can produce substantially ripple-free d-c.
5. Briefly explain the advantages of increasing the number of poles of a generator armature.
6. Briefly explain what is meant by a *self-excited generator.*
7. Show by simple drawings the basic circuits for the shunt-wound generator and the compound-wound generator.
8. Briefly explain what is meant by a *polyphase generator.*
9. What is meant by a *delta* connection? How does this differ from the *star* connection?
10. Briefly explain how current divides in the three wires of a three-phase system.

6

Rectification and Power Supplies

INTRODUCTION

Rectification refers to the process of changing alternating current to direct current in applications where it may be required. Rectification finds extensive usage in the power-supply sections of industrial equipment, as well as in home radio and television receivers.

To effect rectification, either diode-type tubes or solid-state devices are used. As mentioned earlier, these will pass current in only one direction. In vacuum- or gas-tube diodes, current flows from the cathode to the plate and only when the plate is positive with respect to the cathode; when the plate is negative with respect to the cathode, no current flow occurs within the tube. The ordinary solid-state rectifiers such as the selenium and silicon types exhibit a high resistance in the reverse direction and a low resistance in the forward direction, as mentioned earlier, thus these units also may be employed for rectification purposes. However, because there is some resistance in the reverse direction, some current will also flow in a direction opposite to that desired, but this reverse current flow is usually quite low in comparison to the forward current and does not hamper the use of such devices as rectifiers. (See Chapter 1.)

The rectifiers, of whatever type, perform the basic function of producing unidirectional current flow, but other components must be employed in the rectifier circuit for obtaining smooth and ripple-free d-c of the proper amplitude. The amplitude of the output voltage is established by step-up or step-down transformers, and the ripple components of the rectified current are smoothed out by filter networks, or by use of polyphase a-c.

RECTIFIER SYMBOLS

A vacuum-tube diode symbol is shown at A of Fig. 6-1. This tube consists of a filament and a plate, and the direction of current flow is shown by the arrow (from filament to plate). Since the source of the electrons is the filament, it is also referred to as the *cathode* of the circuit. At B, the same basic tube type is shown with a black dot in the symbol, indicating a gas-type tube. The absence of the black dot at A indicates a high-vacuum type tube. At C a diode is shown with a separate cathode. Here the filament is used solely to heat the cathode so it produces electron emission, hence the filament is not considered an active element of the circuit function since the cathode is a separate element. This is still a diode tube because the cathode and anode are the active elements insofar as the circuit is concerned. For simplicity, the filament lines are often omitted from the symbol as shown at C, and when shown in schematics in this manner the filament is presumed to be present.

The selenium, silicon, or other disk-type rectifiers are symbolized as shown at E and F. (See Fig. 1-12 and Fig. 1-14, Chapter 1.) The triangular section may be either as shown at E, or shaded as shown at F, neither method having any particular significance compared to the other. The straight line of the symbol represents the cathode toward which electrons flow and is usually marked with a positive identification on the actual unit. The direction of current flow is shown by the arrows at E and F. (As mentioned earlier, in this text the direction of current flow and electron flow are considered to be in the same direction, starting from the minus terminal and flowing to the positive terminal. This conforms to the modern electronic concept, rather than to the older "conventional" theory.)

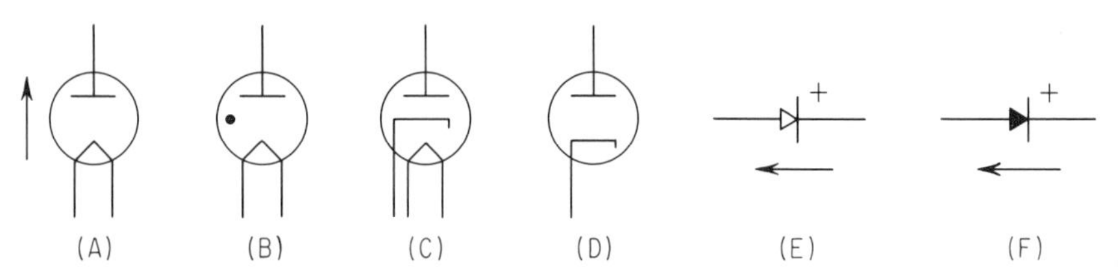

Fig. 6-1. Rectifier symbols

HALF-WAVE RECTIFIER

The basic half-wave rectifier circuit using a vacuum tube is shown at A of Fig. 6-2. (Although a high-vacuum tube is symbolized, a gas-type rectifier could also be employed.) Here, the vacuum tube is in series with one side of the a-c power mains and also with the load resistance (R_L) as shown. If the first alternation of the a-c cycle is positive, as shown at the left of A, terminal T_1 would be positive and terminal T_2 negative. The positive terminal T_1 applies this polarity to the anode, while the negative potential at T_2 applies this polarity to the cathode via resistor R_L. The negative electrons freed by the heated cathode are now attracted to the plate and current flow through the tube occurs. Current flow starts at the zero level, rises to a peak value, and drops to zero again as shown. Consequently, the current flow through R_L also starts at a zero value, rises to a peak value, and drops to zero again. The voltage drop, across resistance R_L, will now have a polarity as shown, and this voltage also has a waveshape similar to the voltage applied to the rectifier circuit.

For the second alternation of the a-c input signal, terminal T_1 becomes negative and terminal T_2 positive. With the anode negative, the electrons at the cathode are repelled and no current flow occurs. Thus, no voltage drop occurs across R_L for a time interval equal to that of the second alternation of the input signal. When the third alternation appears, conduction again occurs and an output alternation is obtained across the resistor. As shown, the output alternations are all positive in polarity, hence the output waveform is known as *pulsating d-c*. For obtaining pure d-c, a filter network as described later is necessary. Because only half of the input cycles are rectified, this is known as a *half-wave rectifier* of the single-phase type.

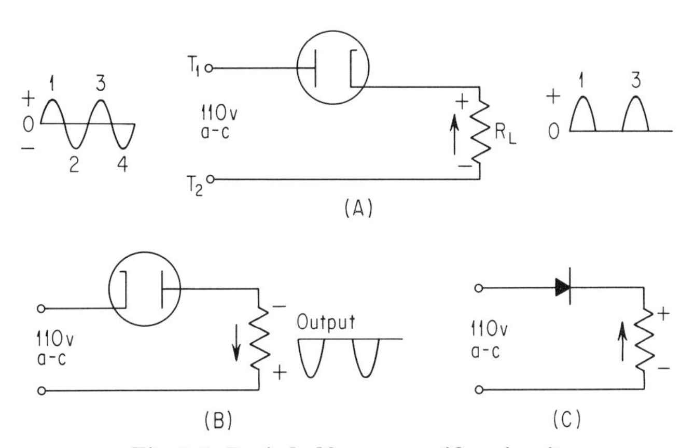

Fig. 6-2. Basic half-wave rectifier circuit

The diode may be reversed as shown at B, and half-wave rectification will still occur. The only difference between the circuits at A and B is that the polarity of the pulsating d-c has been reversed as shown by the voltage-drop polarity across the load resistor. At C a half-wave rectifier is shown, employing the selenium- or silicon-type rectifier. Current flow is in the same direction as that obtained for the circuit shown at A.

With the half-wave rectifier circuit rectifying the line voltage, the amplitude of the rectifying pulsating d-c will be limited by the line voltage. The filtering process will produce an average value which is below the peak value of the input a-c alternations, as more fully described later.

When it is necessary to obtain an amplitude that is different from the line voltage, a transformer is utilized in conjunction with the rectifier circuit so that the line voltage can either be stepped up to a value much greater than the line voltage or stepped down to a low or fractional value of the line voltage. If the line voltage is stepped up, the amount of current available will be decreased, since more power cannot be obtained from the secondary windings of the transformer than is furnished to the primary. When the voltage is stepped down, current is increased proportionately. (See Chapter 4.)

A typical half-wave rectifier circuit employing a transformer is shown at A and B of Fig. 6-3. At A, a directly heated tube having no separate cathode is employed. A secondary winding (S_1) furnishes the proper filament voltage for the rectifier tube, while another secondary winding (S_2) delivers the required voltage to be rectified. Thus, if winding S_2 has more turns of wire than the primary winding (P), a higher output voltage can be obtained than present in the primary. On the other hand, if the secondary winding S_2 has fewer turns than the primary winding, a lower rectified voltage will be available across R_L. As mentioned, the output power cannot exceed that available at the primary, and is limited to an additional degree by the size of the

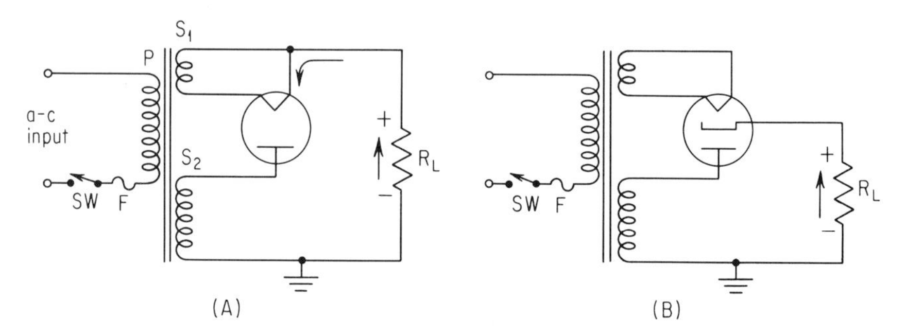

Fig. 6-3. Transformer-type half-wave rectification

secondary-winding wire of S_2 as well as the transfer efficiency of the transformer. With good design, however, the over-all transformer efficiency can be almost 100 per cent.

The operation of the circuit shown at A is similar to that of the half-wave rectifier circuits shown in Fig. 6-2. When the top of the secondary winding S_2 is positive and the bottom of this winding is negative, current flows through the load resistance in the direction shown by the arrow. The current flows to the filament and then to the plate as shown, producing an output alternation. When the top of S_2 is negative, the tube is nonconducting as in the previously explained half-wave rectifier. There is no interaction between the rectified voltage obtained from S_2 and the a-c voltage of S_1 which heats the filament. The voltage appearing across the S_1 winding finds a complete circuit through the filament of the tube and has no return circuit in the S_2 winding. Similarly, the current flow from the S_2 winding has a return circuit through the load resistance, and when it arrives at the filament its return path is to the anode and not to the S_1 winding.

The circuit shown at B is similar to that at A, except that a separate cathode is employed instead of the directly heated cathode shown at A. Circuit function is identical to that previously described. Both circuits are shown with a switch (SW) in the primary side as well as a fuse for protection against overloads or shorts in either the primary or secondary circuits. A ground connection is also shown in the negative line of the rectifier circuits. Such ground usually indicates chassis connection. (The metal chassis on which the circuit is mounted is often used as an interconnecting link for the negative terminals.) In some special applications the positive polarity line is grounded to the chassis, with the negative potential above ground.

FULL-WAVE RECTIFIER SYSTEMS

The pulsating d-c obtained from the half-wave rectifier circuits has a ripple frequency of 60 cycles per second. Because of the time interval between successive alternations, the filtering requirements for obtaining smooth d-c are greater than if there were no gaps between the pulsating d-c alternations. Filtering requirements would also be less rigorous if the ripple frequency were higher, as will be more fully explained. Both the conditions of eliminating the gap between alternations and increasing the ripple frequency can be satisfied by use of the rectifying system known as *full wave.* This consists of rectifying each half of the a-c cycle in such a manner that the output pulses are all of the same polarity. The basic full-wave rectifier system is illustrated at A and B of Fig. 6-4. At A, a vacuum-tube type is shown. Here, two diodes are contained within one tube envelope to form a so-called *dual-diode*

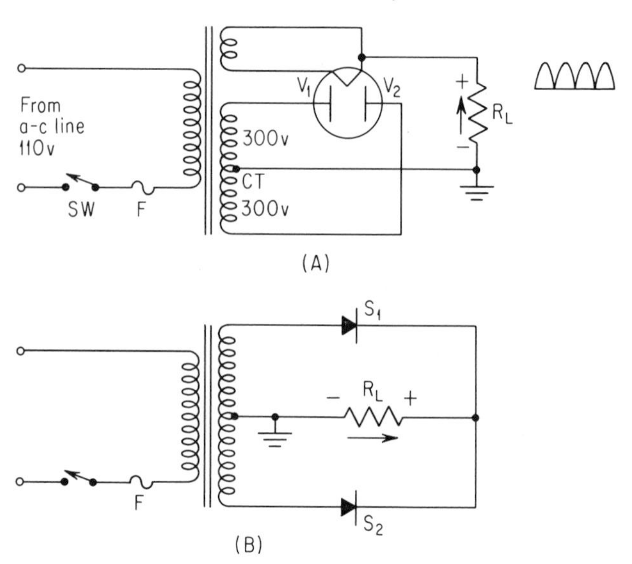

Fig. 6-4. Basic full-wave rectifier systems

rectifier. Separate tubes could, of course, also be employed if desired.

For full-wave rectification of the type shown in Fig. 6-4, a center-tapped transformer is necessary as shown. As an example, the circuit shown at A has a high-voltage secondary of 600 volts, tapped at the center. Actually, the amplitude of the output is no greater than would be obtained from a half-wave rectifier system operating from a single 300-volt winding, because the full-wave rectifier utilizes only one-half of the high-voltage winding at a time. If, for instance, an a-c alternation appeared across the secondary with a positive polarity at the anode of V_1 and a negative polarity at the anode of V_2, the latter would not conduct. Conduction for V_1, however, would occur because the center tap (CT) is negative with respect to the positive polarity at V_1, hence current would flow from the center tap through the load resistance and back to the anode of V_1 via the cathode of the rectifier. When the next alternation of a-c appears across the high-voltage secondary, the anode of V_2 would be positive and the anode of V_1 would be negative. With V_2 positive, the center tap is again negative with respect to the positive anode and current would again flow through the load resistor, through the filament and to the anode of V_2, completing the circuit for the lower half of the high-voltage winding. Successive alternations appearing across the secondary would be rectified alternately by diodes V_1 and V_2, producing a pulsating d-c across the load resistor as shown. The pulsating d-c now occurs at twice the rate which would prevail for half-wave rectification, and the ripple frequency is 120 cps instead of 60 cps. The output voltage has an amplitude which results from rectification of a 300-volt secondary potential, and not of a 600-volt secondary potential.

The full-wave rectifier shown at B is similar to the one shown at A, except for the use of silicon or selenium rectifiers instead of the vacuum-tube rectifiers. As with the vacuum-tube type, the cathodes are common and the load resistor is attached to the cathode sections and to the center tap. The rectifiers conduct alternately and establish a 120-cps ripple frequency of pulsating d-c across the load resistor. The full-wave type shown has the disadvantage of requiring twice as many turns in the secondary winding as would normally be necessary for the half-wave rectifiers.

BRIDGE RECTIFIERS

The necessity for increasing the secondary turns and for using a center tap can be eliminated by use of what is known as a *bridge-rectifier* circuit. Typical examples are shown at A and B of Fig. 6-5. Earlier a half-wave rectifier circuit was shown in series with the a-c mains for direct rectification of the a-c line voltage. In the absence of an intermediate transformer, a bridge rectifier can be employed when full-wave rectification is desired, as shown at A of Fig. 6-5. Here, the bridge rectifier consists of silicon or selenium rectifiers designated S_1, S_2, S_3, and S_4. Full-wave rectification is accomplished because the electrons leaving the negative terminal will automatically find their way through the rectifiers to the positive terminal and, regardless of the polarity of the a-c alternation, conduction through the load resist-

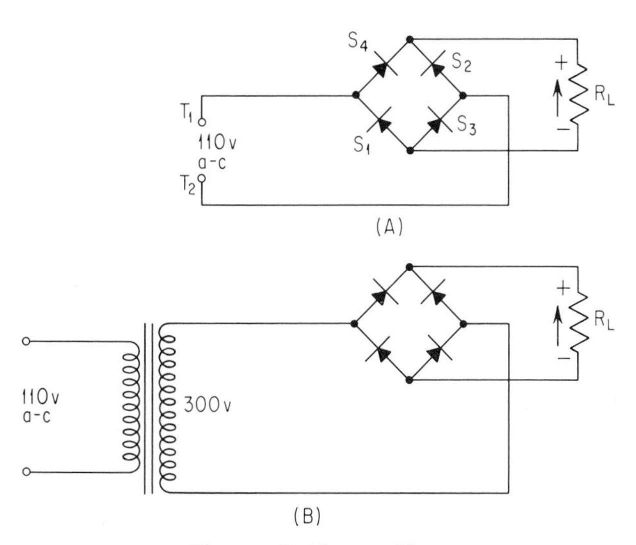

Fig. 6-5. Bridge rectifiers

ance will always be in the same direction. This can be more clearly understood by reference to A, with the assumption that the initial alternation applies a negative polarity to terminal T_1 and a positive polarity to terminal T_2. Current flowing from the negative terminal T_1 will arrive at the junction of S_4 and S_1. Rectifier S_4 is in the reverse direction, however, and current must flow through S_1 to the terminal between S_1 and S_3. Again, S_3 is in the reverse direction, hence current flows up through the load resistance as shown, to the junction between terminals S_2 and S_4, both of which are wired in the forward direction. However, current seeking a return path to terminal T_2 will now flow through rectifier S_2 to the terminal between S_2 and S_3. From here, the return circuit is directly to T_2, even though S_3 is in the forward direction. (Current will not flow through S_3 since it would be in the direction of its source rather than toward its return at terminal T_2.)

When the next alternation of a-c occurs across terminals T_1 and T_2, the polarity at T_1 is positive and the polarity at T_2 is negative. Now, current will flow from the T_2 terminal to the junction of rectifiers S_2 and S_3. In seeking the current-return path to terminal T_1, current now flows through S_3 and up through the load resistor to the junction between terminals S_2 and S_4. From the junction, current flows through S_4 and to its return-circuit terminal T_1. Thus, although each successive alternation flows through two different rectifiers, the direction of flow is always up through the load resistor, establishing a single polarity across the latter. Thus, full-wave rectification is accomplished without the use of a center-tapped transformer.

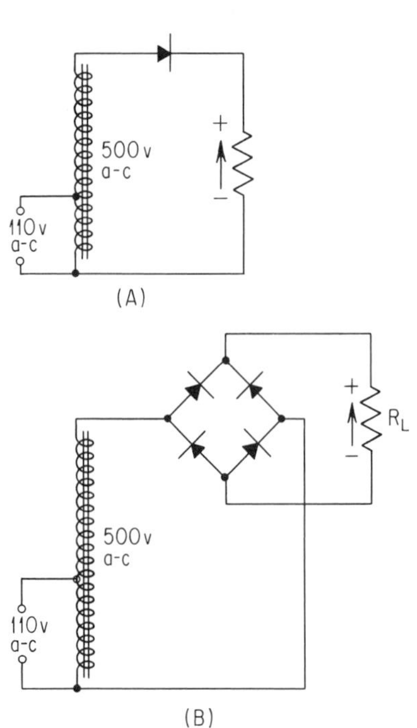

Fig. 6-6. Use of auto-transformers in rectifier circuits

If a transformer is utilized to step up the voltage as shown at B of Fig. 6-5, no additional winding or center tap is necessary. The rectification process is identical to that of the circuit shown at A, with full-wave rectification resulting in unidirectional current flow through the load resistor. This type of circuit is more economical from the standpoint of the transformer, although it requires two additional rectifiers. If the same transformer were used as shown at A of Fig. 6-4, the center tap would not be used and 600 volts would be rectified instead of 300, as in Fig. 6-4. Vacuum tubes, of course, can be employed instead of the rectifiers shown.

A single-winding transformer can be used to step up voltages as shown at A and B of Fig. 6-6 instead of transformers employing both primary and secondary windings. When a single winding is employed, the input a-c voltage is applied across a portion of the total windings as shown. The additional windings step up the 110 volts to the potential required (500 volts in the illustration). The single rectifier at A, however, furnishes only half-wave rectification. Utilizing the same transformer (as shown at B), full-wave rectification is procured by use of the bridge-rectifying principle. Such transformers are known as *auto-transformers,* as discussed in Chapter 4, because the single winding uses itself to step up the voltage to the required amount.

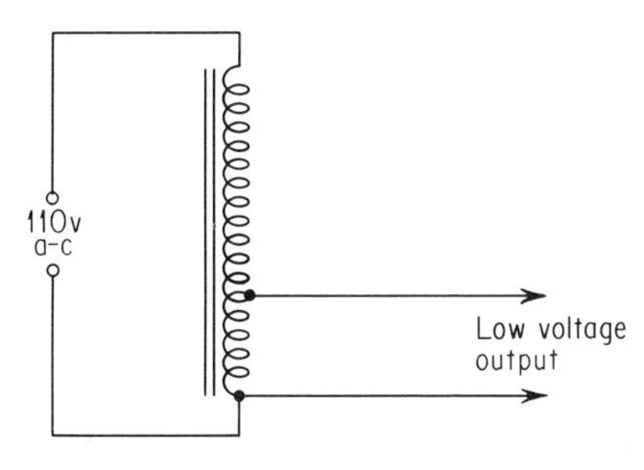

Fig. 6-7. Step-down auto-transformer

As with transformers using a primary and secondary, the auto-transformer can also be employed to step down voltage rather than increase it. For step-down purposes, the transformer schematic would be as shown in Fig. 6-7.

POLYPHASE RECTIFICATION

As discussed in Chapter 5, generators can be designed to furnish not only single-phase, but also polyphase a-c. The single-phase and three-phase generators are most extensively used in industry. For lower-power commercial requirements, the single-phase 110–120 volt, 60 cycle is common, as is also the 220–240 volt three-phase system. Where higher powers are required, it is usual for the power companies to furnish industrial plants with three-phase a-c ranging up to 10,000 volts. At the plant, step-down transformers are employed, using the delta or star circuitry described earlier in Chapter 5.

When filtering high-power a-c, the filter network requirements can be held at a minimum (reducing costs considerably) by increasing the ripple frequency of the pulsating d-c produced by rectification, as mentioned earlier. Thus the three-phase has a decided advantage over the single-phase with respect to filter reduction. A typical rectifier circuit for three-phase is shown at A of Fig. 6–8. Since this is a three-phase system, three diode rectifiers are necessary (D_1, D_2, and

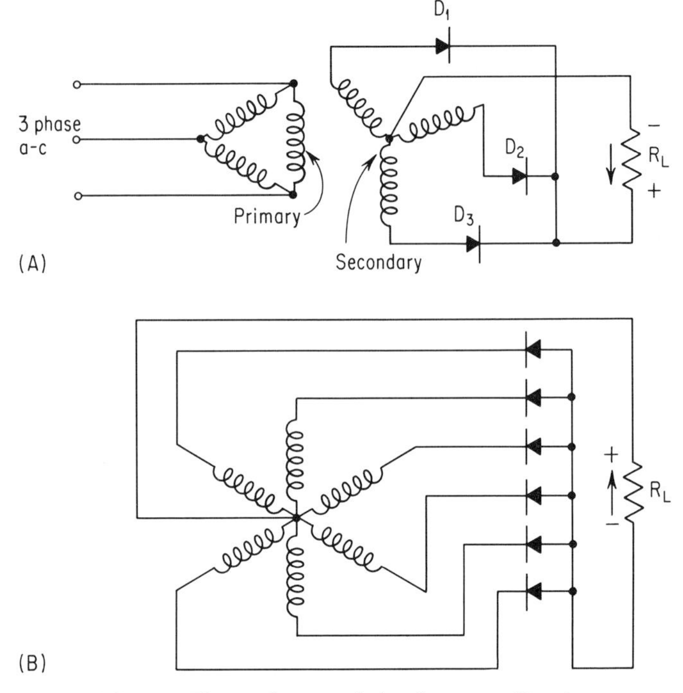

Fig. 6-8. Three-phase and six-phase rectification

D_3). This is full-wave rectification, because each diode will rectify one segment of the three-phase a-c.

Note that the cathode sections of the diodes are all connected to a common lead wire. Current from the center of the star-winding secondary flows down through the load resistor as shown by the arrow, and into the diode which has on its anode the highest positive potential at that time. Although the diodes conduct alternately as the phase changes, a slight sharing of current flow occurs because as the positive polarity on one diode declines, it starts building up on the next.

The polarity indicated across *RL* at A of Fig. 6–8 can be reversed by reversing the diodes. The output d-c across the load resistor can be additionally filtered to any degree required by the filter systems subsequently detailed.

For a much smoother d-c output (requiring even less in the way of filtering) a six-phase transformer, as shown at B of Fig. 6–8, is often employed in industrial applications. In fact, the ripple component in this system is sufficiently low for direct applications to equipment and certain control devices (to be more fully discussed later).

The primary winding for the secondary shown at B is the same as that illustrated for A in Fig. 6–8. Each secondary winding is connected to its individual diode as was the case with the circuit shown at A. Full-wave rectification occurs as each diode, in succession, conducts when its anode is more positive than the others. Again, the polarity across the output load can be altered by reversing the diode connections.

Formerly, banks of large gaseous-tube rectifiers were necessary for the six-phase system (such as the ignitrons discussed later) and many are still in use in industry, occupying large areas by virtue of their bulk. With the advent of the silicon and silicon-controlled rectifiers and other such solid-state devices, many of the older installations are being replaced by the more compact solid-state devices, thus reducing the space necessary for power-supply devices. (See also Chapter 1.)

FILTER NETWORKS

All the rectifier systems previously discussed provide an output of pulsating d-c with a ripple frequency of 60 cycles or more. The rectifier circuits are designed for use in power supplies to furnish d-c from an a-c source. In most instances the power supply, in order to furnish smooth and comparatively ripple-free d-c, must also consist of a filter network in addition to the rectifier circuit. The filter networks are made up of one or more metal-core inductors as well as one or more capacitors. The inductors are known as *filter chokes* or *filter reactors* and the capacitors are referred to as *filter capacitors.*

The filter chokes may have an inductance value from a few henrys up to 20 henrys, depending on how many are used, the degree of smoothing action necessary, and the ripple frequency present. Filter capacitors range from a few microfarads up to as high as 100 microfarads or more in certain applications. The value of the filter capacitors also depends on the smoothness of the d-c required, the ripple frequency, and the number of filter capacitors employed in any particular filter system. The filter chokes are in series with the load circuit resistance, whereas the filter capacitors are in a shunt arrangement across the resistance of the load circuit.

Filter systems fall into two general categories, the *choke input* type and the *capacitor input* type, both of which are illustrated in Fig. 6–9. At A, the choke input filter system is illustrated. Here, L_1 is known as the input choke because it is the first inductance the rectifier circuit encounters. This choke is also referred to as a *smoothing* choke. When a choke input filter is employed, an additional choke is usually utilized as shown, with one filter capacitor between the two chokes and the other connected to the second choke on the load re-

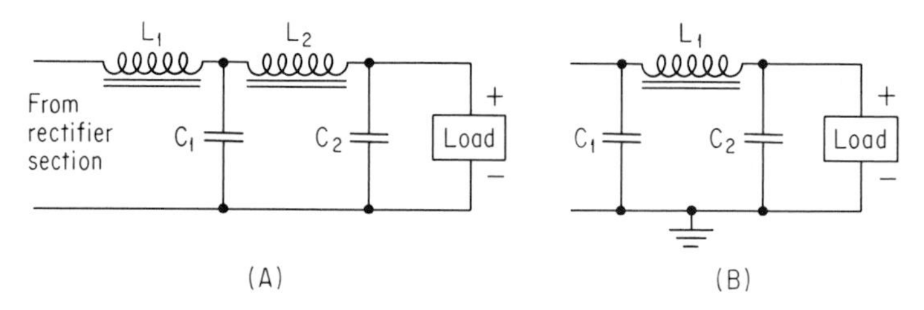

Fig. 6-9. Filter sections

sistor side. The choke input filter contributes towards better voltage stability as detailed in the next section of this chapter. In some applications the second filter choke may be replaced by a resistor, with some decrease in the effectiveness of the filtering. The input choke, because of its reactive characteristics, limits the peak value of the pulsating d-c alternations which result from the rectifying process. The high inductive reactance of the choke coil for the ripple frequency of the pulsating d-c offers opposition to such a ripple frequency and tends to reduce it. The second filter choke has a similar function in presenting a high reactance to the ripple frequency, and since the two inductors are in series, the total reactance presented to the ripple frequency is doubled if each inductor has the same inductive reactance.

The filter capacitors have a low value of capacitive reactance and act as a shunt for the ripple-frequency component of the pulsating d-c. The capacitors become charged to the voltage impressed across them and tend to hold this voltage level, thus helping to produce a ripple-free d-c output.

The filter shown at B of Fig. 6–9 is known as the *capacitor input type filter*. For a given current drain it will provide a higher output voltage than the choke input filter. The ability of this power supply to maintain a fairly constant output voltage, with variations in current drain, is reduced somewhat over the choke input filter type—because the input filter capacitor charges to the peak value of the rectified pulsating d-c alternations and this value is higher than the value which is placed on the first filter capacitor with a choke input filter. Since the current drain from the power supply depletes the charge held by the filter capacitors, it is necessary to replenish constantly the power absorbed from the filter capacitors. This replenishing process is accomplished by the d-c pulses originating in the rectifier circuit. With full-wave rectification, the individual capacitors are replenished at twice the rate which occurs for half-wave rectification. In consequence, the capacitors need not be as large in capacity since they need not store as much energy as they would if replenished at less frequent intervals. With a capacitor input filter, however, peak charging voltage is present for only a short interval. Thus, if the current drain from the system is low, the filter capacitors need furnish only a small amount of their stored power. When current drain increases, however, the filter capacitors give up more power in a given interval and cannot maintain the peak voltage to which they are charged. In consequence, the output voltage declines below that which would prevail for less current drain. With a choke input filter, the amplitude of the charge on the filter capacitors is already below the peak value, hence the capacitors are not influenced to the same degree by current variations, and consequently, the output voltage variations for current changes are not as great.

For the filter systems shown, the ground connection is placed in the negative line, so that the positive polarity of the output voltage is above ground. On occasion, however, when it is necessary to have a negative voltage source such as the bias supplies for vacuum tubes or special amplifier circuits as described subsequently, the positive potential of the supply would be grounded as shown in Fig. 6–10. In this instance, the filter choke is placed in the negative line so that its d-c resistance will not be influential in placing the ground point above the positive voltage reference level of the power supply. Since the filter choke is still in series with the load resistance, the filtering action is no different from the other circuits discussed.

In addition to the resistance presented by the load circuit, an additional resistor is often placed across the power supply as shown. This resistor is known as a *bleeder resistor* because it "bleeds" or causes a constant current drain from the power supply over and above the current drain of the load circuit. The bleeder resistor can be in several sections so that intermediate voltages can be obtained from the various taps at the junction of the several resistors. The bleeder resistor also helps maintain a more constant output voltage because it imposes a constant (though slight) current

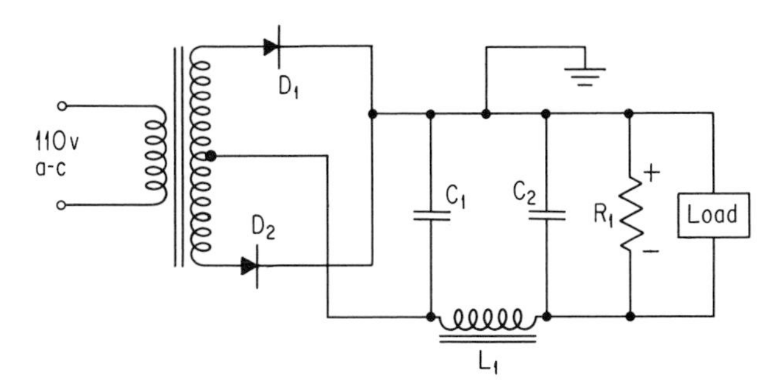

Fig. 6-10. Full-wave bias supply

drain on the system. The bleeder resistor is chosen to have an ohmic value sufficiently high so that only about 5 per cent of the current drawn by the load circuit flows through it. The bleeder resistor must also have a wattage rating high enough so that it will not overheat because of the voltage impressed across it and the current flowing through it.

POWER-SUPPLY REGULATION

The regulation of a power supply relates to its ability to maintain a fairly constant voltage during variations in the current load drawn from the supply. The regulation is affected by the amount of current which flows because of the voltage drops set up within the power supply. Current flow in the power supply sets up a voltage drop across the internal resistance of the vacuum tube and the d-c resistance of the filter chokes, as well as the voltage across a bleeder resistor if used. When the current drain from the supply is low, the voltage at the output terminals will be near a maximum value which the power supply can furnish. As the current drain is increased, however, there is also an increase in the voltage drop across the rectifier and chokes with the result that the voltage at the output terminals decreases. The variation of the output voltage in ratio to the current drain is referred to as *voltage regulation.* With no current drain from the power supply, the output voltage is at its maximum, and with a high current drain (near the safety limits of the unit) the output voltage is at a minimum. The percentage of voltage regulation for power supply can be ascertained by the ratio of output voltages which occur for the minimum and maximum current drains. Considering the current drain as a *load* on the power supply, the voltage is read under a "no-load" condition and under a "full-load" condition and the values set down according to the following formula:

$$\text{percentage of voltage regulation} = \frac{\text{no load } E - \text{full load } E}{\text{full load } E} \times 100$$

Thus, if the power supply output is 500 volts with no current drain, and the voltage drops to 400 under certain load conditions, the voltage regulation would be:

$$\frac{500 - 400}{400} = \frac{100}{400} = 0.25 \times 100 = 25\%$$

Too great a voltage variation with changes of current drain indicates poor regulation, and steps must be taken to stabilize the output voltage. Voltage variations will influence performances in the devices fed by the power supply and, in consequence, erratic results will be obtained. The degree of regulation required depends on the voltage-variation tolerances permitted by the devices which are furnished power. In some instances a voltage regulation of 25 per cent is permissible, whereas in other cases it must be kept below 10 per cent for satisfactory performance. Obviously, if the devices attached to the power supply are such that a constant current drain is maintained, the special precautions taken to improve voltage regulation can be dispensed with.

One method to improve voltage regulation is the use of a gas-type rectifier tube. The gas-filled rectifiers have a very low internal resistance (10 to 20 ohms) during ionization of the gas, hence the voltage drop across the rectifier tube changes little for changes of current through the tube. This is evident when we consider that a change of current from 0.2 ampere to 0.4 ampere will result in a voltage change across a 10-ohm resistor from 2 volts to 4 volts, or a net change of 2 volts. A 200-ohm resistance, however, will result in a voltage change from 40 volts for an 0.2 ampere current to 80 volts for an 0.4 ampere current drain, producing a net change of 40 volts. For industrial applications, the gas-filled tubes are also capable of handling greater power than the high-vacuum types.

Input Filters

Another method for improving regulation is the use of a choke input filter, as shown earlier in Fig. 6-9. The choke input filter reduces the peak level of the a-c alternations and thus reduces the wide variation of output voltage which occurs for a capacitor input filter during changes in the load. With a filter using an input capacitor, the latter changes to the peak a-c voltage of the transformer winding and produces a higher output voltage under "no-load" conditions than would be the case with a choke input filter. With the capacitor input filter, the charge on the filter capacitors is drained off at a rate depending on the load imposed. The decline in voltage from the peak value will thus be greater than if the input choke prevented such an initially high charge from being impressed on the capacitors. The peak voltage value of the input capacitor is replenished only during short time periods, since the peak of the a-c voltage is present only for a fraction of the duration of the alternation. A flattening of the peak as occurs with the choke input filter means a longer charge time for the filter capacitors even though at a lower voltage rate. Hence, the drain from the charged capacitors will still be the same, but the maximum charge of the capacitors is not as high and will be reduced by a smaller value.

An additional improvement in voltage regulation can be obtained from an input filter inductor known as a *swinging choke.* The swinging choke is a metal-core reactor (see Chapter 4) designed to be operated during normal current drains at a point approximately midway between the residual magnetism point (a) and saturation (b) as shown in Fig. 6-11. When current increases through the choke, the magnetizing force increases and the reactor operates at saturation. At or near saturation there is a decrease in the inductive reactance of the choke because of the decrease in permeability (dotted outline) and inductance. With a current decrease through the coil, permeability and inductance increase, and the inductive reactance also increases. Thus, as the current drain varies through the swinging choke, the inductance value also varies and may swing from approximately 10 henrys to 20 or 25 henrys. Consequently, the inductive reactance also varies and becomes less for more current drain. A decrease in inductive reactance decreases the voltage drop across the choke, tending to increase the over-all output voltage. With less current drain (where output voltage from the supply would tend to rise) the inductive reactance increases, a larger voltage drop occurs across the reactor, and the output voltage decreases to compensate for the increase with less load on the supply.

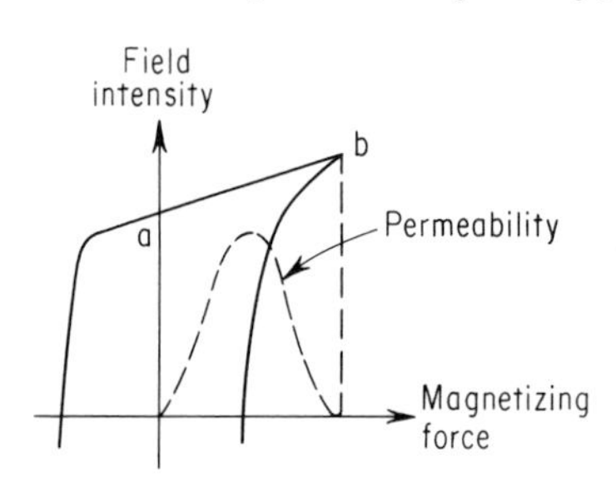

Fig. 6-11. Swinging choke operations

When the swinging choke is used in conjunction with the bleeder resistor mentioned earlier, a fairly stable output voltage can be maintained from the power supply for moderate variations in current drawn by the load.

Voltage-regulator Tubes

Another way to maintain good voltage regulation is to use special voltage-regulator tubes. These are gas-filled tubes that act as independent voltage regulators and do not contribute in any fashion to the rectification characteristics of the power supply nor to the filtering of the ripple component. A typical application of a voltage-regulator tube is shown in Fig. 6-12. In such an application, the voltage-regulator tube helps maintain a constant output voltage for extreme current-drain variations. The voltage-regulator tube is also helpful for maintaining a constant output voltage even though there may be some slight variations in the a-c power main voltages. If the current drain on the power supply decreases from average, the voltage across the output terminals of the power supply tends to rise and, in consequence, the voltage across the regulator tube network also increases. The latter increase will result in a rise of current through the regulator tube with a consequent increase in the voltage drop across the limiting resistor shown in Fig. 6-12.

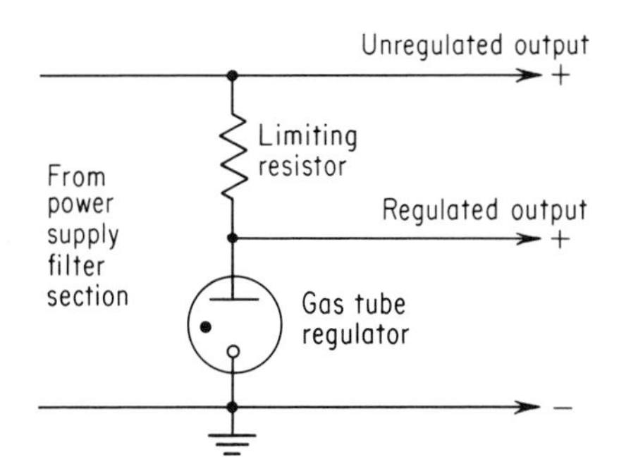

Fig. 6-12. Gas tube regulations

The rise of voltage across the limiting resistor decreases the output voltage of the power-supply terminals, hence it nullifies the rise in output voltage which would result from the current-drain decrease. When an increase in the current drain from the power supply occurs, there would normally be a decrease in the voltage at the output terminals of the supply. The decrease in voltage is also felt across the regulator tube network, and in consequence, the current through the regulator tube declines. Because of the reduced current through the limiting resistor, the voltage drop across the latter decreases, causing the output voltage to rise, and thus again nullifying the voltage decline which would otherwise occur.

Common gas-type regulator tubes are available for operation under constant voltage-drop conditions ranging from 75 volts to 150 volts. One type is the OA3/VR75 which operates within the current range of 5 milliamperes to 40 milliamperes. The OD3/VR150 operates from 5 milliamperes to a 40-milliampere maximum. For higher voltages, the gas tubes may be connected in series without affecting their current ratings. For voltage values below 75, the zener diode regulators described next are used.

The degree of voltage regulation also depends to a considerable extent on the average amount of current drain imposed on the supply. Assume, for instance, that a power supply can deliver a maximum current of 3 amperes, at 1000 volts. This power supply will have much poorer regulation for an average current drain of 2 amperes than it would have for an average current drain of 0.5 ampere, even though the current-drain variations had approximately the same degree of variation at each level.

SOLID-STATE REGULATORS

As mentioned in Chapter 1, the silicon zener diodes are useful in voltage-regulation applications. Like the gas tube, the zener diode has a breakdown characteristic which is not damaging. The breakdown occurs at a specific reverse potential amplitude with the zener diode, whereas in the gas tube the breakdown occurs in the forward direction,

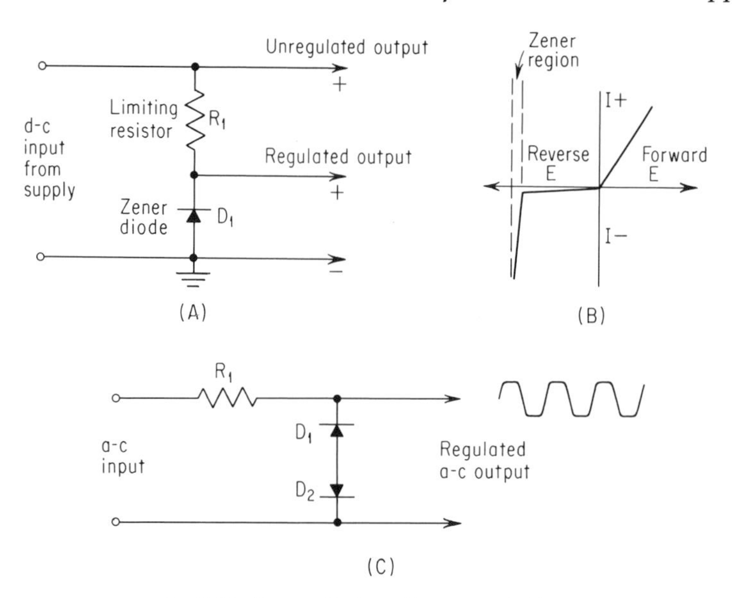

Fig. 6-13. Zener diode voltage regulations

when ionization of the gas occurs and conduction is permitted. In both units the voltage drop remains at a fairly constant amplitude for an increase in current.

A typical voltage-regulator application of the zener diode is shown at A of Fig. 6-13. Note that this circuit is basically similar to that for the gas-tube regulator shown in Fig. 6-12. For the zener regulator, the value of the reverse current limiting resistor R_1 is chosen to hold the diode in the zener region shown at B of Fig. 6-13. (If diode D_1 were reversed, it would be biased in the forward direction because current flow would then be toward the cathode section.) While in the zener region, the voltage drop across the diode remains constant, even though current-drain variations caused by the load alter the voltage of the circuit. Thus, the regulated output voltage will remain substantially constant so long as the diode is operated in the zener region.

The zener diodes can also be used for voltage regulation of a-c, as shown at C of Fig. 6-13. Here, two diodes are placed "back-to-back" so that each half of the a-c cycle is under control. Two separate diodes may be used, or special double-ended diodes, manufactured specifically for this purpose. With separate diodes, units must be chosen which have virtually identical characteristics for symmetrical operation. The a-c output waveform is clipped somewhat, as shown in the illustration.

Although the silicon zener diodes are available in much higher voltage ratings per single unit compared to the gas-tube regulators, they can also be stacked for still higher voltage ratings if necessary,

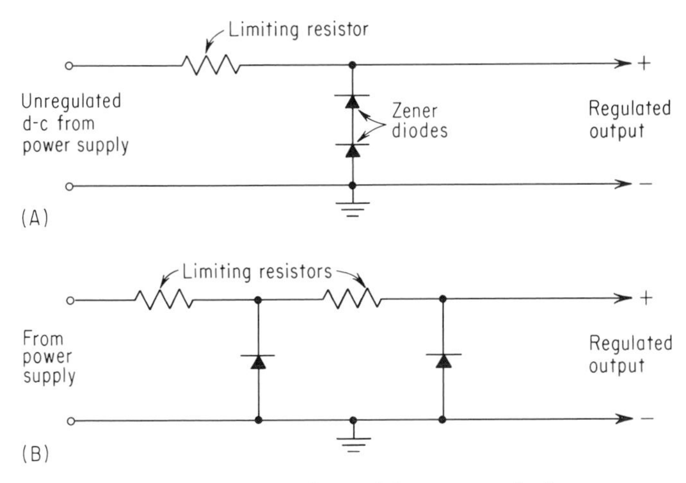

Fig. 6-14. Series and parallel zener regulations

as shown at A of Fig. 6-14. For improved regulation, two units can also be combined in a cascade arrangement as shown at B. As with the other circuits, the current-limiting resistor for the particular diode involved must be of such a value as to hold the reverse current in the zener region.

Thermistor Regulator

As mentioned in Chapter 1, the *thermistor* is a temperature-sensitive resistor, wherein the resistance value changes as the temperature of the thermistor varies. This principle can be employed for voltage regulation, as shown in Fig. 6-15. Regulation can be applied to either d-c or a-c; when d-c is used, the negative terminal can be grounded as shown by the dotted outline in the illustration. As with the previous voltage-regulator circuits shown, a limiting resistor is employed which must have a value for adjusting the current to the correct thermistor characteristics which will produce control effects.

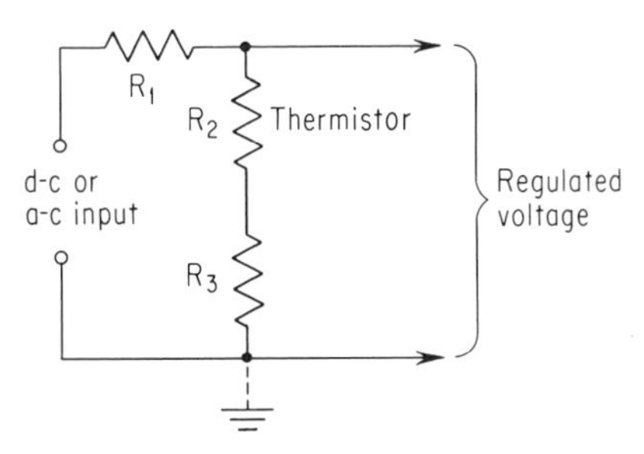

Fig. 6-15. Thermistor voltage regulations

When the load draws more current, the voltage across the output terminals would normally decline. As the voltage across the thermistor circuit drops to a lower value, less current flows through the latter and temperature decreases. With a temperature decrease, the resistance of the thermistor changes and the voltage drop increases to approximately the value it was before the load current changed.

VIBRATORS AND CHOPPERS

For control applications in industrial electronics, it is often necessary to convert a d-c signal to a-c, with the amplitude of the d-c signal regulating the respective amplitude of the a-c resultant. In this manner the output signal can be employed for motor and servo control as shown later, or stepped up for production of an a-c signal of higher amplitude so that it can be rectified to produce d-c which is also of a high-voltage value.

The principle employed is that of using a vibrating metal reed which is made to swing between two contact points to literally "chop" up the d-c into pulses. The d-c, of course, will not transfer through a transformer, but the chopped resultant will; hence the transformer secondary can deliver a voltage with a-c characteristics, and which will have an amplitude depending on the turns ratio of the transformer used. Such devices are variously termed *vibrators, choppers,* or *converters*; the first term usually applies to the devices used in vacuum-tube car radios or portable equipment, and the latter two terms apply to similar devices employed in industrial electronics.

A typical vibrator circuit is shown at A of Fig. 6-16. The metal spring-type reed is mounted so that its end is between two contact

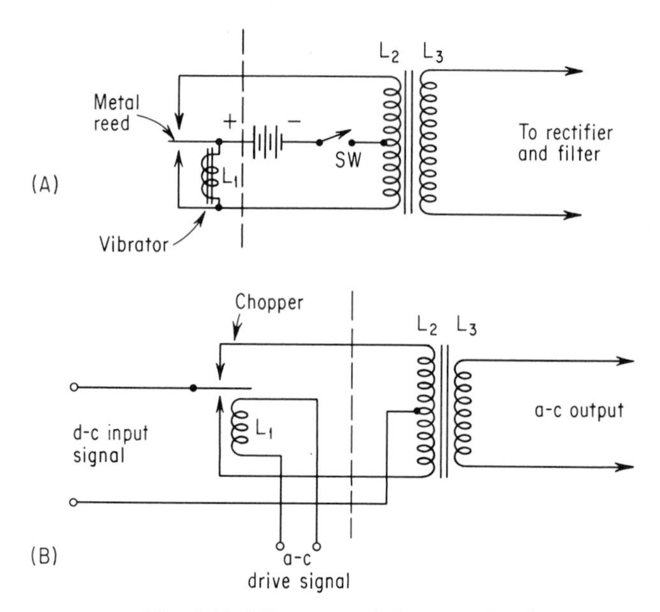

Fig. 6-16. Vibrator and chopper circuits

points as shown. When the switch is closed, current from the battery flows through the solenoid L_1 and the magnetic fields produced pull down the metal reed. As soon as the reed makes contact with the lower terminal, the inductance L_1 is shorted out and no longer produces a magnetic field. The reed, because of its spring action, now swings upward and strikes the top terminal. The magnetic field is again produced in L_1 and the process repeats itself continuously. The alternate "on and off" process applies the battery voltage successively to each half of the primary inductance L_2, and the rapid changes of current flow through the winding induce a voltage across the secondary. In portable equipment, the secondary voltage is stepped up to several hundred volts and is then rectified and filtered to produce d-c voltages higher than would be obtained from the battery.

In industrial electronics, the version shown at B is employed. Here, a control signal is applied to the input shown, and an a-c drive signal is applied to the coil L_1. The alternating magnetic fields of L_1 cause the metal reed to vibrate and again alternately contact the upper and lower terminals, thus chopping up the d-c so that induction occurs in the transformer. The result is an a-c output, the amplitude of which depends on two factors: the turns ratio of the transformer, and the amplitude of the control d-c input signal. As the latter varies in amplitude it will also change the amplitude of the output a-c signal, even though this is many times higher in value than the d-c signal. A typical d-c to a-c chopper (d-c to a-c converter) is shown in Fig. 6-17. This unit is manufactured by Stevens Arnold, Inc., and is available in

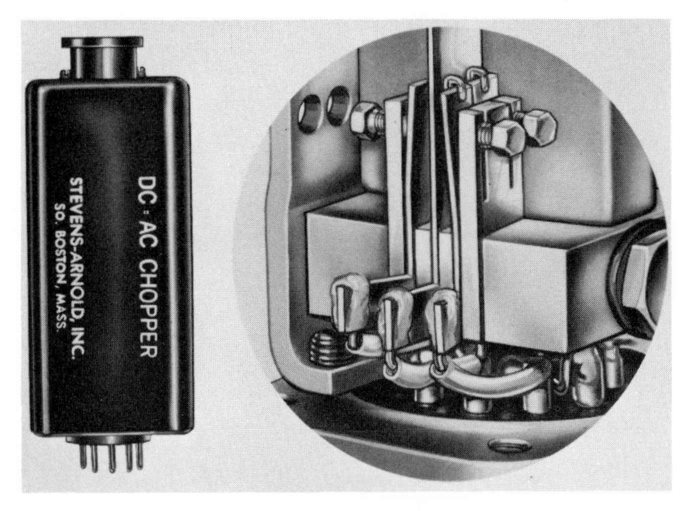

Fig. 6-17. DC-AC Chopper
(Courtesy Stevens-Arnold, Inc.)

several frequency types, including 50/60 cycles and 94/120 cycles, and in various models. Some have single-pole, double-throw (SPDT) switches, while others have double-pole, double-throw (DPDT) units.

These devices are manufactured by a number of other companies also, although, as mentioned, they may not necessarily be known as "choppers." The units manufactured by the Minneapolis-Honeywell Regulator Co., for instance, are known as "Brown Converters" and are also available in a variety of models with different specifications for usage as required.

COMMERCIAL SUPPLIES

Commercial power supplies come in a variety of sizes and models, ranging from the low-voltage types for transistor circuits to units delivering hundreds of volts for higher-power circuity. (High-power thyratrons and ignitrons, which are more strictly control devices rather than power-supply units, are covered in Chapter 7.) Most of the low-power commercial power supplies employ voltage regulation, solid-state rectification, overload protection, and other such features. In many instances they are furnished in units which lend themselves to rack and panel installations and are self-contained for simple removal of the entire unit for service and maintenance. For industrial purposes and for laboratory research work these devices must have rigid specifications and of necessity must adhere to close tolerances with respect to constant voltage output and versatility.

A compact commercial power supply, the LT 1095M, manufactured by the Lambda Electronics Corporation, is shown in Fig. 6-18. It is only $3\frac{1}{2}$ inches high, 19 inches wide, and $14\frac{3}{8}$ inches deep. This

Fig. 6-18. Commercial regulated power supply (Courtesy Lambda Electronics Corp.)

model has a voltage output range from 0 to 32 volts d-c, and a current range of 0 to 1 ampere. The output terminals at the back also have variable adjustment provisions to obtain the voltages in four continuously variable bands: 0 to 8 volts, 8 to 16 volts, 16 to 24 volts, and 24 to 32 volts.

This Lambda supply uses no vacuum tubes, but instead relies solely on solid-state devices for rectification, control, and stability. Rectification is by use of the silicon diode, and the zener diode is used in the regulation circuit. The regulation is better than 0.15 per cent, and the output voltage is constant (with respect to regulation specifications) for 10-volt variations (plus or minus) of the input from 105 to 125 volts a-c. The supply is rated for operation from 50 to 400 cycles with respect to line-voltage frequency.

As shown in Fig. 6-18, an output voltage meter and an output current meter are provided on the front panel. A thermal overload indicator light is provided on the front panel (below the "power on" indicator light) and a thermal overload breaker is contained within the unit for protection against excessive temperature. To comply with industrial requirements, the unit can be operated continuously around the clock without overheating or endangering voltage-amplitude output and regulation factors.

Review Questions for Chapter 6

1. Briefly explain what is meant by *half-wave rectification.*
2. Reproduce a typical half-wave rectifier circuit and briefly explain how rectification occurs.
3. What advantages and disadvantages are there between the full-wave rectifier system and the half-wave rectifier system?
4. Briefly explain the basic characteristics of a bridge-rectifier system.
5. Briefly explain the essential differences between a capacitive input filter and a choke input filter with respect to the filtering process.
6. Briefly explain what is meant by a *bleeder resistor* and give the reasons for its inclusion in some power-supply systems.
7. What is meant by *power-supply regulation?* What formula indicates the percentage of voltage regulation?
8. Describe the types of tubes used for voltage-regulation purposes.
9. Briefly explain how the zener diode can be used for voltage-regulation purposes, and why it is superior to the gas-tube types.
10. What applications do vibrator and chopper devices have in industrial electronics?
11. List some of the characteristics of commercial power supplies.

7

Transducers and Photoelectrics

INTRODUCTION

A *transducer* is a device which converts energy of one type into energy of another type; thus, a unit which converts mechanical energy into electric energy comes under this category, as does a device which converts electric energy to mechanical energy. For instance, a phonograph pickup cartridge is a transducer because it translates the groove variations of a record into needle vibrations which, in turn, are converted to electric impulses by the pickup. A microphone is also a transducer because it produces electric signals from acoustical energy. A loudspeaker is also in the transducer category because it converts electric signals into acoustical signals.

Transducers of various types are extensively employed in industrial electronics for control purposes. They are used to sense deviation, variations, pressures, and other physical changes which they convert into electric signals for purposes of identification, evaluation, fabrication, automation, and control.

Basic transducer principles are covered in this chapter; their specific uses in industry are given in a later chapter. Because a photoelectric tube is also a transducer since it converts incident light energy into electric pulses, photoelectrics will be included.

MECHANICAL TRANSDUCERS

A simple transducer is a lever or piston rod which, under motion, trips a switch or actuates the slide arm of a resistor, as shown in Fig. 7-1. At A, for instance, a lever arm is swiveled so that a lateral movement (left and right, or up and down) can then trip a toggle switch on or off as an overload protection or for some other control purpose. Also, as shown at B, the lever arm, by virtue of its swivel characteristic, can be made to move across a resistance and thereby vary the resistance for indication of the degree of mechanical movement. For liquid, gas, or air pressures, a diaphragm can be used as shown at C, and the pistonlike changes which occur can trip a sensitive microswitch. A roller can also be used as shown at D, whereby a slight movement right or left trips a rotary-type switch (or moves the variable arm of a resistor as at B).

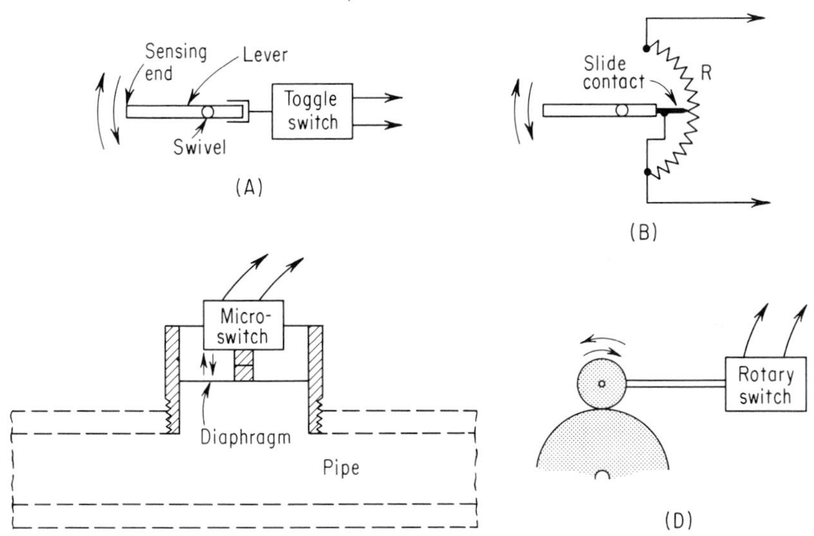

Fig. 7-1. Mechanical transducers

All the devices illustrated in Fig. 7-1 are available from various manufacturers in numerous different models and sizes to meet specific conditions. The type shown at C, for instance, is furnished in a small unit by the United Electric Controls Company, and the dimensions of the Type J6 pressure control are shown in Fig. 7-2. The internal adjustment nut (*A*) is for calibrating the pressure settings for proper tripping during overload. This waterproof pressure-vacuum control unit is designed for air, gas, or liquid applications where close-tolerance on-off differentials are encountered.

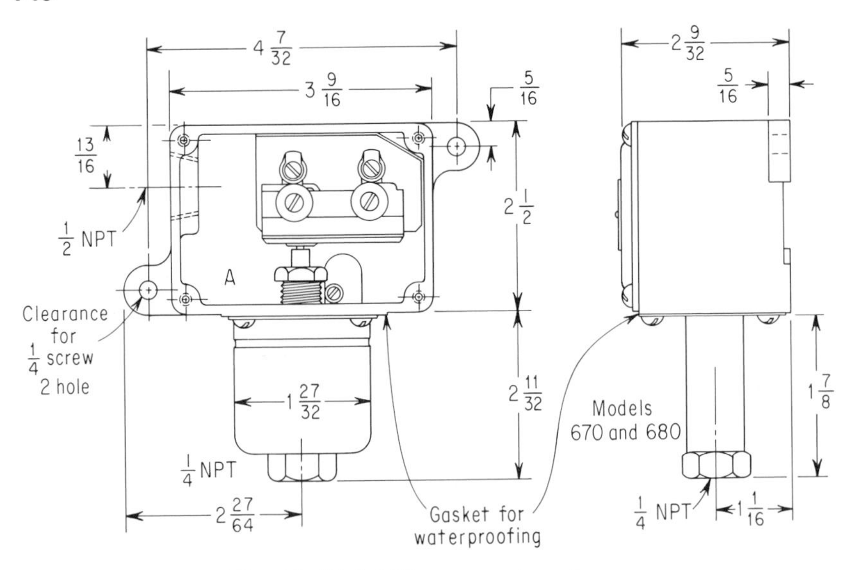

Fig. 7-2. Model J6 pressure transducer (United Electric Controls Co.)

REACTIVE TRANSDUCERS

The principles of an inductive or capacitive change are employed in transducers for sensing mechanical changes and converting them to electric signals. One such device, shown in Fig. 7-3, utilizes the capacitive-reactance principle. Here, a pipe section has an insulating dielectric ring, with the metallic flanges above and below it forming capacitor plates. Fluid pressure, by altering the expansion of the container, either compresses or decompresses the dielectric material, thus changing the capacity and hence the capacitive reactance of the

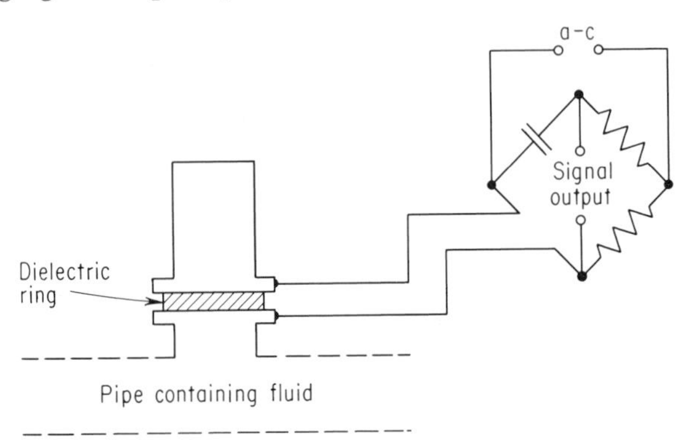

Fig. 7-3. Reactive transducer

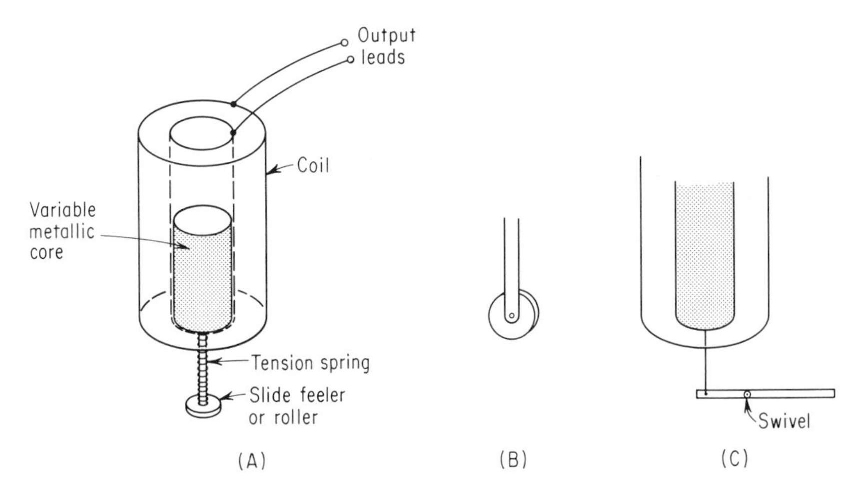

Fig. 7-4. Basic differential reactor

device. The capacity formed by the flanges and dielectric insulating ring becomes one section of a capacitive bridge as shown, hence fluid pressures above and below normal are felt at the bridge terminals by either a positive voltage or a negative voltage. Such voltages are then used for control purposes or for reading the pressures. When the bridge is balanced (see Chapter 10), zero voltage appears at the terminals. A variable capacitor can also be used, with its rotor section connected to a shaft to sense degrees of shaft rotation as discussed and illustrated in Chapter 10.

Inductive-reactance transducers are also extensively employed in industrial applications. As mentioned earlier in Chapter 4, when a plunger-type core is moved in or out of a coil, it changes the characteristics of the coil because the reluctance and permeability are altered accordingly. This principle is applied to create the inductance-type transducer, shown at A of Fig. 7-4. The plunger-type core is attached to a rod, at the bottom of which is a solid section which slides along in material to be measured or sensed. A spring, as shown, keeps the plunger almost out of the coil, and pressure is required to move the plunger into the coil. A roller can be applied to the bottom of the plunger as shown at B, or a lever arm can be used as shown at C. The transducers shown at A and B are used for measuring and controlling variations in thickness or curvature. The transducer shown at C can be used for alignment control of a moving belt of material such as metal or plastic, or for edge control as more fully described subsequently.

A typical inductance-type transducer is shown in Fig. 7-5 which illustrates the Atcotran edge-control device. Because an inductive trans-

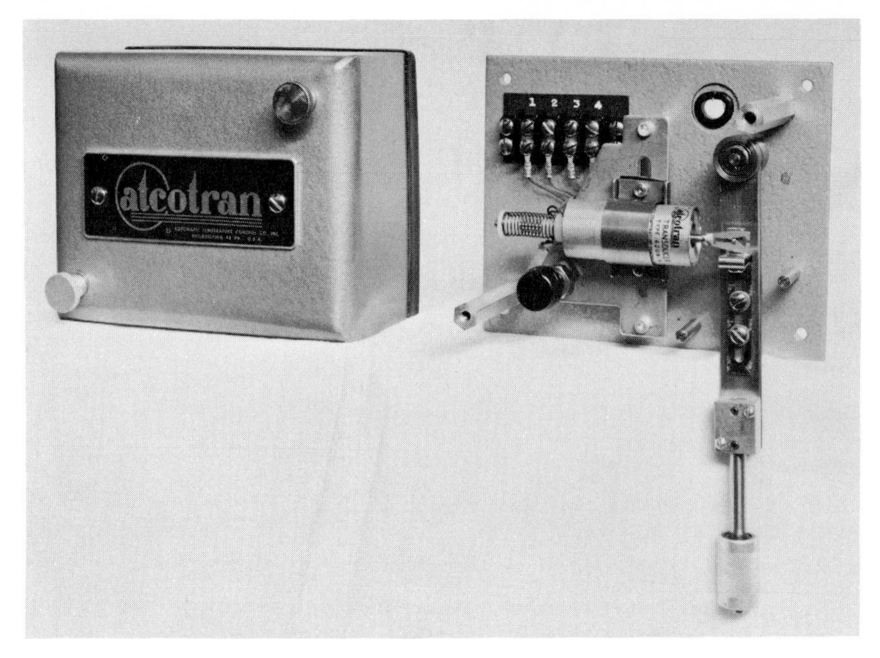

Fig. 7-5. Atcotran transducer
(Courtesy of Automatic Timing & Controls, Inc.)

ducer of this type differentiates between certain variations and transforms them into electrical impulses, it is often referred to as a *differential transformer*. As shown, a swivel arm actuates the plunger; the sensing device at the end of the arm can be a simple feeler as shown in Fig. 7-4, or it can be a roller as shown already mounted on the swivel arm. This device is manufactured by Automatic Timing and Controls, Inc. Applications for its use in edge control and deviation measurements are shown later.

SOLID-STATE TRANSDUCERS

Solid-state transducers contain pressure cells manufactured from rare earths which provide a resistance change when compressed. They are produced by processing the rare earths with zirconium tetrachloride. The cells are mounted in a small metal container and function for any variable physical tension, displacement, strain, or vibration. The basic form and circuit are shown in Fig. 7-6.

A commercial solid-state transducer using the pressure cell is shown in Fig. 7-7. This is the Celab transducer Model 604, manufactured by the Clark Electronic Laboratories. Stock units are made from load cells with ratings from a few grams up to 8 pounds pressure

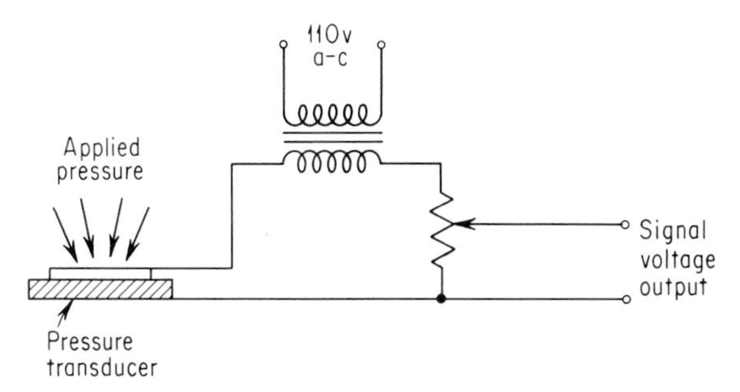

Fig. 7-6. Pressure cell circuit

Fig. 7-7. Celab pressure transducer (Courtesy Clark Electronic Laboratories)

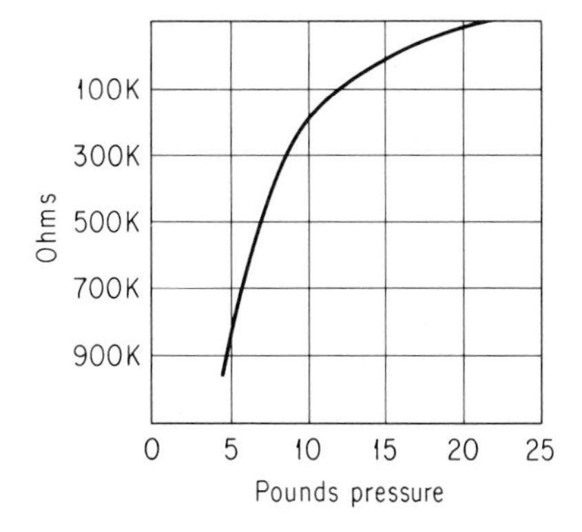

Fig. 7-8. Resistance versus pressure for Celab #48 cell

when used with a 1.5- to 3-volt supply. Output may be sensed in millivolts, microamperes, or ohms. A graph of this company's Model 48 pressure cell is shown in Fig. 7-8. For this transducer, a pressure differential of 15 pounds gives a change in resistance from approximately 0 to 900,000 ohms. Among their other models is the CS-5, with a resistance of about 2.6 megohms at 5000 pounds, and which is sufficiently sensitive to indicate oil leakage of 1 pound in 5000 pounds.

RESISTIVE TYPES

When a section of fine resistance wire is stretched, the increase in length plus the decrease in diameter alters its resistance. This principle is utilized to form transducers for measuring pressure, weight,

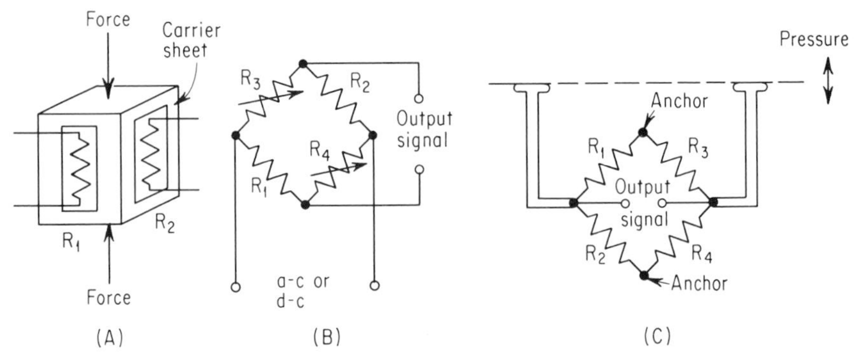

Fig. 7-9. Bonded and unbonded strain gauges

or strain (strain gauge). The resistive change is slight but is detectable in a bridge circuit and can be amplified additionally as required.

Resistive strain gauges are of two types: bonded and unbonded. The bonded gauge is illustrated at A of Fig. 7-9. The resistance strip is cemented to a plastic-treated paper carrier sheet as shown, and this is then bonded directly to the material that is to be sensed for pressure, strain, or stress present in it. When force is applied to both the top and bottom, creating pressure, the resistance of R_1 and R_2 strips decreases, causing a bridge unbalance. The two resistors are part of the bridge circuit as shown at B, with R_3 and R_4 variable for null balancing of the bridge for normal (or zero) pressure. The wire lengths are usually from a fraction of an inch to about 6 inches, with an average diameter of 0.001 inch. Average resistance without stress is approximately 100 ohms.

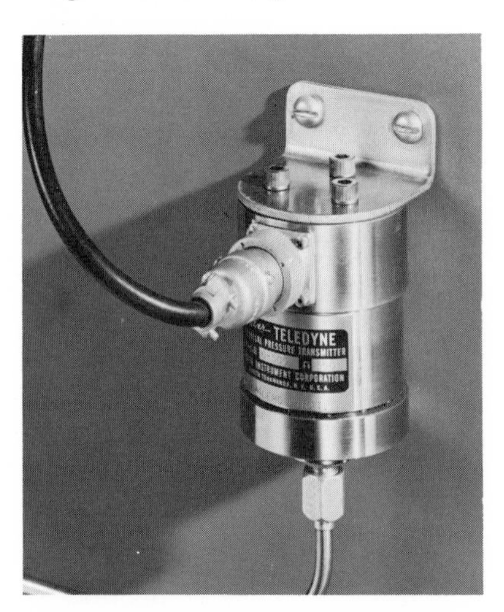

Fig. 7-10. Teledyne 206 pressure transducer (Courtesy Faber Instrument Co.)

The unbonded strain gauge in its basic form is shown at C of Fig. 7-9. Here, all four resistors are part of the strain gauge, with the upper resistors (R_1 and R_3) at opposite tension with respect to the lower resistors (R_2 and R_4). As shown, with the anchor points keeping the resistors in place, a pressure applied to the L-shaped arms forming an armature at the left and right will increase the strain of one set of resistors and decrease it in the other set, thus producing an output signal. (For basic bridge theory, see Chapter

10.) The unbonded strain gauge finds its greatest usefulness
manently installed weighing systems.

A typical application of the bonded strain gauge in a transd
Teledyne Model 206 pressure transducer illustrated in Fi
(Taber Instrument Co.). Here, dual metal diaphragms are used to sense the pressure variations, and these, in turn, press against a ring which has bonded to its circumference strain-gauge resistive elements. When pressure is applied to these elements, a linear resistance change occurs which is proportional to the pressure applied to the diaphragms. (Other solid-state transducers include the photocells described later.)

TACHOMETER TRANSDUCERS

When the shaft of a generator is made to rotate, the voltage produced will have an amplitude proportional to the speed (see Chapter 5). This transducer principle (conversion of revolutions to voltage) is utilized in industrial electronics for testing the number of revolutions per minute of various rotating devices such as spindles, motors, servos, machine shafts, etc. The generator is a small one, with a shaft extending beyond the housing. This shaft is pressed against the revolving unit to be tested and the resultant voltage is read on a calibrated meter. The generator transducer is called a *tachometer.*

Commercial Tachometer

A direct-current tachometer generator and the indicator unit are shown in Fig. 7-11. This is the Servo-Tek Products Company's speed-indicating device, which requires no batteries or external power because of the generator characteristics of the tachometer. The Servo-Tek speed indicator is available with indicators calibrated for a number of different speeds as required, ranging as high as 12,000 rpm. Scales are also available to read "0 to 100 per cent of full speed" for indus-

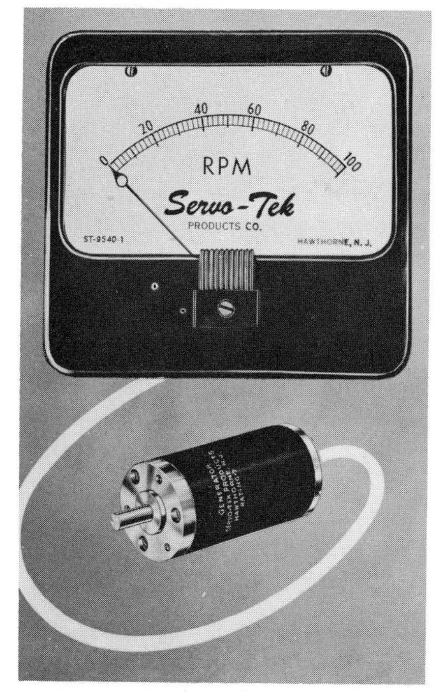

Fig. 7-11. Tachometer speed indicator (Servo-Tek Products Co.)

trial speed-comparison purposes. Various couplings are also furnished for proper coupling to the revolving or moving unit under test. The transducer is bidirectional, that is, it can sense speed for either clockwise or counterclockwise rotations. (See also Chapter 12.)

TEMPERATURE-SENSITIVE TRANSDUCERS

There are a variety of heat-sensitive transducers, most of which are constructed with bimetal elements. The principle of bimetal temperature sensitivity is shown in Fig. 7-12. Two dissimilar metals,

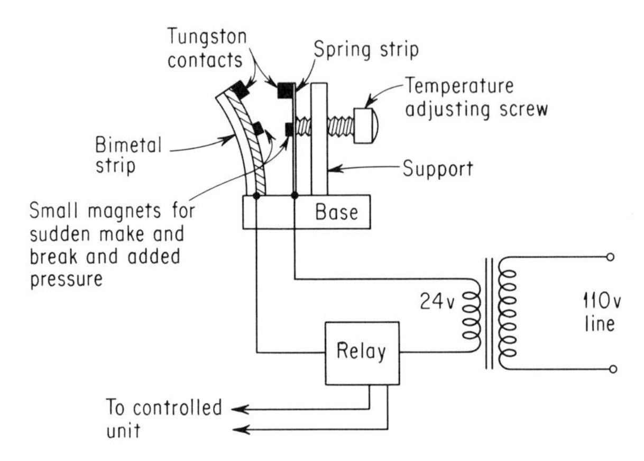

Fig. 7-12. Thermostat system

with different coefficients of expansion, are fused together. For a temperature change, the difference in contraction in one metal with respect to the other causes the metal to bend. Thus, it can be used to open a circuit for a rise in temperature or to close a circuit as shown in Fig. 7-12. The thermistor can also be employed. (The principle of the thermistor is covered in Chapter 1.) The thermistor, because of a change in its resistance for temperature changes, can be used as a transducer as shown in Fig. 7-13.

On occasion a spiral bimetal strip is utilized, as shown in Fig. 7-14 which illustrates a typical unit used in oil heating systems. The spiral temperature-sensitive element is placed within the heater and at a certain temperature trips a relay which is mounted on the framework on the outside of the heat chamber. As can be seen from the figure, the spiral ele-

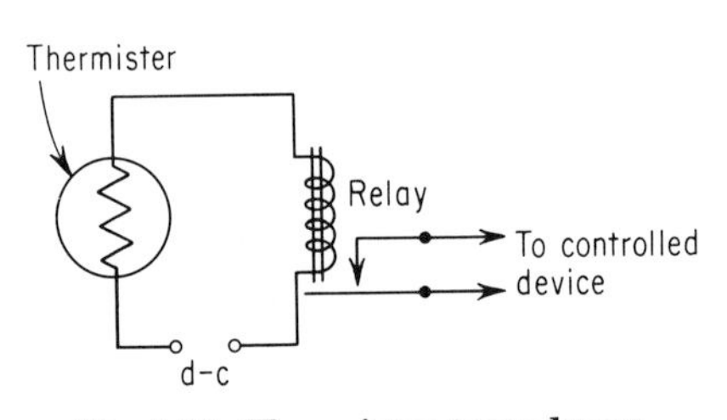

Fig. 7-13. Thermister transducer

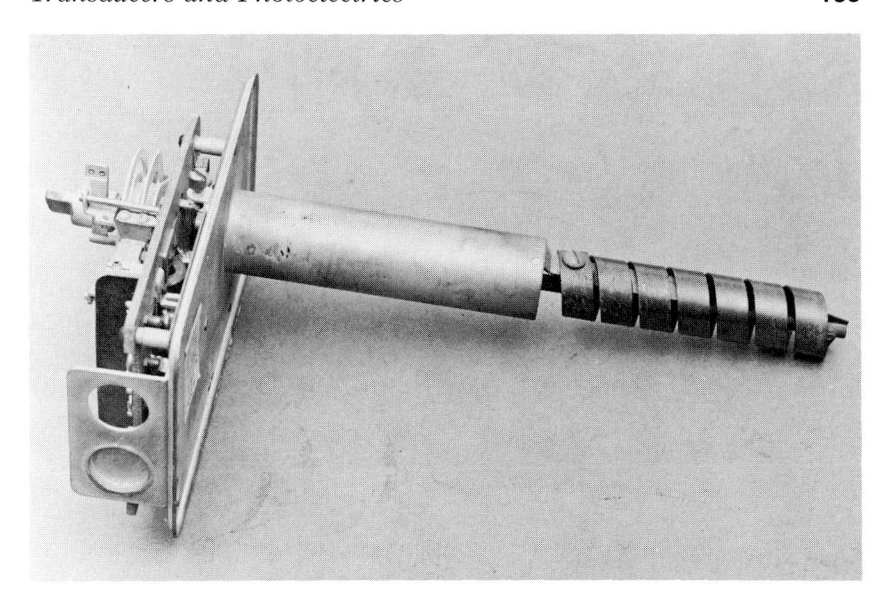

Fig. 7-14. Spiral transducer

ment, which is connected to a center rod, forces the rod to move in or out with respect to the housing. The other end of the rod connects to appropriate relays for turning on blowers, opening relays for safety protection, etc., as covered more fully in Chapter 10.

PHOTOELECTRIC DEVICES

As mentioned earlier, the photoelectric device is a transducer because it will convert changes in light waves to electric signals. There are a variety of photoelectric units employed in industrial electronics, for turning equipment on or off, counting moving objects, or otherwise regulating electric or mechanical devices.

Sensitive units are available in the following types: vacuum tubes, gas-filled tubes, diode photocells, resistive photocells, and transistor photocells. Because of this variety available, the photoelectric device is versatile. It can, for instance, be used to turn equipment on at daybreak or shut it off at nightfall. It can also be used to sense missing items or count a progression of merchandise on an assembly line. When used with a beam of light, the interruption of the latter finds use in such devices as burglar alarms and traffic counters, and is used for the ordinary opening of doors when the light beam is interrupted by an approaching person. Applications in basic circuitry are covered in this chapter.

BASIC PHOTOTUBE

The basic photoelectric tube (Fig. 7-15) consists of an anode and a cathode in an evacuated glass envelope. It compares generally to an ordinary vacuum-tube diode, except that no heater or filaments are employed. The cathode is a half-cylinder usually formed of silver-plated copper, the concave side of which is coated with a light-sensitive material such as cesium. When incidental light strikes the cathode structure, it gives up electrons which are attracted to a positive anode to establish current flow. The anode, as shown in Fig. 7-15, has applied a positive potential to it to attract the electrons which are loosened by the incident light; since current flow is low, the anode can be a thin vertical rod or wire as shown, the latter having the advantage of imposing a minimum of obstruction to the light striking the cathode.

Space-charge factors present in normal vacuum tubes are absent in the phototube, hence only a small positive potential need to be applied to the anode structure. The amount of electrons flowing to the anode depends on the amount of light energy which falls on the cathode structure as well as the wavelength of the light energy. Normal daylight need not be the sole light source. Ultraviolet light can also be used, with a special glass envelope to prevent the absorption of the ultraviolet rays before they reach the cathode. Light from a tungsten filament lamp can also be used, although as the wavelength of the light is decreased, the sensitivity of the tube would have to be increased to produce an equal amount of current flow. Sensitivity can be increased by using a gas-filled tube as described more fully later.

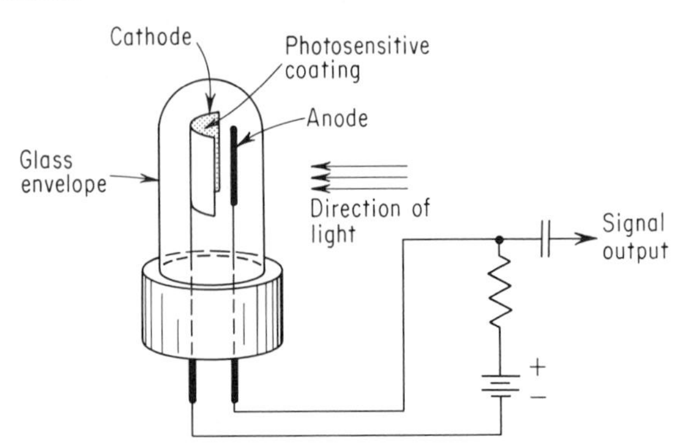

Fig. 7-15. Basic phototube and circuit

UNITS OF RADIANT ENERGY

Photoelectric tubes, cells, and other similar devices are calibrated on the basis of units of light, and in consequence are rated according to their sensitivity to such light units. Radiant energy can be expressed in units by relating the energy which is present to that which occupies a unit area, as for instance, the number of watt-hours or fractional watt-hours per square meter or per square centimeter. The total radiation can also be indicated in relation to the amount of energy in a given area with respect to the time in units. An example of such a rating would be the energy in watts or fractional watts for a given length of time per square centimeter or per square meter.

With respect to light, the unit measurements are based on comparisons with a known standard. Light, when striking the retina of the eye, produces a sensation of vision which has an intensity depending on the degree or brightness of light reaching the eye. The radiant energy producing such a visual sensation is termed *luminous flux,* of which the unit is known as the *lumen.* The light emitted from a candle burning under normal conditions is considered as the unit of intensity of light; a one-candle light source is designated as emitting a total flux of 4×3.14 (pi) lumens. The illumination created on a spherical surface by the light from a single candle placed at the center of a sphere having a one-foot radius is known as the *foot-candle.* The foot-candle represents 1 lumen per square foot. From the foregoing it becomes evident that the light intensity from a given source decreases inversely with the square of the distance.

The international unit of illumination is known as the *lux,* equivalent to the direct illumination which falls on a surface that is exactly 1 meter away from a light source equal to 1 international candle. Thus, a lux is equal to 1 lumen per square meter, and with respect to the foot-candle mentioned earlier, it has a value of 0.0929 foot-candle.

The high-vacuum phototubes have less sensitivity than the gas-filled types, although the high-vacuum types have a response superior to the other types discussed herein. The vacuum phototubes can be operated with variations in light intensity having a repetition rate up in the megacycles, whereas the gas-filled types are limited to frequencies below 10,000 cycles per second. The vacuum type's sensitivity is such that it produces about a microampere of current per lux with normal levels of illumination, hence the signal derived from such a tube must undergo amplification before application to control devices or indicators.

VACUUM-PHOTOTUBE CIRCUITRY

One application of the high-vacuum phototube is for sound reproduction from motion picture film, wherein the frequency of the signals is represented by alternate light and dark areas, and the volume of the audio is regulated by the intensity of the light and dark areas. An analysis of this circuit will serve as an introduction to the basic amplifiers used for phototubes.

The basic phototube circuit for sound reproduction is shown in Fig. 7-16. The phototube, V_1, has a positive potential applied to its plate from a d-c source as shown. The potential of the d-c voltage is determined by the characteristics of the phototube, and voltages as high as 90 volts are common. Capacitor C_1 bypasses the d-c voltage so that the internal resistance of the battery or d-c generator does not have signal variations developed across it. Since the internal resistance of the d-c source is bypassed, the signal voltages developed by the phototube will appear across resistor R_1 and will be coupled via capacitor C_2 to the standard amplifier circuit comprised of vacuum tube V_2 and its associated components.

Variations in light intensity such as those produced by passing light rays through the sound strip of motion picture film are impressed on the photo cathode of V_1. The resultant current flow from cathode to plate will pass through R_1 and set up signal-voltage variations across R_1 which conform to the variations of light intensity impinging on the phototube. These signals are then amplified by V_2 and appear across the load resistor R_4 for subsequent amplification to the level desired.

Resistors R_1 and R_2 range from 1 to 5 megohms, depending on the characteristics of the phototube used. The value of capacitor C_2 is such that it will have a sufficiently low reactance for the audio frequencies involved. A value of 0.1 microfarad is usually satisfactory.

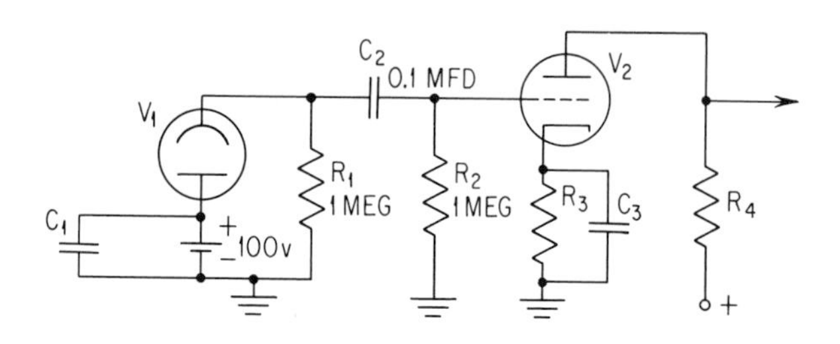

Fig. 7-16. Phototube sound reproduction

GAS PHOTOTUBE

The introduction of an inert gas such as argon into the basic phototube envelope increases the sensitivity of the phototube to an appreciable extent because of the increase in current flow during the time incident light is impressed on the cathode. Gas pressure within the tube is kept below the arc level, although sufficient pressure is maintained to cause ionization. Although the sensitivity of the gas-filled phototube is increased, the internal resistance is decreased and the sensitivity is not maintained at as constant a level throughout the tube's life as it is with the high-vacuum types. Also, the gas types are more susceptible to damage by accidental overload conditions such as the application of a higher than normal voltage to the anode. The gas types, however, find preference where high sensitivity is desired, although the high-vacuum types are often preferred where relays are to be operated by light-intensity variations or where light measurements are to be made.

The sensitivity of the gas phototube is increased because of the ionization of the gas atoms which occurs during current flow. When light strikes the cathode, the electrons which travel from the cathode to the anode strike gas atoms. When this occurs, an electron is knocked out of the atom and the latter becomes a positive ion. The dislodged electron, being a negative particle, is attracted to the anode while the positive ion is repelled by the anode but attracted by the cathode. Hence, the positive ions within the gas tube travel to the cathode, and in striking the latter, dislodge other electrons in the form of secondary emission. The secondary-emission electrons, in their travel to the anode, increase the sum total of electrons which flow from cathode to anode. Hence, the current flow for a given amount of light is greater in a gas phototube than in a vacuum phototube. The increase may be as much as four or five times that which would occur in an equivalent vacuum phototube.

In a phototube, the start and stop of current flow should correspond closely in terms of time to the beginning and ending of the lighting source which impinges on the photosensitive cathode. In a high-vacuum phototube the response is excellent for both the low- and high-frequency light changes. In the high-vacuum type, the light striking the cathode liberates electrons which immediately flow to the anode. In the gas phototube, however, there is a dual action of electron flow, since the light striking the cathode emits the primary electrons, which after a specific time interval release the secondary-emission electrons. Thus, the primary electrons cause ionization, and the ions must then reach the cathode before secondary-emission electrons are produced. With a low-frequency incident light change, the response of electron flow to the light striking the photosensitive surface is fairly good. For a higher-frequency light change, however, the current variations will not follow the starting and stopping of the light waves as rapidly, hence response is poorer. With rapid changes, the light strikes the cathode for only a short interval. Current flow starts and ionization occurs, but the light source may be gone before the secondary emission occurs, hence the cathode-to-anode current change lags the incident light change. The response of the current changes to the light changes is known as the *dynamic response* and has reference to the rapidity with which the current changes follow the light changes. Gas phototubes also find application in sound reproduction from films and, in addition, are used in some measurement and calibration procedures, accounting operations, control of indoor lighting or sign illumination, and other industrial processes as shown in subsequent chapters.

The luminous sensitivity of a phototube which is operated by a steady light source may be defined as the quotient which results from dividing the direct anode current by the flux intensity of the incident light. This calculated sensitivity is referred to as the *static luminous sensitivity.* This corresponds to the static conditions observed in an ordinary amplifier vacuum tube where the grid-voltage, plate-current, and plate-voltage values are constant. When the light striking the phototube cathode varies, such as in sound reproduction from film, the luminous sensitivity of the tube is known as its *dynamic sensitivity.* The dynamic sensitivity is a function of the quotient which is obtained by dividing the amplitude of variations in the anode current by the amplitude of variations in the light striking the cathode. The dynamic sensitivity decreases as the audio-frequency rate increases, as mentioned earlier.

The gas-type phototubes must be operated at or below their indicated ratings to prevent what is known as *gas discharge.* Once the gas starts to discharge, a blue glow occurs within the tube and the discharge continues whether or not radiant energy strikes the cathode. The discharge must be stopped by removing the anode voltage, and it should be stopped as soon as discovered in order to avoid damage to the tube. The photosensitive material can be paralyzed for a period of time by overexposure to intense illumination, which can occur with or without an anode voltage. The degree of cathode paralyzation depends on the intensity and length of exposure. Hence, in addition to operating the tube within the proper voltage ratings, care must be taken to prevent overexposure to high-intensity illumination. Overexposure, for instance, can occur in a sound movie projector when the exciter lamp is in operation with no film in the projector. Under such a condition the phototube receives the high-intensity light directly from the exciter lamp without the intervening film which normally brings the incident light to normal operating levels.

When phototubes are operated with high-frequency signals, precautions should be observed similar to those which are taken with conventional vacuum-tube amplifiers operating at high frequencies. Shielding of the phototube and the associate leads may be necessary when the phototube feeds an amplifier having high gain. In the high-vacuum phototubes, lead shielding may also be necessary because of the higher load resistance which is employed. All interconnecting leads should be made as short as possible and spaced away from the metal chassis to reduce shunt-capacity effects. Long leads, routed close to the chassis, could create capacity between the leads and the chassis, and in consequence, the higher frequencies will find a low reactance path and some signal energy will be shunted and hence lost. When phototubes are used to actuate relays or in measuring circuits, the phototube is required to be sensitive to small changes or low levels of light. In such instances, additional precautions must be observed with respect to leakage and losses.

SOLID-STATE PHOTOVOLTAIC DEVICES

In addition to the vacuum and gas-filled phototubes, other devices exhibit photoelectric characteristics, including copper oxide, selenium, silicon, and germanium in specially constructed units. Copper oxide or selenium coatings on iron, and other similar devices, are commonly used as rectifiers because they exhibit a high resistance for current flow in one direction and a low resistance for current flow in the other direction. Such devices, however, also act as photosensitive devices because they create a current flow in a closed circuit when incident light rays strike the copper oxide or selenium.

Basically, solid-state photosensitive cells fall into two general classifications: *photovoltaic* and *photoconductive*. The photovoltaic are similar to the photoelectric tubes, that is, such cells are self-generating in that they generate a d-c voltage proportional to the illumination falling on the photosensitive material. The photoconductive types, however, have their resistance altered in proportion to the light striking them, and the greater the light intensity, the greater the conductivity (lower resistance). Figure 7-17 shows the basic circuits for both types. At A the photovoltaic circuit is shown, and the d-c output can be applied directly to a sensitive relay as shown, or can be applied to measuring devices or d-c amplifiers. The photoconductive-cell circuit is shown at B, and as with the photovoltaic-*tube*

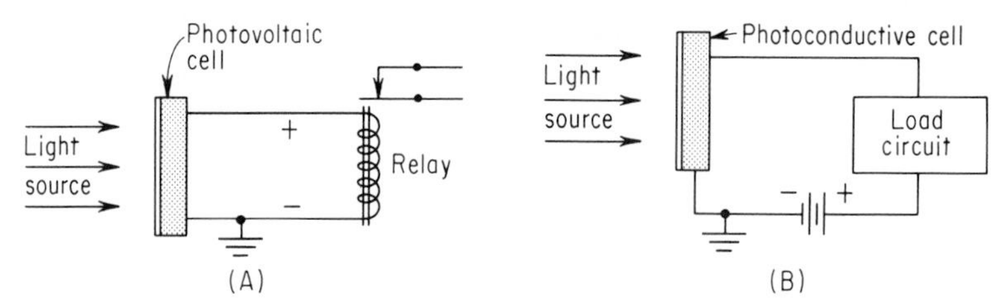

Fig. 7-17. Basic photovoltaic and photoconductive circuits

photo devices, a d-c potential must be applied in series with the load and the photocell.

The selenium photovoltaic cell has found wide application in the exposure meters used in photography. It has a high degree of sensitivity, although in commercial applications other than photography its usage is limited to circuitry where light-intensity variations are confined to those below approximately 2000 cps. Selenium photoconductive devices, although developed, have generally been superseded by the germanium point-contact diode, the germanium phototransistor, and similar devices. The phototransistors have a high lumen sensitivity and are capable of operating at considerably higher light-variation repetition rates than the selenium photovoltaic devices.

In the photoconductive class are the so-called light-dependent resistors formed from cadmium sulphide, which exhibit a high degree of lumen sensitivity although limited in light changes to low-frequency pulse signals in switching applications.

POINT-CONTACT PHOTODIODE

The internal construction of the point-contact photodiode is shown at A of Fig. 7-18. Here, a germanium wafer with an indention is used, as shown, with this section making a point contact with a conducting rod. By way of comparison with the transistor types de-

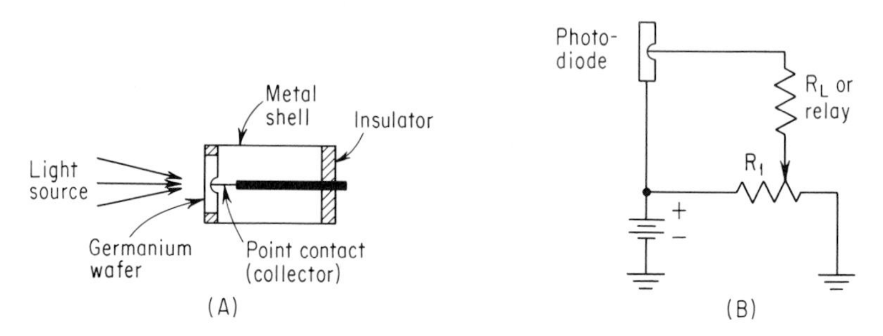

Fig. 7-18. Point-contact photodiode

scribed in Chapter 2, the outer metal conducting shell contacts the germanium wafer, and the shell can be considered as the base. The incident light striking the wafer performs the function of the emitter, and the point-contact element acts as the collector.

The germanium wafer is ground extremely thin at the center as shown, forming what is sometimes referred to as a *dimpled* wafer section. The collector electrode is made negative with respect to the wafer, as shown at B. The variable arm of resistor R_1, when moved toward the ground end of the resistor, permits adjustment of the negative potential applied, and this collector potential attracts the positive energy carriers which are liberated when light strikes the front section of the photodiode. The return circuit for the electron flow which is created is through the load resistor and back to the transistor via the ground conducting path. The load may be a circuit or a sensitive relay. By use of the latter, a large amount of power can be switched on or off as desired by the arrival of light at the transistor.

A static response curve for the photodiode is shown in Fig. 7-19 for several load-resistor values. Here, the collector current is plotted along the vertical axis and the collector voltage along the horizontal axis. As shown by the response curve of the phototransistor, the latter's response tends to peak in the infrared wavelength region of light (around 1 micron). Satisfactory response, however, is obtainable in the visible light portion of the spectrum.

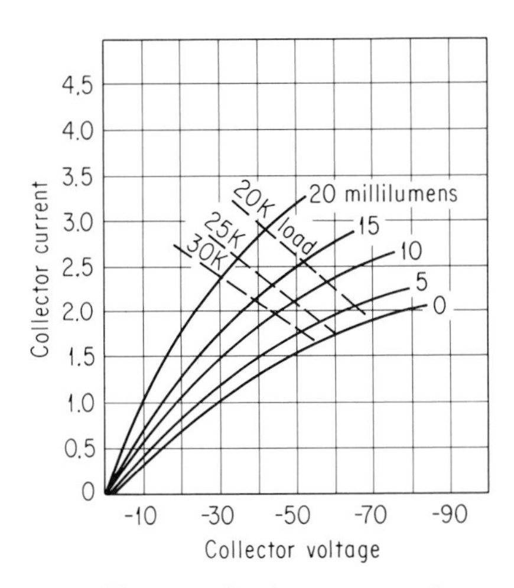

Fig. 7-19. Static response of photodiode

In the tube-type photoelectric devices previously discussed, the light-sensitive area was fairly large in diameter compared to the phototransistor's. In the latter, the light-sensitive area is extremely small, and only light which falls on that portion of the germanium section directly opposite the collector results in a current output. The light-sensitive area is a spot only about 0.01 inch in diameter. Such pinpoint localization of the photosensitive region makes this device considerably useful in a number of applications where a large area of light-sensitivity is detrimental.

JUNCTION PHOTOCELLS

The two fundamental types of junction phototransistors are shown in Fig. 7-20. At A the P-N junction photocell is illustrated. This also uses a basic germanium wafer formed by a P-N junction with a lead wire connected to each end as shown. As with the point-contact type previously described, light must be pinpointed because the area of sensitivity is quite small. For the unit shown at A, the light must be focused precisely at the area of the P-N junction.

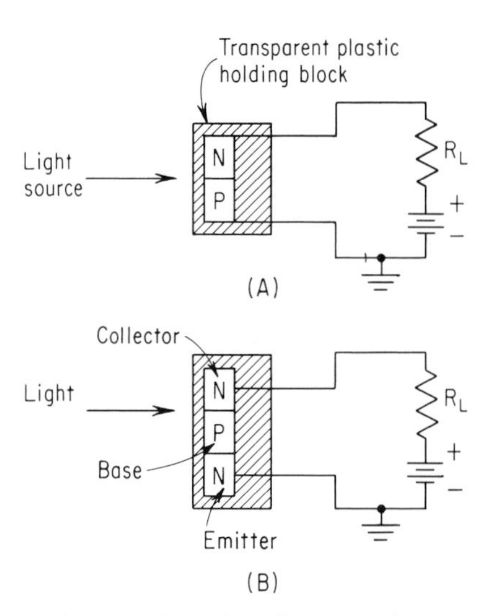

Fig. 7-20. Junction phototransistors

A phototransistor using N-P-N junction sections is illustrated at B of Fig. 7-20. This is also a two-contact photocell, as was the case with the P-N cell at A. This type of phototransistor is much more sensitive to light than the P-N junction type, although as with the latter, the light must be focused carefully at the N-P junction as shown at B of Fig. 7-20. As with the N-P type, a plastic block is used for housing the transistor element, with the light-sensitive side made transparent.

COMMERCIAL PHOTOCELLS

Typical light-dependent cadmium-sulphide photocell resistors are illustrated in Fig. 7–21. These units, less than a dime in diameter, are the Ferroxcube LDR cells, manufactured by the Ferroxcube Corporation of America. These cells have a resistance ratio in excess of 25,000 to 1 for a light intensity change from total darkness to 1400 foot-candles. They are sensitive throughout the entire visible range of light as well as through a portion of the infrared band. The light-dependent resistors do not follow rapid changes in illumination intensity, although the more intense the incident light, the more quickly they respond. This factor, however, although limiting them with respect to rapid light fluctuations, makes them useful for delay-type relay tripping in some industrial applications.

As illustrated in Fig. 7-21, the LDR units consist of a glass envelope containing a plate of photoconductive material 0.028 inch thick. The

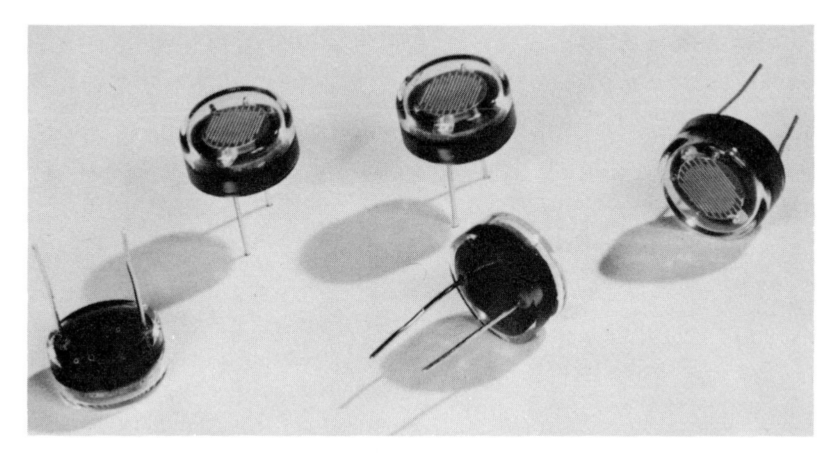

Fig. 7-21. Ferroxcube light dependent resistor LDR (Courtesy Ferroxcube Corp. of America)

coating on one side consists of metal film electrodes forming two interlocking combs as shown at A of Fig. 7-22. Using electrodes in this manner increases the sensitivity as well as enlarging the sensitive area of the unit.

As with all such devices, there are many applications in industrial electronics, and two practical systems are shown at B and C of Fig. 7-22. At B the cell is shown acting as a relay. When light from the lamp strikes the cell the resistance of the cell decreases, thus (in effect) closing any circuit to which it is connected. At C a gain-limiting control application is shown. When the signal input reaches a value high enough to light the lamp, the latter will cause the cell to have a decreased resist-

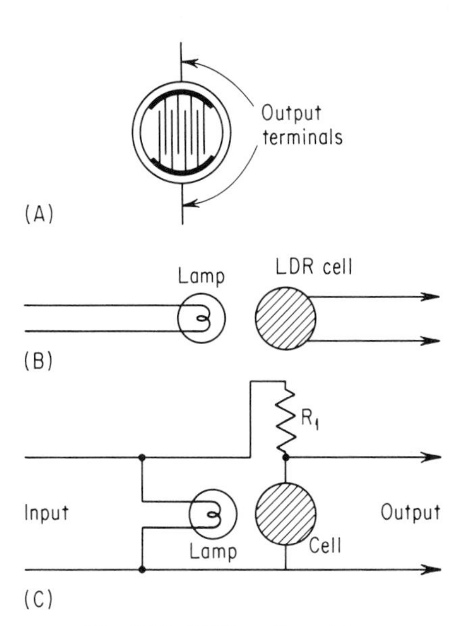

Fig. 7-22. LDR unit and two applications

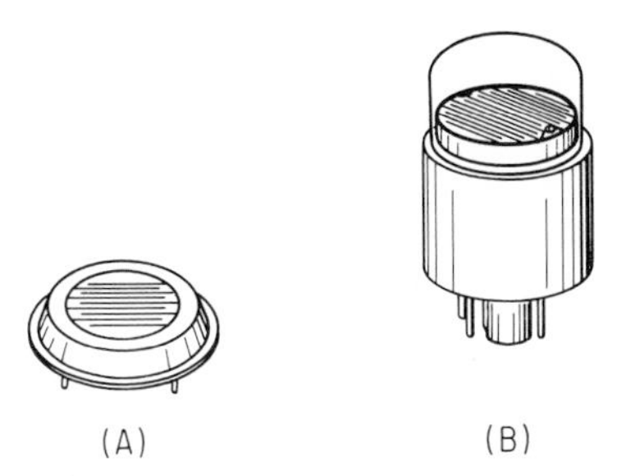

Fig. 7-23. RCA photoconductive cells

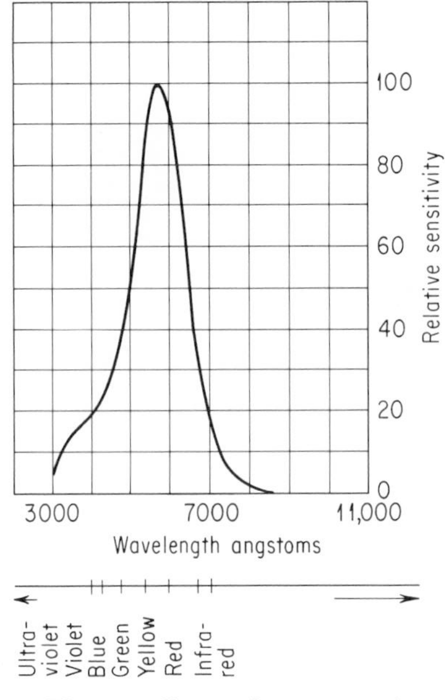

Fig. 7-24. Spectral response of RCA photocells 6957 and 7163

ance, thus acting as a low-conductance shunt across the output and decreasing the signal level.

The general shape of two RCA cadmium-sulfide photoconductive cells are shown at A and B of Fig. 7-23. At A is shown the type 7163 which is a "head-on" type cell suitable for such applications as automatic street lighting control and other relay applications related to light-intensity changes. A larger version is the 6957 shown at B, with correspondingly greater sensitivity. The spectral response for both these types is shown in Fig. 7-24, which illustrates the relative sensitivity for various wavelengths of light. As shown, these units have their highest sensitivity in the yellow-red light regions. RCA also manufactures photo junction cells, one of which (type 7224) is sensitive in the infrared region and, among other applications, finds usage in the sensing and control of industrial processes where the light to be used for triggering falls primarily into this region.

ELECTRON-MULTIPLIER TUBES

The principles of photoelectric emission are used in devices known as *electron-multiplier tubes,* wherein the secondary emission principle is utilized. The secondary-emission principle has already been mentioned with respect to the gas-filled phototubes. In the latter, the primary electrons emitted because of incident light striking the photosensitive surface travel from cathode to anode. In transit, the electrons strike the atoms of the inert gas and knock off electrons from the outer orbits of the atoms. Ions are formed which are attracted by the cathode, hence they travel toward it. Upon their striking the cathode, secondary-emission electrons are produced which in turn combine with the primary electrons in their travel toward the anode. This is a form of electron amplification or multiplication because the light energy striking the photosensitive surface liberated only a certain quantity of electrons, but the secondary-emission characteristics increased the quantity of electrons flowing between cathode and plate.

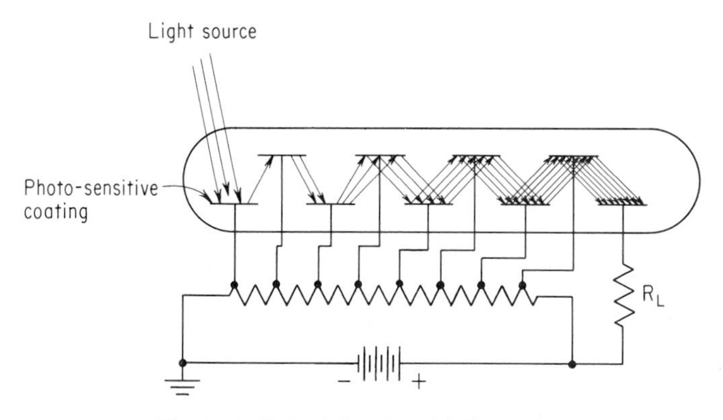

Fig. 7-25. Principle of multiplier tubes

In electron-multiplier tubes, a similar principle is employed. Initially, primary electrons are released from a photosensitive surface and are attracted by a positive anode structure called a *dynode.* This dynode has a low positive potential applied to it and when electrons strike the dynode, secondary-emission electrons are liberated. A second dynode is placed at such an angle from the first dynode that is intercepts the secondary-emission electrons produced by the first dynode. The second dynode has a higher positive potential applied to it than the first dynode so that the secondary-emission electrons leaving the first dynode are attracted it. Hence, the electrons traveling from the first dynode to the second have increased velocity because of the increased potential of the second dynode. When the electrons reach the second dynode, their velocity is sufficiently high to strike the second dynode with sufficient force to liberate an additional quantity of electrons by secondary emission.

As shown in Fig. 7-25, a third dynode is placed at such an angle that it intercepts the electron emission from the second dynode. The third dynode has a positive potential applied to it which is higher than the second dynode, hence the electrons reach a still higher velocity and liberate a greater quantity of electrons when striking dynode no. 3. Successive dynodes have increasing potentials applied to them for additional multiplication of the original quantity of electrons emitted by the photosensitive cathode. Whereas from the theoretical standpoint electron multiplication could be continued indefinitely by adding successive dynodes with greater potentials, a limit is reached when approximately ten dynodes are used because of the space-charge effects established around the dynode areas and also because of the heating of the final dynodes which dissipates considerable power.

The electron emission from the final dynode is accelerated and aimed at an anode which is then connected to the load resistor of the circuit as shown in Fig 7-25. The multiplier tube, by virtue of its high gain, eliminates the necessity for using as many amplifier stages as with a normal phototube. If some of the amplifier stages normally necessary are eliminated, some of the characteristic drawbacks of amplifiers are minimized, such as circuit losses, stray capacities, shunt capacities, and interelectrode capacities. In vacuum-tube amplifier circuits, interelectrode capacities have a decreasing capacitive reactance for increasing frequencies and tend to shunt some of the signal energy of the latter. Losses also occur because of stray capacities existing between the wiring of the amplifier and the shunt capacities set up by the wiring and the chassis.

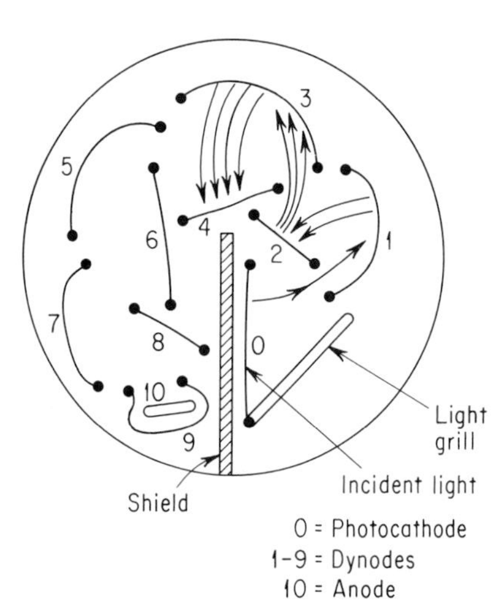

Fig. 7-26. RCA 951-A electron-multiplier tube, schematic

A typical layout of dynodes in an electron-multiplier tube is shown in cross-section form in Fig. 7-26. The various elements are numbered from 0 to 10, with 0 representing the photocathode and 10 representing the anode. Electrodes 1 to 9 consist of the multiplier dynodes. Because of judicious layout and design with respect to the anodes, the tube illustrated in Fig. 7-26 has a diameter of only $1\frac{1}{8}$ inches (RCA 931-A). As shown, incident light is directed toward the photocathode and then the path of electrons is toward dynode 1 and then successively to the other dynodes. Since the layout of the dynodes is circular, the electrons are rerouted in a circular fashion and up at the anode no. 10 as shown. An internal shield composed of mica separates the input and output electrodes as shown.

Review Questions for Chapter 7

1. Briefly describe the underlying principles of the reactive transducers.
2. In what industrial applications are the solid-state transducers useful?
3. Explain what essential differences there are between the bonded and unbonded strain gauges.
4. Show how a temperature-sensitive transducer can be used to control the turning on and off of heat sources.
5. Summarize the definitions for the terms *luminous flux* and *foot-candle.*

6. Briefly explain the basic differences in the characteristics of the gas phototubes and the high-vacuum types.
7. Define the terms *dynamic response* and *dynamic sensitivity.*
8. In a phototube, what causes the condition known as *gas discharge,* and how may this condition be corrected?
9. What are the differences in characteristics between the photoconductive and photovoltaic devices?
10. Briefly define the essential differences between the point-contact photodiode and the N-P-N-junction type.
11. To what light bands are the cadmium-sulfide commercial photocells generally sensitive?
12. Briefly explain how electron multiplication occurs in an electron-multiplier phototube.

8

Thyratrons, Gates, and Switches

INTRODUCTION

Transducers and generators originate the signals which are used for industrial control purposes. After the signals have been obtained, they often must be applied to an amplifier to bring them to the level necessary for the work they are to do. Once the proper signal level has been obtained, the signal can be used for triggering, switching, or control purposes. On a number of occasions, however, the signal must be applied to a circuit or some other load at a certain time or during certain time intervals. In such an instance it must be held in readiness until needed—then released at the predetermined time. The latter process is known as *gating* and differs somewhat from *switching*.

Essentially, switching consists of an opening or closing process, accomplished by a simple mechanical switch, an amplifier or flip-flop, or a relay. The gate, on the other hand, is often used to hold a signal in abeyance until another signal (called the *gating signal*) arrives. The gating signal then opens the circuit and permits the signal which was held to pass through. A control circuit is another type of switching or gating device, although the control circuit usually does more than merely turning a unit on or off. It can also regulate the *amount* of power applied to a device, hence it actually controls the function of the latter (see Chapter 13). There is some overlapping of functions, however, with respect to gating, switching, and control, and therefore a control circuit might be referred to as a "switch," or a switch might be called a "gate" on occasion. Therefore, a study of the circuit or device is necessary to ascertain its true function.

Thyratrons and ignitrons, as well as relays, are the devices which are under control of signals, and they are essentially switching devices. The thyratrons and ignitrons are units wherein a very large amount of current flow can be controlled by a relatively small signal. Relays are essentially low-power devices, although they in turn can switch in high power by use of relatively low electric energy. Large relays, however, suffer the disadvantages of arcing, pitting of contacts, etc., hence they are primarily confined to lower power than the thyratrons and ignitrons.

Gates, relays, and switching are covered in this chapter, as well as the thyratron and ignitron principles. Other devices under the control of signals include the magnetic and dielectric amplifiers, servos, counters, and indicators, etc., discussed elsewhere herein.

TUBE GATES

As mentioned earlier, the basic function of the gating circuit is to hold back a signal until a predetermined time. Such a circuit is very useful in industrial electronics for process control, counting, and logic systems such as found in computers. A typical gating circuit using two vacuum-tube triodes is shown in Fig. 8-1. This circuit functions on the principle that the bias requirements for a tube differ for various values of plate voltage. With a high anode potential, a greater negative bias is required at the grid to reach cutoff. For low plate-voltage values, however, a lower negative potential of bias will provide tube cutoff.

In Fig. 8-1, vacuum tube V_1 has a high anode voltage, while vacuum tube V_2 has a low potential. The cathode of each tube is connected to

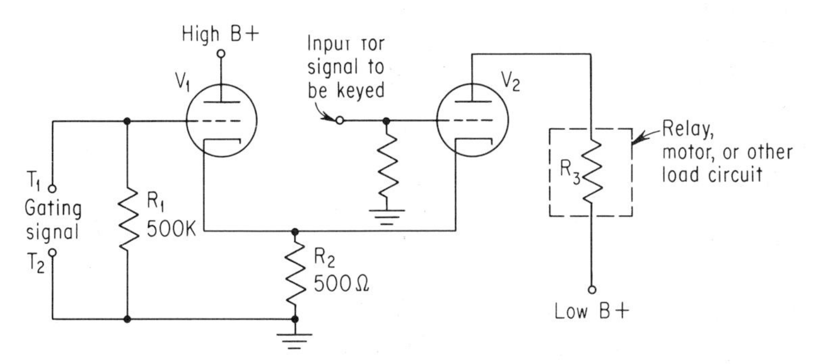

Fig. 8-1. Basic triode gating circuit

a common resistor, R_2. Because of the latter, any plate current flowing in either tube must flow through the cathode resistor. A high plate potential for vacuum tube V_1 causes a high amount of current to flow through this tube, and hence through the cathode resistor R_2. The high current flow through the cathode resistor produces a voltage drop across the latter having a value sufficient to produce cutoff bias for vacuum tube V_2, since the latter has a lower anode voltage than V_1. Now, vacuum tube V_1 is conducting, while vacuum tube V_2 is cut off. The input signal to be keyed or gated through the circuit is applied to the grid of V_2. Such a signal can consist of squarewaves, sinewaves, pulses, or any complex waveform which must be applied to some load device at a specific time. The *gating* signal is applied to the grid of V_1, and can consist of a d-c potential, or a negative pulse.

For the purposes of this discussion, assume that a series of pulses are present at the grid of V_2. Since the latter tube is at cutoff, the pulses which appear at its grid are not amplified and do not appear across the load resistance R_3. When these pulses are to be gated through vacuum tube V_2, however, a negative potential is applied across terminals T_1 and T_2 in the grid circuit of V_1. The negative signal applied across terminals T_1 and T_2 will make terminal T_1 negative and terminal T_2 positive. Under this condition, the negative voltage at the grid of V_1 reduces plate-current flow through this tube. The reduction in plate-current flow also occurs through resistor R_2, hence the bias for vacuum tube V_2 is lowered sufficiently to cause the latter tube to go into conduction. When V_2 conducts, the gate is "open" and the signal which is applied to the grid of V_2 will appear across the load resistance R_3. If a series of pulses are applied to the grid of V_2, such pulses will appear across R_3 for as long as the negative gating signal is present at the grid of V_1. When the gating signal is removed from the grid of V_1, plate current for the latter again increases and raises the voltage drop across resistor R_2, to bias vacuum tube V_2 to cutoff again. This results in "closing" the gate and preventing the signal applied to the grid of V_2 from appearing across the load resistance R_3. Of course, the signal appearing at the grid of V_2 need not be pulses. It could also be a sinewave signal, a squarewave, or a complex waveform.

When the circuit shown in Fig. 8-1 is employed in the manner just discussed, it is known as a *gating-in* circuit, because the gating signal will *open* the gate and permit the signal to enter the gated tube V_2 and appear across the load resistance R_3. The same circuit can, however, also be used as a *gating-out* circuit. For gating-out purposes, the high anode potential appearing at the plate of V_1 is reduced sufficiently to reduce the current flow through R_2 to the point where the bias is no longer high enough to cut off vacuum tube V_2. Now, signals which are applied to the grid of V_2 will appear across R_3, because when V_2 is not at cutoff, an open-gate condition prevails. To gate out the signals entering the open-gate condition of V_2, it is necessary to apply a positive gating signal to the grid of V_1. Such a gating signal can be a steady-state d-c voltage which will then close the gate for as long an interval as desired, or the gating signal can be a short duration positive pulse, which will close the gate for a short time interval only. When a positive signal appears at the grid of V_1, the current flow through the latter and also through the common cathode resistor R_2 increases. The result is an increase in the negative potential applied to the grid of V_2, and the latter reaches cutoff. With V_2 cut off, the gate is closed and the signals applied to the grid of V_2 no longer appear across the load resistance R_3. The circuit is now a *gating-out* circuit instead of a gating-in circuit.

Pentode Coincidence Gate

Another gating-in circuit, also known as a *coincidence gate,* is shown in Fig. 8-2. Here, a single pentode tube is employed, although the screen grid does not have a positive potential applied to it as in normal pentode amplifier circuitry. Instead, the screen-grid resistor is returned to ground as is the control-grid resistor, R_1. A positive potential is applied to the cathode of the tube so that a voltage drop across resistor R_2 is sufficiently high to cause the tube to reach the cutoff region. Since both the control grid and the screen grid are biased negatively, either one has the ability to hold the tube at cut-off. Thus, if a positive potential is applied to the control grid, the tube will still be cut off, because the screen grid has a negative potential high enough to prevent current flow. Similarly, if a positive potential were applied to the screen grid only, the tube would still be cut off because of the negative bias developed for the control grid by virtue of the positive potential applied to the cathode. Thus, in order to cause conduction of the tube, both the control grid and the screen grid must have high enough (positive) potentials applied to them to

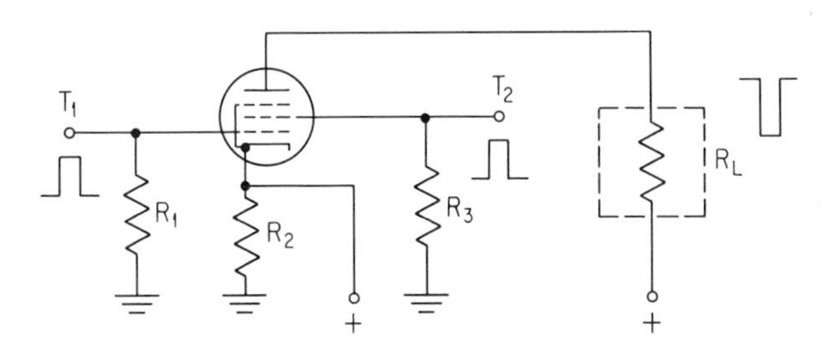

Fig. 8-2. Pentode coincidence gates

overcome the negative potentials of the control grid and screen grid with respect to the common cathode.

Thus, if a positive pulse is applied to terminal T_1, and at the same time a positive pulse is applied to terminal T_2, the tube will conduct and an amplified pulse will appear across the load resistance as shown. (The amplified pulse, will, of course, appear in an inverted condition because of the usual 180-degree phase reversal over a vacuum tube utilizing this circuit.) When pulses are used to actuate the circuit, they must coincide in their timing to produce an output, hence this circuit is known as a *coincidence gate*. The pulse applied to terminal T_1 can be considered as being gated in by the pulse which appears at the screen-grid terminal T_2. The circuit shown in Fig. 8-2 is also used in digital computers, and in this application is often referred to as an *and* circuit. An output occurs only for a signal applied simultaneously to terminals T_1 *and* T_2.

The load can consist of a fast-acting relay or another vacuum-tube circuit. For the control of motors or slower-acting devices, the coincidence circuit requires the application of a d-c steady-state potential at both the control grid and the screen grid.

If this circuit is to be used as a gating-in circuit instead of a gating-out circuit, a positive potential is applied to the screen grid instead of returning R_3 to ground. With a positive potential on the screen grid, the tube will conduct and any signals appearing at terminal T_1 will appear across the load. When it is necessary to gate out such signals, a negative potential is applied to terminal T_2, driving the screen grid into the negative region with an amplitude sufficiently high to cause tube cutoff.

SOLID-STATE GATES

A gating circuit which employs two diodes is shown in Fig. 8-3. Here, in the absence of a signal at the input terminals T_1 and T_2, both diodes conduct fully because of the battery potential across them. The current flow for both diodes is in the direction shown by the

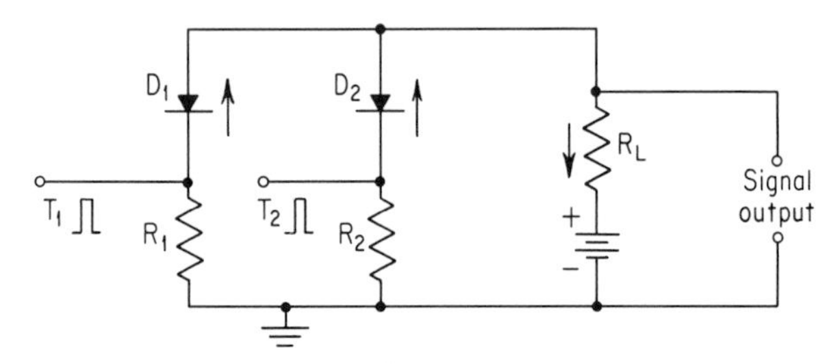

Fig. 8-3. Diode coincidence gates

arrows, and flows through the load resistance R_L as shown. Because of such current flow, there is a high-amplitude voltage drop which occurs as the battery potential establishes a steady-state low-amplitude d-c signal at the output terminals.

When a pulse of sufficient amplitude appears at terminal T_1, its positive-polarity voltage drop across R_1 overcomes the battery potential across the diode network D_1 and R_1. Since the positive pulse is opposite in polarity to the battery potential, the voltage drop across the diode network is canceled and no current flow occurs through diode D_1. However, diode D_2 still conducts current, hence there is only a slight change in voltage drop across the load resistance R_L. The same condition occurs for a positive pulse applied to terminal T_2, in the absence of a pulse at terminal T_1.

When pulses appear simultaneously at terminals T_1 and T_2, both diodes stop conducting and current flow through load resistance R_L ceases. Now, the battery potential predominates and a rising positive polarity signal appears at the output. This signal will have a flat-top amplitude which equals the duration of the pulses applied at terminals T_1 and T_2. As with the other circuits previously discussed, the circuit can be actuated by the application of d-c potentials at terminals T_1 and T_2 so that current flow through the circuit is controlled. Current flow through the load circuit can be stopped by the continuous application of a positive polarity voltage to terminals T_1 and T_2, but the application of only one of these voltages would not prevent current flow through the load circuit. Thus, a coincidence-gate circuit condition prevails.

Transistor Coincidence Gate

A coincidence gate employing the triode-type transistors is shown at A of Fig. 8-4. Here, reverse bias for the collectors of the P-N-P transistors is provided by the battery in series with the load circuit as shown. Forward bias, however, has been omitted for each of the transistors. In consequence, each transistor acts as a Class B circuit, because in the absence of forward bias between the base and emitter of the transistor, the latter is in its cutoff state and no current flows. Only when forward bias is applied will the high-potential barrier in the collector side permit current flow through the transistor. Thus, the gating signal which is used has a negative polarity, so that the base is made negative with respect to the emitter.

When a negative signal is applied to the input terminals no. 1, the upper transistor could conduct but is unable to, because the conducting path for current is also through the collector emitter circuit of the lower transistor. In the absence of a signal across the input termi-

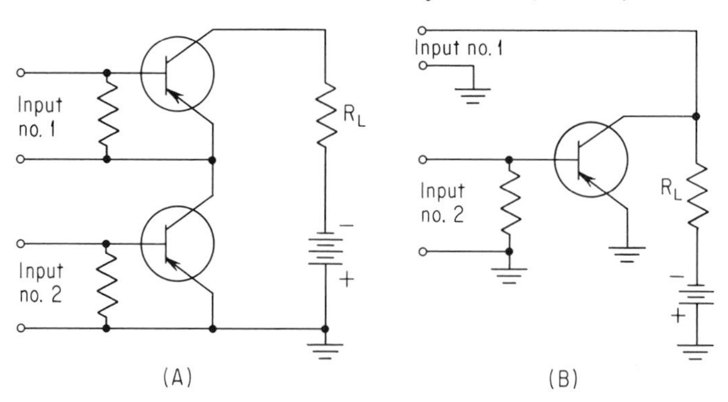

Fig. 8-4. Transistor coincidence and gating out circuits

nals of the lower transistor, no conduction can occur through this transistor, and no current flow occurs through the load resistance R_L. An identical condition prevails if a signal is applied to input no. 2 for the lower transistor, in the absence of a signal at the input terminals of the upper transistor. Again, even though the lower transistor could conduct, current flow cannot occur because of the cutoff status of the upper transistor. However, when a negative-polarity voltage or pulse is applied to both the upper and lower inputs, the potential barriers of both transistors are reduced substantially, and current flows through each transistor and through the circuit. The signal which develops across the load resistance is opposite in polarity to the signals applied by inputs nos. 1 and 2. Thus, the circuit acts as a coincidence gate or an *and* circuit in a fashion similar to that described previously for the vacuum tubes and diodes.

The Class B operational characteristics in transistors, where no forward bias is applied to the base emitter circuit, can also be employed for other gating purposes. At B, for instance, a *gating-out* transistor circuit is shown, wherein the lack of forward bias on the transistor permits the input terminals 1 to 2 to be employed as the keying or gating input; the latter will then control the application of the signal to no. 1 input. Assume, for instance, that a series of pulses appears across input no. 1. So long as the transistor is at cutoff, it presents a high impedance across the load circuit and there is virtually no shunting effect—hence no disturbance of the signals across the load circuit. However, when a negative pulse is applied to input no. 2, the base will be made negative with respect to the emitter (emitter is now positive with respect to base) and the transistor conducts. In the conduction state, the transistor presents a very low impedance and shunts the load circuit. Thus, any signals which would appear across the load circuit are shunted by the low impedance of the transistor and are effectively gated out by the signals which appear at input no. 2. Again, as with the previous circuits discussed, steady-state d-c voltages can be employed at inputs nos. 1 and 2 to turn off and on and otherwise control the device which is utilized for the load circuit.

RELAY SWITCHING

Basic relays, which have been discussed previously, consist of a solenoid which produces a magnetic field upon the application of electric power. This magnetic field is utilized to attract a metal spring or hinge for opening or closing contacts. Relays come in a variety of switching arrangements; a few basic types are shown in Fig. 8-5. At A, the single-pole, single-throw (SPST) normally closed type is illustrated; at B is shown the SPST normally open unit; at C, the single-pole, double-throw (SPDT) design; and at D, the design provides a double-pole, single-throw (DPST) normally open switch. The latter could also be designed for a normally closed position. At E a triple-pole, double-throw (TPDT) type is illustrated.

The relays at D and E have insulating washers so that the moveable poles will not short together. A swivel rocker arm (L-shaped) is pulled in when the solenoid is actuated, and this in turn forces the moveable poles upward, engaging the upper contact points. This is more clearly illustrated in Fig. 8-6, which is a double-pole, double-

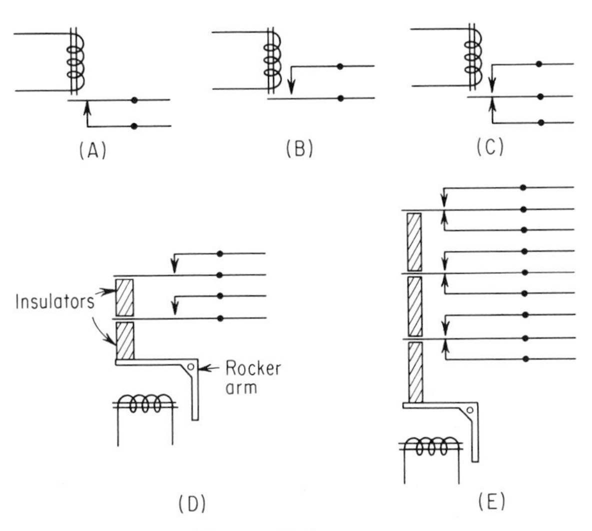

Fig. 8-5. Relay types

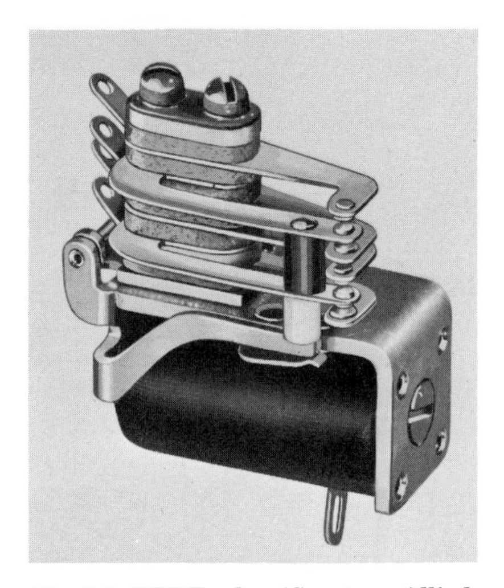

Fig. 8-6. DPDT relay (Courtesy Allied Control Co.)

Fig. 8-7. Meter relay (Courtesy Assembly Products, Inc.)

throw (DPDT) relay, model TSL of the Allied Control Company. As with most relays of this type, various models are available for handling different current ranges. The TSL type 1 shown is available in models handling 0.027 ampere to 1 ampere, with coil resistances ranging from 1.5 ohms to 2000 ohms and operating from 1.5 volts to 55 volts.

Relays can be an integral part of instrumentation for combining metering and triggering. One example of such a device is the model CR (continuous-reading) meter relay manufactured by Assembly Products, Inc., and illustrated in Fig. 8-7. This consists of a microammeter with a built-in relay that is actuated for a predetermined setpoint. The latter is manually placed by setting the moving adjustable pointer to the unit value on the scale where the relay is to function. The meter is switched into the circuit and reads current changes. When the current reaches the preset value—that is, when the indicating needle coincides with the adjustable needle—a contact on the point touches a contact on a toggle (see Fig. 8-8) and a circuit is closed to the solenoid of a multipole load relay. A booster coil is also switched in for increasing contact torque at the setpoint to assure positive actuation of the relay.

The relay remains energized as long as the current to the meter is either higher or lower than the setpoint. When the meter needle returns to the setpoint, the contact again touches a terminal on the toggle, and both the booster coil and the relay are disengaged from the circuit. The relay can also be switched by use of a voltmeter, or any other measurement meter.

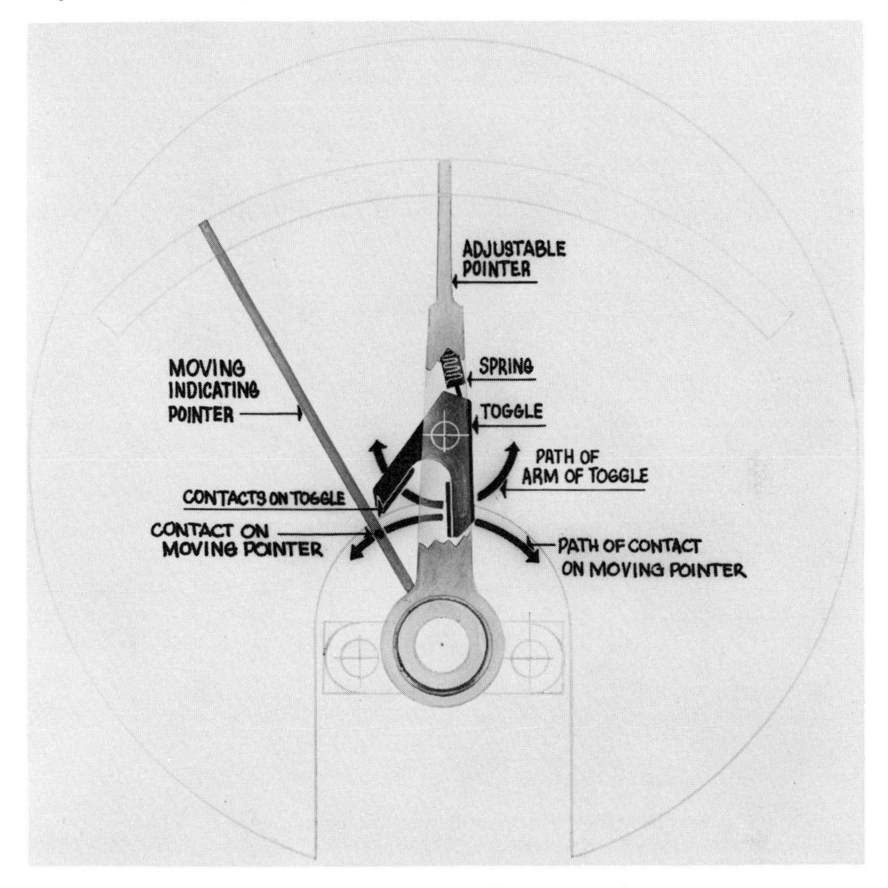

Fig. 8-8. Continuous reading meter relay

Sequence Switching

Relays, in conjunction with delay circuitry, can be used to switch load circuits in or out in sequence rather than simultaneously. One method is illustrated at A of Fig. 8-9. Here thermistors are used having a temperature coefficient such that current flow through the unit increases as temperature rises.

As shown, the d-c power source is switched or gated to the various load circuits. The three (or more) thermistors provide a delaying action, the degree of which depends on the thermistor construction and the value of the resistors in series with it. When the switch is closed, power is applied immediately to the first load resistance (R_{L1}). The second load, R_{L2}, however, receives power slightly later than the first

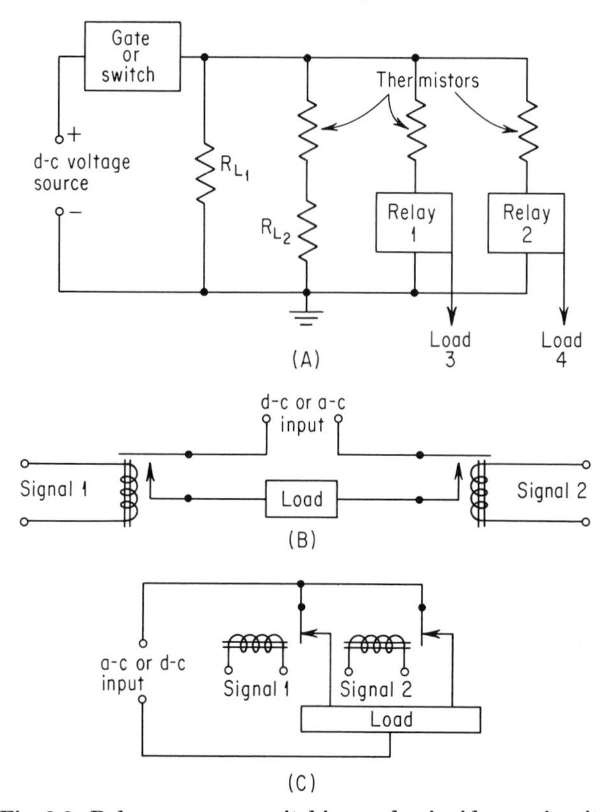

Fig. 8-9. Relay sequence switching and coincidence circuits

load. Similarly, the second thermistor releases sufficient current for actuating relay no. 1 at a still later time. Relay no. 2 is the last to be energized. This type of circuit is referred to as a *sequential switching* circuit and is used when specific time intervals are required between applying power to various load systems.

Relay Coincidence Circuit

As shown at B of Fig. 8-9, relays can also be used to form coincidence circuits which function in a fashion similar to the tube and solid-state devices shown earlier. Here, a-c or d-c power is applied to the load only if energizing current flows through both relay solenoids at the same time. Signal no. 1 alone, or Signal no. 2 alone, closes only one relay—hence an open circuit still exists.

Such a relay coincidence gate can be formed with additional relays if needed, with the relay contact terminals all placed in series, so that a three-, four-, or five-input-signal coincidence gate can be formed.

Normally closed relays instead of the normally open types shown can also can be employed. For the normally closed relays, power is applied continuously to the load for the circuit shown at C of Fig. 8-9, until *both* relays are energized. With a signal at either relay alone, the d-c (or a-c) power is still connected to the load circuit.

THYRATRON DEVICES

Thyratron units, like the mechanical relays just discussed, can be switched on with low power and thus release considerable power to some load circuit. Unlike the relays, however, the thyratrons (and ignitrons discussed later) can be designed to handle very high power without overload or damage, and can be triggered at a much faster rate. In addition, phased signals can be used for precise triggering and the application to the load of short bursts of energy if required.

Because of the advantages of the thyratron devices, they are used extensively in all branches of industrial electronics for power application and control of welding systems, speed control of d-c motors, and milling and process operations. Thyratron devices include the gas-tube types, and the solid-state types such as the General Electric silicon-controlled rectifier, the RCA Thyristor, the Westinghouse Trinistor, and the GE unijunction transistor. The basic characteristics of the solid-state thyratrons have been discussed in Chapter 1, to which reference should be made for review purposes. Circuits are covered later in this chapter.

The gas-tube thyratron is a hot-cathode type which differs from the gaseous diode rectifier previously discussed because it possesses a grid structure, thus forming a triode-type tube. The thyratron contains an inert gas (sometimes mercury vapor) under low pressure. The inclusion of a gas in the thyratron provides the low internal voltage drop which is a characteristic of the gas-type tubes, and the inclusion of the grid provides a method for control of plate-current flow. The presence of gas within the tube, however, modifies the control-grid function so that amplification cannot be accomplished. Instead, the grid of the thyratron tube is employed to control a large amount of power by use of much lower power in the grid circuit. The control factor relates to the release of plate-current flow within a tube at a specific time or during certain time intervals. Thus, a few watts of power at the grid can switch on hundreds of watts of power in the anode circuit.

As shown in Fig. 8-10, the grid structure of the thyratron differs radically from that of the conventional high-vacuum type. The grid is a cylindrical affair which contains a baffle plate spaced between the anode and the cathode. The baffle plate has one or more perforations through it for electron flow between cathode and plate. The shielding effect of the grid is such that it provides a complete electrostatic isolation between cathode and anode structures except for the necessary perforations for the current flow. As with a high-vacuum type, the control grid will hold the plate current at cutoff. Unlike the vacuum tube, however, once the bias of the control grid has been reduced sufficiently to permit current flow, the thyratron control grid is ineffective in bringing the tube back to the cutoff region—because of the presence of gas within the tube. While the tube is at cutoff, there is no current flow within the tube and no ionization of the gas atoms. Hence, the electrostatic fields of the grid structure are sufficient to repel any electrons attracted by the positive anode. When the grid-bias potential has been reduced to a value sufficient to permit plate-current flow, the electrons in transit to the anode collide with the gas atoms and knock off electrons from the atoms, forming positive ions. As with other gas-type tubes, the positive ions are attracted by the negative cathode and, in transit to it, neutralize the space charge; thus they permit a greater current flow within the tube while reducing internal resistance. The presence of the grid within the thyratron, however, provides an additional electrode, also subject to the ionization which occurs.

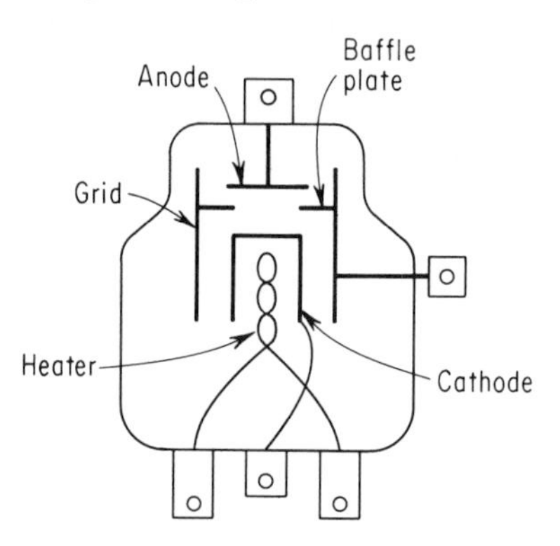

Fig. 8-10. Basic thyratron construction

Once ionization and plate-current flow have been established, the grid structure is in the path of both the electron flow and the current flow between cathode and anode. If a negative potential were now applied to the grid in an effort to cut off plate-current flow, the electrostatic fields created by the negative grid structure would attract the positive ions which would then cluster around the grid structure. Such an ionic cluster around the grid element establishes a space-charge condition similar to that which occurs in a hot cathode. With the latter, the space charge consists of negative electrons which repel other electrons and thus hinder plate-current flow. The space charge surrounding the grid structure, however, is composed of positive ions, and their aggregate fields may be compared to that of a positive grid structure which would accelerate electrons to the plate by virtue of the attraction set up by the additional positive charge established between cathode and anode. Thus, the electron flow is accelerated rather than repelled. Increasing the negative potential on the control grid would increase the positive-ion space-charge effect around the grid structure.

In order to stop conduction in a thyratron which has been fired so that the ionization has been established, it is necessary to open the anode circuit and at the same time apply a negative potential to the grid. This circuit is shown in Fig. 8-11. Here, a bias battery is used. with a variable resistor, R_1, placed across the battery terminals. The moveable arm of the resistor is attached to the grid of the thyratron. In this anode circuit a d-c power source is in series with the anode-cathode elements, with the positive potential applied to the anode as shown. A switch, SW_1, is also included in series with the anode circuit of the thyratron. When the moveable arm of the variable resistor R_1 is near the negative terminal of the battery, a bias is supplied to the thyratron which is sufficiently negative for cutoff purposes. If the switch in the anode circuit is now closed, there will be no plate-current flow because of the high negative bias applied to the grid circuit. As the moveable arm of R_1 is moved toward the positive terminal, the negative grid bias is reduced until a value is reached which will permit the thyratron to fire. When the latter occurs, a maximum value of current flow occurs, the value being established by the potential of the power source and the value of the load circuit represented by R_L.

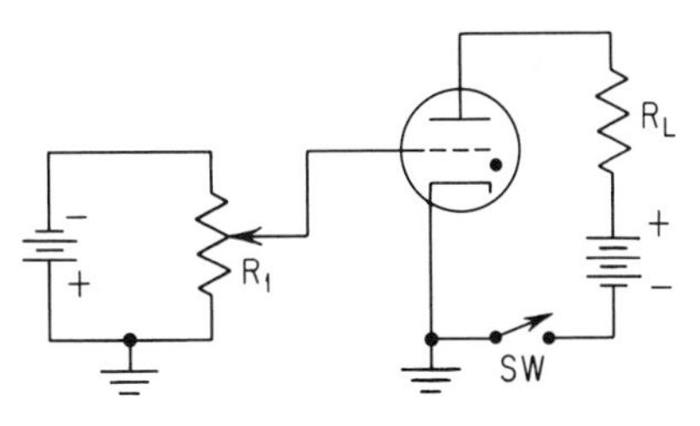

Fig. 8-11. Thyratron circuit factors

The bias may now be increased toward the negative direction by again moving the variable arm of R_1 toward the negative terminal of the battery. Despite the application of a negative potential to the grid, however, the tube conduction remains at the maximum established by the power source and R_L, and the grid is ineffective in restoring the cutoff condition. To achieve cutoff, switch SW_1 would have to be opened to cut plate-current flow completely. With bias at a negative value, however, the switch may now be closed and the tube will remain at cutoff because the grid is now effective again. With the grid negative, the opening of switch SW_1 causes the current flow to stop within the tube, hence the gas within the tube is deionized. The positive-ion space charge around the grid also becomes deionized and hence obliterated. If a negative bias is now applied to the grid, the electrostatic fields set up by the grid structure are again effective in preventing plate-current flow. Until the latter occurs, there is no ionization and hence no nullifying of the repelling forces set up by the electrostatic fields of the grid structure.

Thus, as show in Fig. 8-11, very low power can be utilized to turn on very high power in the anode circuit. Consequently, the flow of current and hence the application of power to the load circuit can be controlled by the relatively low potential applied to the grid structure.

The time at which the tube will fire is related to the amount of anode potential present and the amount of internal gas pressure, as well as the type of gas. The internal structure of the tube influences firing because it determines the sensitivity of the grid wires. In some applications the thyratrons are of the negative-grid type, and these operate under conditions where the grid is negative for the normal operational range. Other thyratrons have a grid structure consisting of two or more grid baffles. With such a grid structure, there is more complete shielding between the cathode and the anode, and it is necessary to reduce the negative grid-bias potential to zero or to a positive value before the tube will fire.

General Characteristics

The general characteristics of thyratrons must be known so that the tube may be used properly in various industrial electronic applications. One of the characteristics is the ionization time of the tube. The *ionization time* refers to the elapsed interval between the application of the voltage to the plate and the full ionization of the gas atoms within the tube. The time is ascertained on the basis of the rapidity with which ionization occurs without hindrance from the control grid, the latter having zero or a positive potential on it which would permit conduction. The ionization time in many thyratrons is less than 5 microseconds.

Another characteristic which must often be ascertained with respect to thyratrons is the *deionization time*. This refers to the minimum interval of time required for neutralization of the positive ion space charge which surrounds the grid structure after the plate-current flow has been interrupted. Thus, the latter is an indication of the rapidity with which the grid can regain control of plate-current cutoff when the plate is again made plus. The deionization time in many thyratrons averages around 500 microseconds, although some thyratrons have a deionization time of less than 100 microseconds, and others more than 1000 microseconds, depending on the amount of gas pressure, the density of current flow within the tube, and the physical design of the grid structure and other internal elements. The deionization time determines the operation of the thyratrons at higher frequencies. When the deionization time interval is long, the applications of the thyratron are limited to power sources having a frequency of 60 cycles per second; a shorter deionization time permits the use of power sources of higher frequency.

a-c Operation

The thyratron tube is especially adaptable for operation with alternating current at the grid and anode circuits. When an a-c signal is applied at both these circuits, the control of the power developed in the load circuit is established by the relative phase of the grid signal versus the anode signal. Because the grid loses control once the tube is conducting, the use of an a-c signal in the anode circuit permits the grid to regain control; because the successive alternations of the a-c signal in the anode circuit apply a negative potential to the anode and cause the current flow through the tube to stop, regardless of whether the grid is made negative or positive. The basic circuit for a-c operation is shown in Fig. 8-12. Here again, the application of the a-c power to the load circuit (R_L) is controlled by the a-c signal at the grid, just as the grid circuit controls the turning on of the anode power for the d-c operated thyratron.

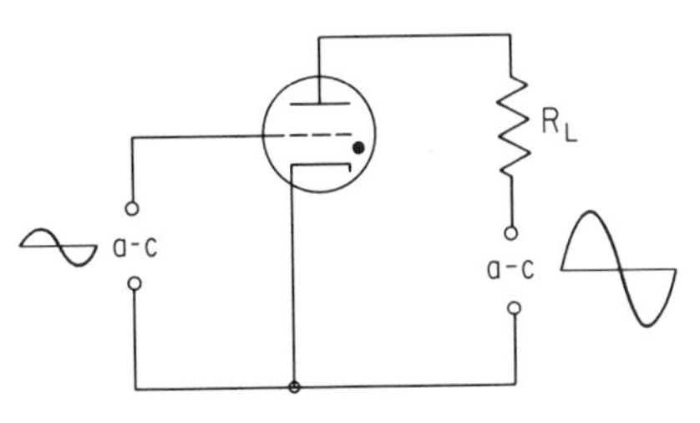

Fig. 8-12. a-c thyratron circuit

The grid and anode phase relationships shown in Fig. 8-13 will aid in understanding the characteristics of the a-c operated thyratron. At A of Fig. 8-13, the plate voltage (E_p) is shown on the top line of the drawing. The grid voltage (E_g) is shown on the second line, and the resultant plate current (I_p) is shown on the bottom line. When the plate-voltage and grid-voltage signals are *in phase* as shown at A, the tube acts as a conventional half-wave rectifier and a series of positive alternations are applied to the load circuit. Such a signal can be filtered to obtain a low-ripple-component d-c. With the signals in phase as at A, the grid becomes positive at the same instant that the plate signal becomes positive, but firing of the thyratron is delayed because the anode potential must reach an amplitude high enough to cause ionization.

Similarly, both alternations of the input and output signal decline simultaneously, and the tube stops conducting before the grid signal reaches a negative value—because deionization occurs when the anode potential reaches a low level.

If the phase of the grid signal shown at A is inverted 180 degrees as shown at B, it will shut off the tube entirely because the grid

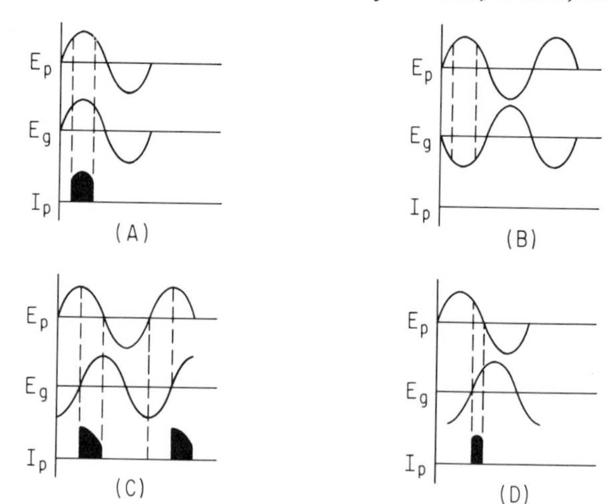

Fig. 8-13. Trigger phasing

signal is becoming increasingly negative as the plate signal becomes increasingly positive. Thus, when the plate signal reaches an amplitude which normally is sufficient to fire the tube, the grid potential is sufficiently negative to prevent such firing. Also, by the time the grid signal is reduced sufficiently to permit firing, the anode signal has declined to such a low value that it is insufficient to cause firing. Thus, the use of a-c signals at both the grid and anode circuits permits the turning on and off of the power applied to the load circuit as exemplified by the drawings at A and B. Intermediate phase relationships will reduce the average power output as shown at C and D of Fig. 8-13. At C, the grid signal lags the plate signal by 90 degrees. (This can also be expressed as the plate signal leading the grid signal.) Under these conditions, the rising amplitude of the plate voltage brings the potential above the firing level, but this occurs at a time when the grid signal is holding the tube at cutoff.

As the negative grid potential decreases, it reaches a point where it permits the firing of the tube, and this occurs when the plate voltage is in the peak-value region. The tube conducts fully, then conduction declines as the a-c signal in the anode circuit declines to zero. When the amplitude of the plate voltage has declined sufficiently to stop conduction, then deionization occurs. The tube remains at cutoff during the negative portion of the plate voltage and conduction will not occur again until the grid voltage declines enough to release plate-current flow. In consequence, the successive bursts of plate-current flow consist of virtual half-alternations as shown on the bottom I_p line shown at C.

The bursts of plate-current flow can be controlled so that they have even shorter durations, as shown at D of Fig. 8-13. Here, the phase difference between the plate and grid signals is greater 90 degrees, although not quite 180 degrees. As shown, the rise of plate voltage does not cause conduction because the grid signal is highly negative during this time. Hence, the plate voltage reaches its peak and starts to decline before the grid signal reaches a value sufficiently low to permit conduction. In consequence, conduction starts at a time interval following the peak amplitude of the plate voltage. Since the grid signal now goes through a positive alternation, the tube continues to conduct until the plate potential has reached such a low value that deionization occurs. For a greater phase difference, there would be a more narrow time interval of tube conduction until the 180-degree phase difference occurred, as shown earlier in drawing B of Fig. 8-13.

Phase shifting between the grid and plate signals can be accomplished by use of a phase-shifting circuit such as illustrated in Fig. 8-14. Here, the power source for the anode and load circuit of the thyratron is the secondary of a transformer, the latter having a center tap so that a voltage with a 180-degree phase difference can be obtained. A coil (L_3) and a variable resistor (R_1) are used to form a resistive-inductive phase-shifting device. A capacitor could also be utilized instead of the inductance L_3. In lieu of a variable resistor, a saturable-reactance type of inductor can be employed, and the phase of the signal shifted by varying the reactance and hence the inductance of the coil. The inductance of the latter can be varied to a considerable degree by altering the amount of direct current flowing through the winding which controls saturation, as described in Chapters 4 and 11. Usually only a few milliamperes of current are required to produce a considerable reactive change. When a fixed value of inductance or a fixed capacitor value is employed, the variable-resistor type of phase-shifting device such as shown at Fig. 8-14 must be employed.

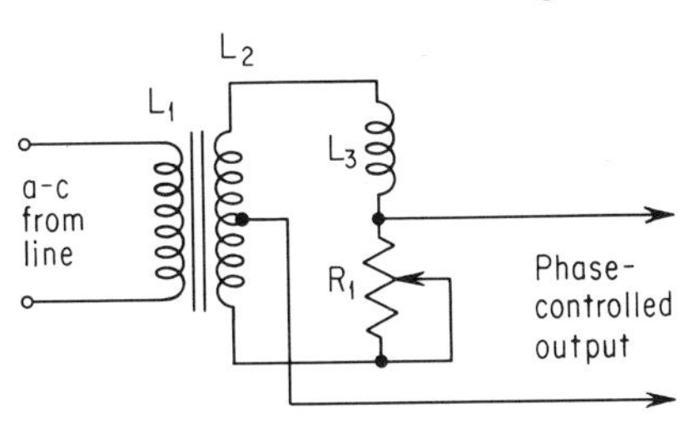

Fig. 8-14. Thyratron phasing circuit

In certain industrial applications, the phase-shifting device, in conjunction with a-c signals, is sufficient for most practical applications. For high-order precision firing, however, unsatisfactory results may occur because of line-voltage variations, tube- or circuit-characteristic variations, or both. If the characteristic curve of the tube alters because of temperature changes or aging, precise firing can be altered. If the grid waveform has a sharp rise time, however, it will nullify the critical aspects of the tube's characteristic curve at the firing interval.

The steep waveform required should be in the form of a sharp spike with sufficient amplitude to cause firing. If such a sharp spike has a short duration, it will turn on plate-current flow and immediately cause the grid to revert to a cutoff-bias status so that the tube will be shut off as soon as the plate voltage reaches a level sufficiently low to cause deionization.

A process for obtaining the necessary sharp firing spike is by use of a multivibrator or blocking oscillator of the type described earlier for generating a squarewave signal as shown at A of Fig. 8-15. This squarewave is then modified prior to its application to the grid of the thyratron by using a *differentiating circuit.* (See Chapter 1.) At A of Fig. 8-15, the differentiating circuit consists of capacitor C_1 and resistor R_1, and the values of this resistor-capacitor combination are so chosen that the circuit has a short time constant. Thus the capacitor becomes fully charged early with respect to the arrival of the squarewave. This can be understood by referring to the illustration and noting the relationship of the squarewave at the top of the drawing to the differentiated waveform below. When a squarewave with a rising voltage is applied to the terminals T_1 and T_2, terminal T_1 becomes positive and terminal T_2 negative. Current will then flow through resistor R_1 and will charge capacitor C_1. (Assume that the bias battery has a low internal resistance, or that it is bypassed with a capacitor of large value so as to provide a low-reactance shunt path.)

Since C_1 and R_1 have a short time constant, the leading current in the capacitor when the signal is first applied causes current to flow through R_1 in the direction shown by the solid arrow. This establishes a voltage drop of positive polarity across R_1 as shown, and thus the initial rise of the spike waveform shown at A. After the capacitor has charged to the peak value of the squarewave, current no longer flows to the capacitor and there is a current decline as the capacitor reaches its full charge. The current decline across resistor R_1 causes the spiked waveform to decline to zero again as shown in the drawing at A. During the flat-top portion of the input squarewave, there is no change

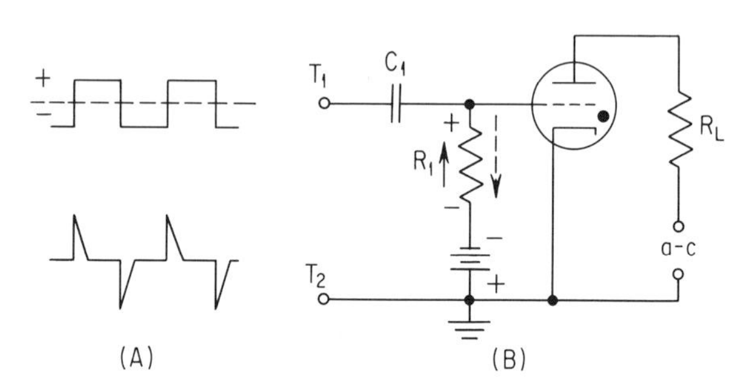

Fig. 8-15. Triggering waveform and circuit

in the differentiating circuit because the capacitor is charged fully and a steady-state potential is obtained from the flat top of the squarewave. When the squarewave amplitude declines, a negative voltage appears at terminal T_1 and a positive potential at terminal T_2. The result of the latter is a reversal of current through the input circuit, and now the capacitor not only discharges through R_1 but recharges in the negative direction. During the latter course of events, the current flow through R_1 is in the direction shown by the dotted arrow and this develops the negative-going spiked waveform shown at A. After capacitor C_1 has been charged to the peak value of the negative alternation of the input squarewave, current flow through R_1 will again have dropped to zero.

Thus, for each positive alternation of the squarewave, a positive spiked waveform is produced, and for every negative alternation of the squarewave, a negative spiked wave form is developed. Because of the short time constant of the differentiating circuit, the leading edge of the differentiated waveform is very sharp, that is, it rises from a minimum to a maximum in a very short time, making it an ideal triggering pulse. Such differentiation of squarewaves in order to obtain a sharp spike with a steep leading edge is also employed extensively in computer circuitry, television transmission and reception, and in other applications where abrupt gating characteristics are desirable.

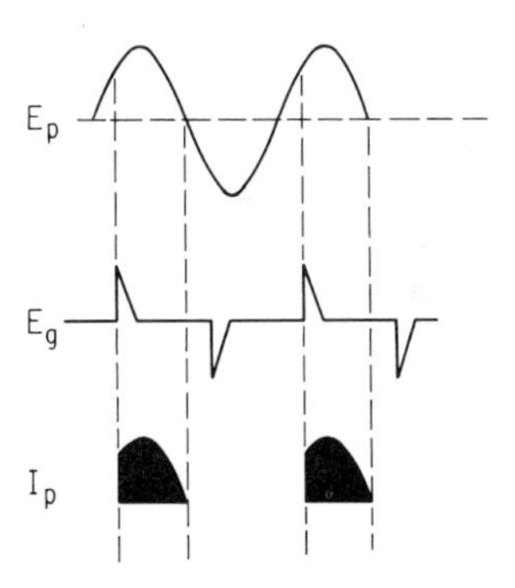

Fig. 8-16. Spiked trigger waveforms

The differentiated waveform as applied to the thyratron control characteristics is shown in Fig. 8-16. The phase of the differentiated waveform is controlled and set at a point where firing is to occur. Only the positive spike of the differentiated waveform causes firing, because the negative spike occurs at a time when the plate voltage is already negative, hence the second spike is ineffectual.

The grid input circuit of a thyratron can also be controlled by a fixed d-c bias in conjunction with an a-c waveform instead of a spiked waveform, using a circuit similar to that shown at B of Fig. 8-15. For a sinewave input which it not to be differentiated, capacitor C_1 and resistor R_1 have values which produce a long time constant. A differentiating circuit will not alter the waveshape of a sinewave signal, but will effect its amplitude, because a small value of C_1 will have a high reactance for the signal frequency. If C_1 has a high reactance, the signal will develop across it as well as across resistor R_1. Hence, if the reactance in ohms of C_1 is equal to the resistance of R_1, the grid only receives half the voltage applied to terminals T_1 and T_2. Thus, for a sinewave signal input, capacitor C_1 should have a very low reactance for the input signal.

THE IGNITRON

The ignitron is another three-element tube of the gaseous type. The cathode is not thermionic, as in the thyratron, but instead it consists of a pool of mercury as shown in Fig. 8-17. The anode structure is conventional as with other tubes, and as with most high-power tubes it is usually constructed of graphite since this has better heat-dissipating characteristics than the metal plates. The third element consists of an *ignitor* which has a pointed tip of silicon carbide or boron carbide which dips into the mercury pool. The ignitor tip is rough-surfaced, as shown at B of Fig. 8-17, and presents a number of sharp contact points to the mercury. When a voltage is impressed across the ignitor rod and the mercury pool, a potential difference is established between them with a number of small flash points sufficient to cause electron emission. With the anode positive, electron flow will result and the consequent bombardment of the gas atoms causes ionization.

A typical circuit is shown in Fig. 8-18. Without any voltage applied to the ignitor, a voltage applied across the anode and cathode, with the anode positive, will not cause conduction because a potential difference across the anode and cathode will not produce electron movement or emission from the cold mercury which forms the cathode. It is only when the ignitor causes sparking with its contact at the mercury surface that electron flow and ionization occur. As shown in Fig. 8-18, a diode rectifier, D_1, is employed between the anode and the ignitor circuit. The a-c supply power is in series with the load circuit (R_L) and the mercury pool of the tube as shown.

During the time the a-c supply voltage is negative at terminal T_1

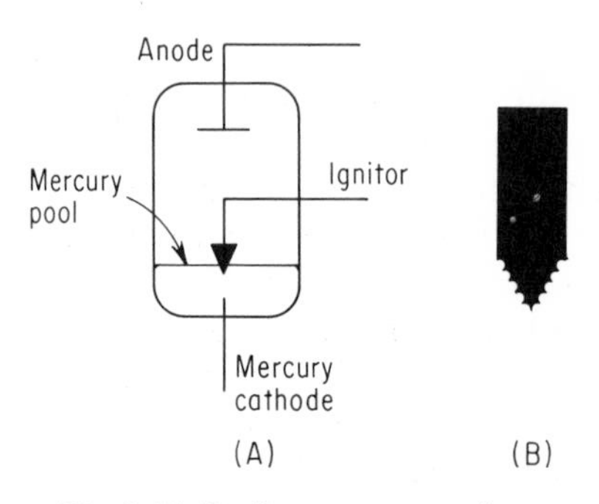

Fig. 8-17. Ignitron construction

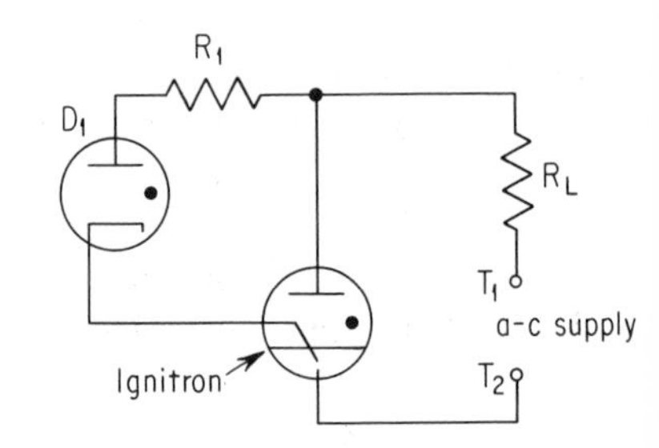

Fig. 8-18. Ignitron circuit

and positive at terminal T_2, nothing occurs because the anodes of both the diode D_1 and the ignitron tube are negative. Since diode D_1 does not conduct, there is no flash point established between the ignitor and the mercury. Similarly, the negative potential at the ignitron plate also prevents the latter from conducting. When terminal T_1 is positive and terminal T_2 negative, both the diode D_1 anode and the ignitron anode are positive. Conduction occurs through diode D_1 as soon as there is arcing between the ignitor and the mercury pool, and when this occurs, ionization is created and the ignitron conducts fully. During the time of conduction, the internal voltage drop is at a low value since the internal resistance becomes quite low. The danger of arcback—that is, a flash from plate to cathode—is reduced because the inverse peak voltage is on the ignitron only when the gas vapor within the tube is in a deionized state. Only at the initiation of the positive cycle at terminal T_1 will there be ionization, and this is under the forward-current conditions. When the ignitron is not conducting, the inverse peak voltage is present across a resistance which is considerably higher than it would be for an ionized-tube condition such as occurs in the mercury-vapor rectifiers and others.

The ignitron has a number of advantages over the thyratron. No excitation must be maintained, such as current flow through a filament winding, to maintain proper temperature. The ignitron can be fired at any point on the cycle, thus providing complete control as with the thyratron. For varying the firing along the points on the input a-c cycle, diode D_1 anode would have a phase-shifting device incorporated in it. Another advantage with the ignitron is that the anode can be placed in close proximity to the mercury pool to obtain a low internal resistance and increased efficiency. In a tube where ionization prevails during the presence of inverse peak voltage, the danger of arcing prevents the anode's being spaced too closely to the cathode structure.

Ignitrons with mercury-pool cathodes have unlimited life since there is no danger of cathode burn-out as there is with thermionic tubes that have heated filaments or cathodes. The mercury pool has unlimited life and will withstand very high overloads without this disintegration or impairment of function. Disadvantages are bulk, cost, and the necessity for vertical operation because of the mercury pool.

Several methods may be employed for firing the ignitron as shown in Fig. 8-19. At A, the a-c power source which the ignitron releases to the load circuit is also employed to initiate the arc between the ignitor and the cathode. Resistor R_1 prevents the full voltage of the a-c power source from appearing across the ignitor-cathode circuit and drops the voltage to that required for creating the initial arc at the igniter. The diode D_1 prevents the application of a reverse-polarity voltage across cathode and ignitor. (The ignitor may be damaged for

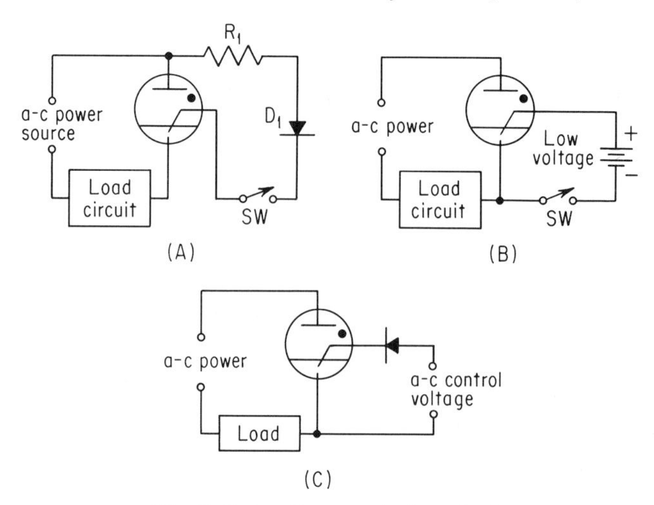

Fig. 8-19. Ignitron control methods

even low values of reverse current flow, that is, current flow from the ignitor to cathode.) The switch (SW) is used to start conduction through the ignitron. It can be a relay type, or an electronic gate which closes the circuit at proper time intervals as required by the industrial processes involved.

Another method is shown for initiating the arc between the cathode and the ignitor at B of Fig. 8-19. Here, a low voltage from a battery, power supply, or d-c generator is employed. Since the polarity applied to the ignitor and cathode does not vary as with the circuit shown at A, the diode rectifier is not required. When the switch is closed for the circuit shown at B, firing occurs for the first alternation of the a-c power which applies a positive potential to the anode with respect to the cathode. As with the circuit shown at A, the ignitron delivers a pulsating d-c to the load circuit, since only every other alternation of the a-c waveform is passed by the ignitron.

An a-c control voltage may be employed as shown at C. Such a low-voltage alternating current may be obtained from the a-c power source by use of a step-down transformer and phasing controls of a type similar to that used for the thyratron. By appropriate phase-shifting, precise firing control can be obtained with the ignitron in a fashion similar to that obtained with the thyratron.

DUAL-TUBE IGNITRON CIRCUITS

The ignitron circuits previously shown were of the single-tube type and delivered pulsating d-c to the load circuit. Such pulsating d-c can be filtered to produce d-c with a minimum of ripple. However, since

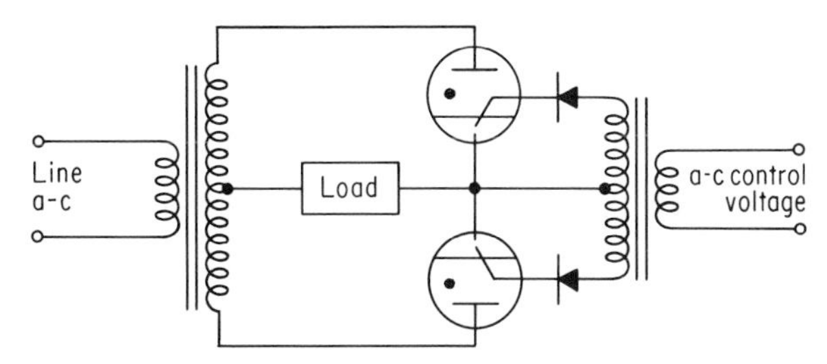

Fig. 8-20. Full-wave ignitron operation

alternate halves of the cycle are employed, the intervening gaps between the pulsating d-c make filtering more difficult than if no gaps were present as in full-wave rectification. Ignitrons can be employed in a full-wave circuit as with other diodes, and a typical basic circuit is shown in Fig. 8-20. The mode of operation is similar to that of any full-wave rectifier circuit. (See Chapter 6.) Each tube conducts alternately, and the circuit is so arranged that the resultant current flow for each tube is in the same direction through the load circuit and filter section. As with other full-wave supply systems, the ripple frequency is 120 cycles per second instead of the 60 cycles per second obtained with half-wave rectification.

When the ignitron must be capable of turning on and off *alternating currents* without converting them to pulsating d-c, it is necessary to employ two ignitrons in a circuit such as shown in Fig. 8-21. In this arrangement, the ignitron V_1 will conduct current in one direction through the load circuit, while V_2 will conduct current in the opposite direction. The result is the application of both alternations of the a-c cycle of the power source to the load circuit.

Any one of the previously illustrated ignitor-cathode circuits can be employed for initiating the ignitor spark. For the circuit shown in Fig. 8-21, low-voltage a-c signals can be employed at terminals desig-

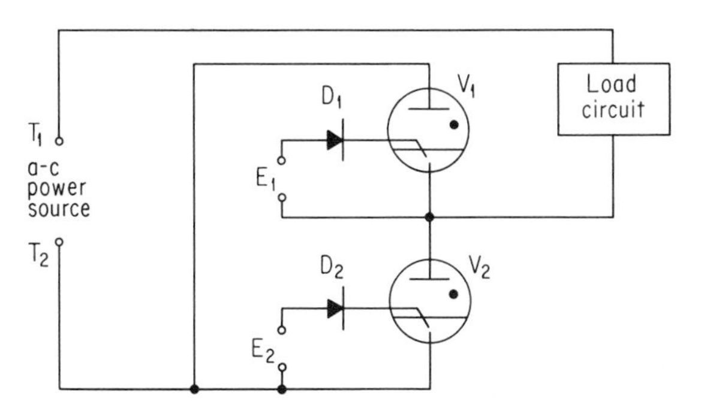

Fig. 8-21. Dual ignitron a-c control

nated E_1 and E_2. For direct-current sources, diodes D_1 and D_2 may be eliminated. Instead of the load circuit shown, the power switched by the ignitrons can be applied to the secondary of a transformer and the voltage stepped up or down as required. For arc-welding purposes, a low-voltage, high-current secondary winding would be employed.

The circuit shown in Fig. 8-21 must not be confused with that of a full-wave rectifier. Even though the ignitrons V_1 and V_2 pass current in only one direction, the power delivered to the load circuit has alternating-current characteristics and not pulsating d-c. When one alternation of the a-c power source is such that terminal T_1 is positive and terminal T_2 negative, current will flow from T_2 to the cathode of V_2. If the ignitor polarity is applied to permit firing, the ignitron V_2 will conduct and current will flow from cathode to anode, and thence through the load circuit to terminal T_1. During this time the ignitron V_1 is nonconducting because the negative polarity at terminal T_2 appears at the anode of V_1 and prevents tube conduction. At the next alternation of the a-c power-source cycle, terminal T_1 is negative and terminal T_2 is positive. When terminal T_1 is negative, current flows from T_1 through the load resistor and to the cathode circuit of V_1. Because the latter tube has a positive anode (from T_2) this ignitron will conduct, providing the ignitor initiates the current flow by starting ionization. Hence when V_2 conducts, current flows up through the load circuit shown in Fig. 8-21; when V_1 conducts, current flows down through the load circuit, thus furnishing it with a-c power.

SOLID-STATE THYRATRON

The solid-state thyratrons such as the silicon controlled rectifiers have characteristics quite similar to the gas-tube types, but they offer a number of advantages. The gas-tube thyratrons use more electric power because of their heaters, and they also generate much more heat than the solid-state devices. High-power thyratrons and ignitrons are forced-air or water cooled, thus requiring either a blower or a water-circulating system which must constantly cool the tube by use of a water jacket surrounding the anode-envelope structure. The jacket housing also adds to the bulk of the unit.

The solid-state thyratrons need no warm-up, and switching is faster than in the gas-tube thyratrons, with speeds involving only a dozen or so microseconds. The lifespan of the solid-state thyratrons is also considerably greater than the tube types, because of the decreased heat, no filament deterioration, and less internal resistance during conduction.

Basic Circuit

As with the gas-tube thyratron, the silicon-controlled rectifier has a control element for switching on current flow through the device. Once current flows, however, the element looses control until the anode voltage is removed. This is illustrated in Fig. 8-22, which resembles the circuit discussed earlier in Fig. 8-11 for the gas-tube thyratron. The additional terminal is the gating electrode, which compares to the grid of the tube thyratron. The rectifier is triggered when the resistance arm moves up from the negative (ground) terminal and applies a positive potential to the gate. With the anode switch closed, current flows through the diode and continues to flow even though the resistor arm is moved down to the ground side. Thus, even though the gate potential has been removed, the rectifier continues to conduct, just as the tube thyratron continues to conduct with a negative grid potential after firing. To stop conduction in the silicon-controlled rectifier, the anode switch must be opened during the time no positive voltage appears at the gate. The gate-to-cathode voltage characteristic of the silicon-controlled rectifier is similar to that of a conventional solid-state diode which is forward-biased, thus only a few volts are necessary to produce sufficient current in the gate-cathode circuit for firing. Therefore, this device can be utilized to switch high electric power to load circuits by the application of very low power to the gate, just as the tube thyratron switches considerable power by low-power grid signals.

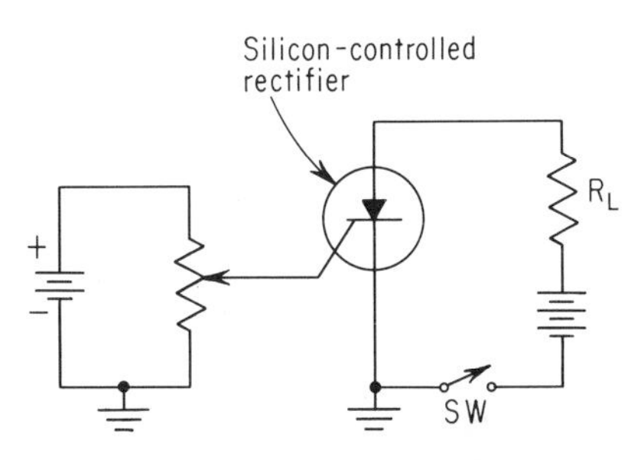

Fig. 8-22. Silicon-controlled rectifier circuit factors

The tube thyratrons do not conduct until current flow is released by the grid structure. The controlled rectifier, however, will conduct in the forward direction when sufficient voltage amplitude is present to break the rectifier into conduction in the forward direction. Thus, without employing the gate terminal, the controlled rectifier can be used as a standard half-wave rectifier as shown at A of Fig. 8-23. If the reverse breakdown-voltage rating is not reached by the amplitude swings of the negative a-c alternations, the output will be in the form of pulses occurring at the line a-c rate. These can be filtered additionally, if necessary, in conventional fashion as described earlier in Chapter 6.

If the pulsating d-c (or filtered d-c) is to be switched to a load at a specific time as in typical thyratron applications, a d-c trigger voltage

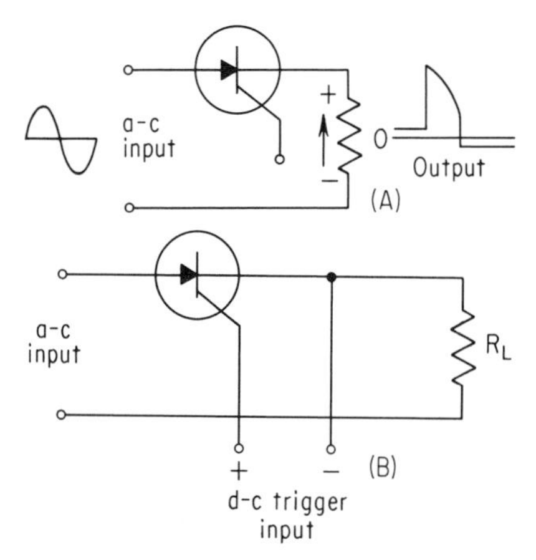

Fig. 8-23. Basic circuits of controlled rectifiers

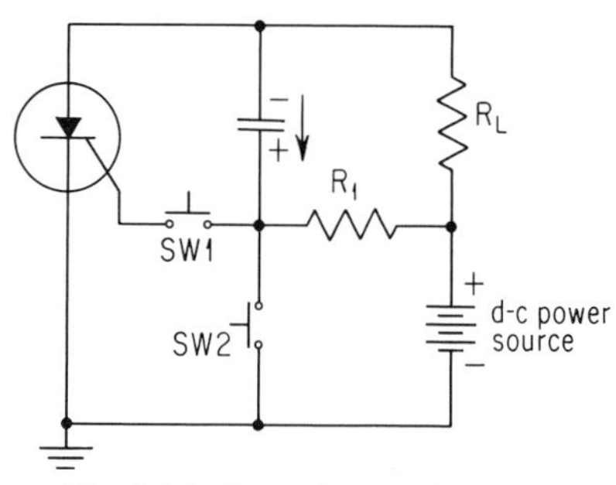

Fig. 8-24. d-c switch using controlled rectifier

is applied between the gate terminal and the cathode, as shown at B of Fig. 8-23. This trigger voltage must be applied at the time a positive alternation of the a-c input signal is present, just as with the tube thyratron previously discussed. By applying timed or phased pulse signals to the gate, conduction can be set for the precise moment required.

As with the silicon-rectifier circuits discussed in Chapter 6, full-wave circuits can be employed to reduce the ripple component, or three-phase systems with multiple rectifier units can be employed for the production of low-ripple d-c without using filter circuits. The phasing circuits previously discussed for the thyratron gas-tubes can also be employed with the thyratron silicon-controlled rectifiers.

The controlled rectifier can be used for switching d-c, as shown earler in Fig. 8-22. The circuit can be designed to use the d-c power source for switching both on and off, as shown in Fig. 8-24. Push-button switches are indicated, although any relay or gating system can be employed, or triggering can be by use of pressure-sensitive switches, thermostats, or voltage-sensitive devices. When switch no. 1 is depressed, the necessary positive triggering potential is supplied from the d-c power source in series with resistor R_1. This starts the current flow through the rectifier and through the load circuit R_L. The capacitor which is connected to the anode now charges, because the conduction of the rectifier closed the circuit for the capacitor so that the latter can charge up from the d-c power source. Thus, the start switch SW_1 applies power to the load circuit and charges the capacitor to the full value of the d-c power supply. When power is to be removed from the load, the stop switch SW_2 is closed momentarily. The closing of SW_2 places the charged capacitor directly across the controlled rectifier and applies thereto a reverse voltage sufficient to stop conduction until the start switch SW_1 is again depressed.

Where a-c is to be switched to the load without rectification, the circuit shown in Fig. 8-25 can be employed. Here, two controlled rectifiers are in parallel, and the parallel combination is in series with

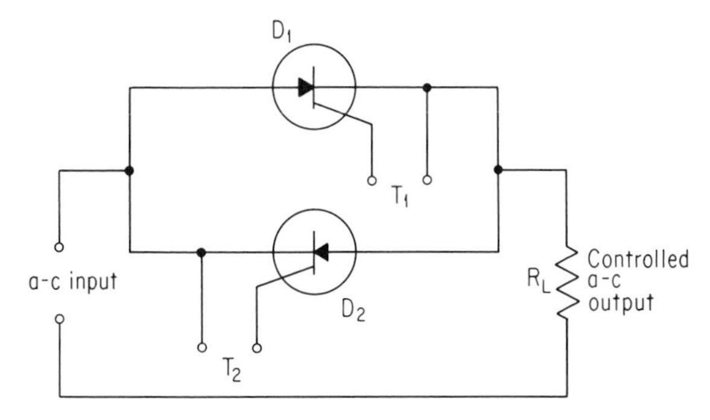

Fig. 8-25. a-c Switch using controlled rectifier

the line. This circuit is similar to the dual-ignitron a-c control circuit shown earlier in Fig. 8-21. When the gates of the controlled rectifiers D_1 and D_2 of Fig. 8-25 are triggered, the diodes conduct alternately for each positive and negative half-cycle of the a-c, thus producing both alternations across the load circuit R_L.

Review Questions for Chapter 8

1. Briefly explain how tubes can be used in circuits for gating-in and gating-out signals.
2. Why is a coincidence gate sometimes referred to as an *and circuit?*
3. Briefly summarize the circuit function of the gate in Fig. 8-3.
4. Submit a schematic diagram of the type illustrated in Fig. 8-5 for the DPDT relay illustrated in Fig. 8-6.
5. Reproduce the relay schematic at D of Fig. 8-5, and add a push-button switch and battery to energize the relay, and also apply one set of relay terminals to switch voltage to a load resistor and the terminals of the other relay to apply voltage to a variable-reactor transducer.
6. Draw a schematic of a sequence switching circuit using four thermistors controlling four load circuits, plus one load circuit without delay.
7. Draw a three-relay coincidence circuit.
8. Explain the basic principles of the gas-tube thyratron.
9. Explain the basic principles of the ignitron.
10. Briefly explain how the circuit shown at B of Fig. 8-15 *differentiates.* (Refer to Chapter 1 for review.)
11. List some advantages of the solid-state thyratrons over the gas-tube types.
12. Submit a diagram using silicon-controlled rectifiers in a three-phase power system, similar to the silicon-diode circuit of this type given in Chapter 6.

Motors

INTRODUCTION

Both a-c and d-c motors are employed in industry. The a-c motors are used extensively where the control factor is primarily one of turning a device continuously or intermittently. The d-c motor is employed where speed regulation as well as the turning on and off of the motor is required.

The basic principles of generators previously discussed also apply to motors, and reference should be made to Chapter 5 for review purposes regarding their basic similarities. As was mentioned, a generator can be converted into a motor or vice versa by the proper application of voltage to the terminals. In generators, an output voltage is procured from the armature windings, whereas in the motor an external voltage source is used to apply voltage to the armature in order to cause current to flow through the armature and in turn rotate it. With these similarities in mind, the more advanced aspects of motors will be detailed in this chapter.

THE BASIC MOTOR

Reference to the cross-section diagram of the two-pole generator (Fig. 5-5, Chapter 5) will aid in understanding basic motor principle. Here, the cross-sectional wires at the left in the armature have a negative polarity while the wires at the right have positive polarity. Because the field-coil wires at the left also have a negative polarity, there will be a repelling force set up between the field coils at the left with respect to the left-hand armature coils. Also, the positive polarity of the field coils at the right repels the positive polarity of the armature coils. Thus, a force (*torque*) is exerted on the armature causing it to turn. By this process a motor is formed from the basic generator device.

As with generators, there are two basic types of motors, a-c and d-c. The a-c motors are less expensive than d-c motors. They are universally employed in all types of applications, from very low power to extremely high power.

Where speed regulation is important, the d-c motor is used extensively. Because of its constructional and electric characteristics, its speed can be readily controlled electronically without disturbing to any appreciable extent the regulation and torque characteristics. Thus, the d-c motor is extensively used in industrial electronics. However, because of the widespread use of a-c in power-distribution systems, some means must be provided to furnish the necessary d-c electric power for operating the d-c motors properly, as more fully explained later.

In Fig. 9-1, the basic types of electric motors are shown—the alternating-current type, the direct-current type, and the universal motor which can be operated on either a-c or d-c. The direct-current types are divided into three basic categories, the *shunt* motor, the *series* motor, and the *compound* motor.

There are a variety of alternating-current motors, each especially suitable in a given application. As shown in the block diagram, the two primary types are the *synchronous,* and the *induction,* which has the

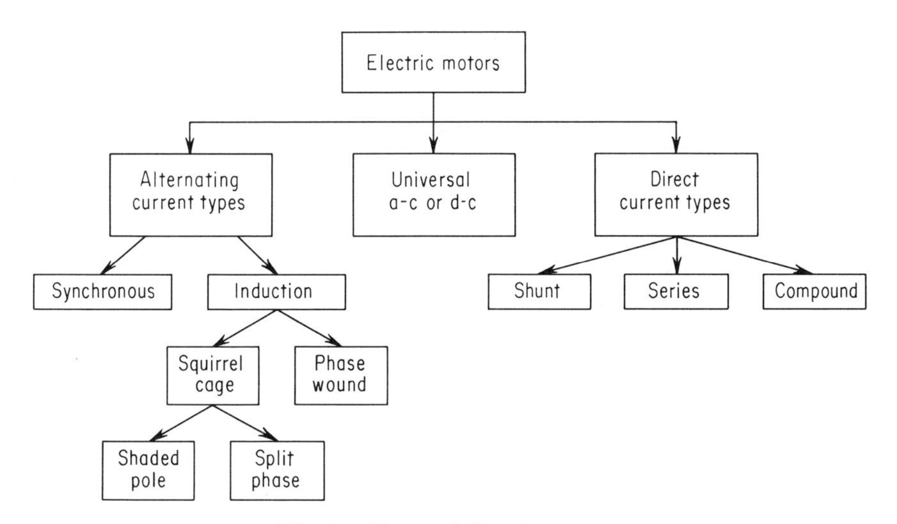

Fig. 9-1. Types of electric motors

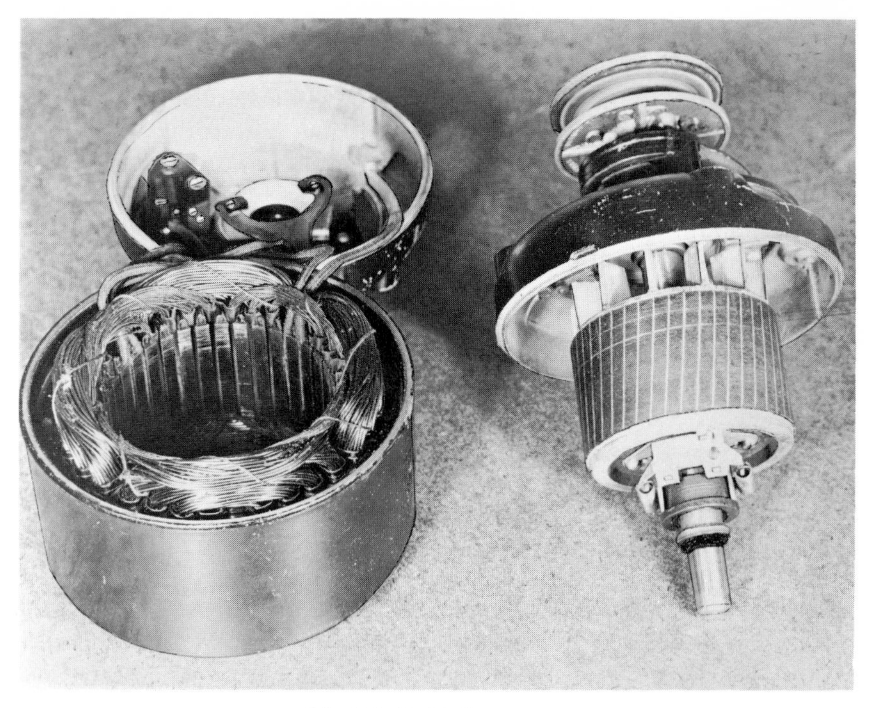

Fig. 9-2. Induction motor

greater number of variations. The synchronous types are used where a constant speed is required. The constant speed of the synchronous a-c motor is related to the constant frequency of the 60-cycle line voltage. The frequency of the line voltage is maintained within extremely close frequency tolerances by the power companies, hence the synchronous motor will also maintain a constant speed when used within its power range. The induction motors are used in various applications from low power to high power, for operating blowers, fans, power tools, air-conditioners, etc., as will be more fully discussed. A typical one-third horsepower motor (with rotor out of frame) is shown in Fig. 9-2.

THE d-c MOTOR

The speed of the d-c motor depends on a voltage drop which occurs across the armature coils and on the strength of the field. Because the strength of the field is related to motor speed, the speed of a d-c motor can thus be regulated by the amount of voltage applied to the field. For this reason the d-c motor is an important item in industrial applications where variable speeds are necessary. As discussed later, motor speed control can be accomplished by electric or electronic means for greater efficiency, reliability, and ease of establishing automatic speed control.

As with d-c generators, d-c motors have three basic types of internal circuitry; the *series, shunt,* and *compound.* Also, as with the d-c generators, there are two compound categories, the *cumulative* and the *differential.*

In the series-type motor, since the load current flows through both the armature and the field coils, there is a considerable variation in speed for changes in the load, as with the series-type generator. For the series-type motor, the starting torque and the starting current are high. In a d-c motor, the amount of torque produced is proportional to the number of conductors of wire in the armature coil and the amount of current flowing through the conductors, as well as the magnetic field density. Thus, in the series motor, if the load is increased to the point where more current is drawn through the armature and field coils, the flux density will increase. Hence, in the series motor, the torque varies almost as the square of the current. In consequence, the torque is increased approximately four times as the current through the armature and field coils doubles. For the series motor, a decrease in load increases motor speed. With no load on the series motor the speed may become extremely fast and result in motor damage.

The series-type motor is used in industrial cranes and industrial hoisting devices, including some elevator motor applications. It is used in street cars and also as the starter motor in automobiles.

If the voltage polarity on both the armature and field of the series motor is reversed, the direction of the torque remains the same as it was before the field reversal. Consequently, such motors will operate on either d-c or a-c and are known as *universal* motors. These find extensive applications in vacuum cleaners and other home electric appliances. For prolonged a-c operation, a rotor core coil is used which must be supplied with current to build up a field. Consequently, carbon brushes must be employed for current-carrying connections to the rotor section.

In the shunt-type motor, as in the shunt-type generator, the field coils are in shunt (parallel) with the armature coils. A change in the load will alter the armature current, hence the voltage drop across it. The change is small, however, because of its low resistance (the field coil having a high resistance). Because of the small voltage change across the armature coils, the speed of the shunt motor changes very little with wide variations in loads. The shunt motor has medium starting torque and current. Because the field current remains fairly constant for variations in load, the doubling of the armature current would cause the torque to double. Thus, in this motor, the torque produced is directly proportional to the current flowing in the armature.

The shunt motor is used in motor-generator sets, in centrifugal pumps, in fans and blower devices for forced-air usage, in printing presses, and in general-purpose work.

The differential compound motor has characteristics similar to the differential compound generator. The magnetic fields generated by the series field and the shunt field are in opposite directions, hence they oppose each other. The current flowing through the armature when the motor is started tends to be quite large, but the torque quite small. Because of an inherent instability, the differential compound motor is used infrequently.

A more desirable arrangement of the compound motor with both the series and shunt coils is where the coils are so wound that they aid each other with respect to the magnetic fields produced. This, of course, is similar to the cumulative compound arrangement used with the d-c generator. If the proper number of turns is assigned to the coils, the speed of the motor can be kept fairly constant despite variations in the load. The cumulative compound motor is used in such commercial devices as punch presses, rock crushers, and also in some elevators.

THE a-c MOTOR

The a-c motor differs somewhat from the d-c motor because there is no electrical connection between the rotor and the stator windings. Instead, the stator (field) coil is the one to which the line voltage is attached. The magnetic fields which build up and collapse for each alternation of the a-c cycle will induce a voltage into the rotor coil. Thus, because the rotor receives its power by magnetic induction, a transformer reaction occurs and for this reason the field coils or the stator section of an a-c motor is sometimes referred to as the "primary" whereas the rotor is called the "secondary," as is the case with a conventional transformer. Torque to turn the motor shaft is created by the attraction set up between the magnetic fields of the stator and those induced into the rotor.

The a-c motor turns because the fields in the stator section are essentially *rotating*. The rotating field can be understood by reference to Fig. 9-3. Two-phase, three-phase, or other polyphase currents are employed for rotation of the field. For purposes of illustration, assume a two-phase a-c is employed as shown at A of Fig. 9-3. Also, assume that we have a stator section with four pole pieces as shown at D. The vertical pole pieces are energized by the coils which are fed currents through X windings. The horizontal poles are energized by coils

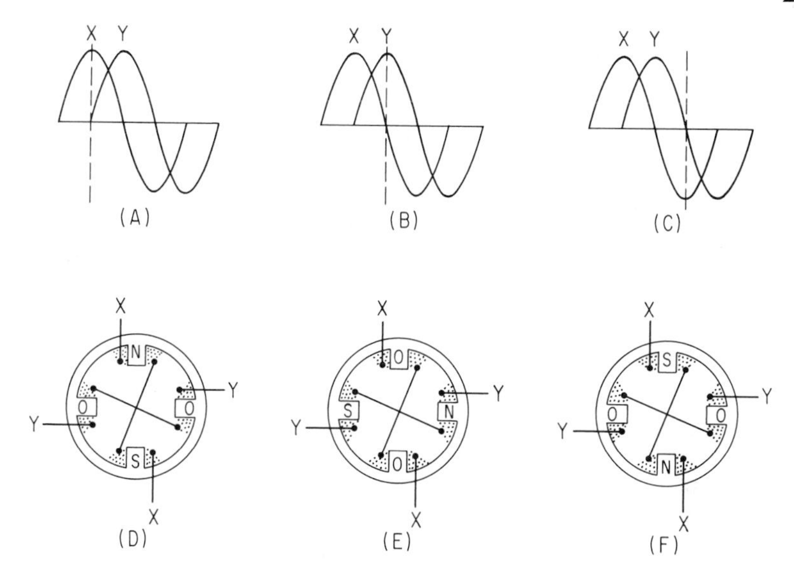

Fig. 9-3. Rotating field

because of the energy applied to the *Y* terminals. The two-phase currents shown at A are also marked *X* and *Y* respectively, and the *X* voltage is applied to the *X* terminals of the stator and the *Y* a-c power is applied to the *Y* terminals of the stator shown at D. When this is done, the *X* coils are the only ones which will be energized, because for the time interval indicated by the dashed line at A the *X* power is at its peak, but the *Y* power is at its zero level. Thus, the vertical poles of the stator as shown at D will have a north-pole polarity at the top and a south-pole polarity at the bottom as shown.

At a later time interval, as shown by the dashed line at B, the *Y* a-c power will be at its maximum, but the *X* a-c power will be at zero. Now, the *Y* coils of the stator shown at E will be energized while the *X* coils will have no current flow through them. Thus, the horizontal poles shown at E are now north-pole polarity at the right and south-pole polarity at the left, and the change from the north pole at D to the north pole at E is as though the pole had rotated in a clockwise direction from the vertical position at D to the horizontal position at the right as at E.

At a still later time interval, as shown by the dashed line at C, the *Y* current is again at zero, but the *X* current is at a peak value, although it is now in a *negative* direction as compared to the peak value which prevailed for the current at A. Since the *X* coils are again energized, there will be a polarity of north and south poles developed as shown at F. Because of the negative polarity of the a-c at C, the *X* poles are now energized with a polarity opposite to that which prevailed for the polarity at E. In consequence, the north-pole polarity is now at the bottom for the vertical poles shown at F. Again, the result is as though the north-pole polarity had moved from the right-hand side down to the bottom around the circumference of the stator frame.

A quarter-cycle later, the north-pole polarity would shift around in a clockwise direction again and would appear at the left-hand pole of the stator frame. At the end of a complete cycle, the condition shown at D would prevail again, with the north-pole polarity at the top. Thus, the revolving magnetic field makes one complete revolution around the circumference of the stator during the time the current in one set of coils passes through one a-c cycle. As the voltage through one set of coils is gradually declining, the voltage in the other set of coils is building up, and in consequence a fairly constantly moving field is generated. When a three-phase motor is employed, three currents are involved as detailed earlier for the three-phase generator. Each current differs from the others by one-third of a cycle, as illustrated earlier. With the three-phase motor, the polarity also revolves around the frame, and a number of poles can be used for reduction of speed as mentioned with respect to the three-phase generator. As with the three-phase generator, the delta or Y connections can be employed. The coils are also placed in slots, similar to the stationary-armature arrangement of the a-c generator discussed earlier.

When a circular framework has a rotating magnetic field, it will cause a rotation of any metal section which is placed at its center. The induced current in the metal section at the center will create a magnetic field which will be attracted by the magnetic field of the circular frame. In consequence, the rotation of the magnetic field of the circular frame will cause the metal section at the center to rotate in unison with the speed of the field rotation. The rotor section follows the magnetic-field rotation of the stator section, but does not attain exactly the same speed.

There are several types of rotors used in the practical a-c motor. A simple, commonly used rotor is the so-called *squirrel-cage* type. The squirrel-cage rotor has a circular, laminated metallic core. Heavy-gauge copper wires are placed around the core, in slots so that the copper cores of wire are somewhat beneath the outer circular surface of the laminated core. The copper wire bars are short-circuited together so that they form a single closed circuit. The copper rods thus form coils, but these have no electric connection with the stator coils —hence no slip rings or commutator rings are necessary. As mentioned, the rotating field acting on the squirrel-cage rotor causes the latter to rotate to form the necessary torque.

Another type of rotor used with the induction motor is the so-called

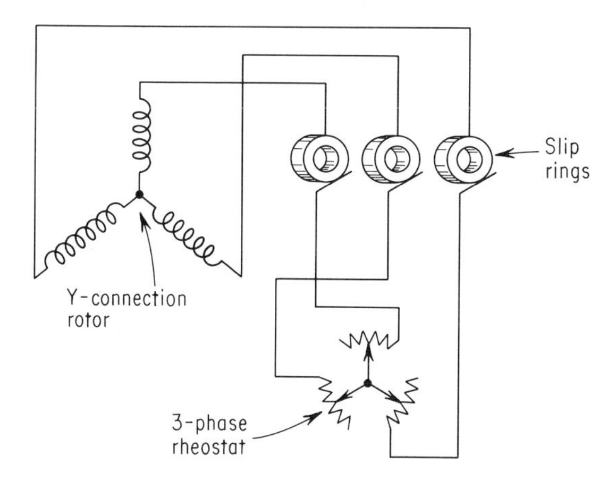

Fig. 9-4. Rotor and starter for wound-rotor induction motor

phase-wound rotor. This rotor also has a laminated iron core, but coils are wound around it in a way resembling the construction of the armature for the d-c generator. The coils are wired in a three-phase circuit, using Y connections. This produces three terminals which are then brought out to three slip rings, as shown in Fig. 9-4. The slip-ring terminals permit the application of a resistance to the rotor coils for starting purposes where increased energy is required to overcome the inertia of the rotor core. After the starting mechanism has brought the rotor up to the proper speed, the starting resistance is removed and the rotor then operates like the squirrel-cage, wherein the electromagnet formed by the magnetic induction from the field causes the rotor to follow the stator rotating field. As mentioned earlier, the rotor speed follows, but does not equal the stator speed. This lag is known as *slip*.

As shown in Fig. 9-4, a three-phase rheostat is used, and the three sliding arms of the variable resistors are all common. Under these conditions, the rotor is a closed circuit at all times. For starting, each sliding arm is at the far end from the slip-ring terminals, providing maximum resistance. As the sliding arms are moved to the right (by a common control knob or lever) the resistance is reduced as the motor increases speed, until finally no resistance is in the circuit and the Y rotor coils are connected directly together.

This type of motor is known as a *wound-rotor* induction motor and is used for cranes, hoists, and other applications where variable speed is required initially so that no sudden, damaging power is applied. With the three-phase rheostat, a gradual power application is possible.

The wound-rotor motor is more costly than the ordinary squirrel-cage motor. In addition, more components are present which might give trouble, including the three slip rings, their brushes, and the rheostat.

When a squirrel-cage a-c motor is to be run from single-phase a-c, some methods must be employed to obtain a rotating flux for starting the motor, because the magnetic flux from a single-phase winding is stationary. In the single-phase induction motors used in the home and in low-power industrial applications (small drill presses, light hoists, etc.), an additional winding is included in the motor, and this secondary winding is known as the *starter* winding. By displacing the secondary winding a quarter phase from the standard winding, a rotating flux is procured. Such a motor is known as a *split-phase* motor because of the way the a-c phase is split up for polyphase starting purposes. In such motors, the starting-winding wire is smaller in diameter than the main winding, and if it were left in the circuit after the motor has come up to speed, the high operating currents would overheat the winding and burn it out. For this reason a mechanism must be included in the motor housing for disconnecting the starter winding when the rotor has reached normal speed.

There are several ways to disconnect the starting winding; that shown in Fig. 9-5 is commonly used. A fixed-position ring, marked *A* in the drawing, is fastened to the rotor section. Attached to this is a double-hinged joint arrangement as shown, which in turn is fastened to a moveable ring marked *B*. The *B* ring is held away from the *A* ring by spring tension. The *B* ring, in turn, presses against a U-shaped copper strip as shown in detail in the lower drawing of Fig. 9-5, and as also shown at the left in Fig. 9-2.

With the *B* section held away from the *A*, the pressure of the *B* ring against the copper U-strip causes the latter to press against two contact points to close the circuit to the starter winding. This is the condition when the motor is first turned on. When the motor reaches normal speed, the centrifugal force exerted on the hinged joint forces it outward and pulls the *B* ring toward the rotor, thus removing the tension from the U-strip. In turn, the latter disengages from the

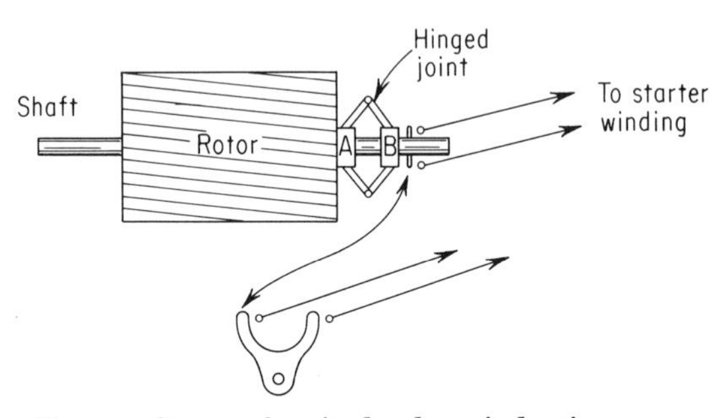

Fig. 9-5. Starter for single-phase induction motor

starter-winding contacts, thus opening the circuit for the latter. When the motor slows down (when being shut off, or when under excess load) the *B*-ring section is again pushed against the U section and the starting winding is thrown into the circuit again.

Once the starter winding is removed, the rotor will continue to spin because of the fields building up and collapsing in the stator, even though the latter is not actually a rotating-type field.

The starting characteristics of the split-phase motor can be improved by use of a capacitor in series with the starter winding. The capacitor will create a leading current in the starter winding with respect to the voltage, and thus produce a rotating field that is more uniform in amplitude than without the capacitor. In consequence, the starting current is reduced and the starting performance upgraded. Such a motor is known as a *capacitor-type* motor and it is extensively used in single-phase a-c operation such as in home workshops and in some industrial applications. As with the split-phase motor previously discussed, the starter winding is disengaged after the motor reaches a certain speed.

For very light starting loads, the squirrel-cage induction motor can be started with an oscillating field generated by the shaded-pole design. This type of motor design is shown in Fig. 9-6. As shown, two copper straps are employed to form what is known as a *shaded-pole* area. The normal pole area is formed by the laminated framework, with the coil at the lower end supplying the necessary field between the split area of the pole pieces. The copper strap consists of a one-turn piece of wire wound around the portion of the pole shown. A single short-circuited turn of copper wire is, in essence, a type of short-circuited coil which will have a voltage induced in it and current flow through it. The magnetic field will not build up as rapidly in the area of the pole which surrounds the copper strap, because of the short-circuited action of the latter. Because the shaded area has a lagging magnetic field, it is as though it were a separate pole. Thus, each copper strap forms a shaded area of lagging magnetic density, hence there are essentially four pole

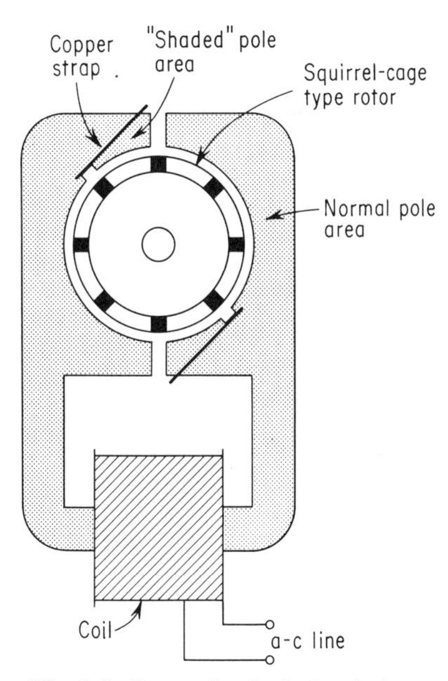

Fig. 9-6. Two-pole shaded pole induction motor

areas, two shaded and two normal. Because the shaded portions are between the normal pole portions, the rise and fall of the magnetic fields, lagged by the shaded areas, simulates a rotating field. A magnetic peak builds up a normal pole area and a lagging peak builds up in the adjacent shaded pole area. As the normal pole area magnetic peak declines, there is a lag in the decline of the shaded pole area. Thus, the magnetic field which is generated appears to rotate insofar as its action on the rotor goes. In consequence, the squirrel-cage rotor has sufficient magnetic fields of the rotating type applied to it to establish not only the running torque but the starting torque.

Applications of the squirrel-cage induction motor are numerous. As mentioned earlier, they are used in home appliances quite extensively. They are also used in industry—as line shaft drives, in woodworking machinery, textile and paper manufacturing machinery, and also in cranes and hoists. The phase-wound rotor induction motor finds applications in air compressors, belt conveyors, elevators, electric shovels, hoists, and other similar applications. Squirrel-cage motors of the shaded-pole variety are also found in phonographs and tape recorders in the home as well as in small and medium-sized fans.

SYNCHRONOUS MOTOR

The synchronous motor, as its name implies, is synchronized in relation to the frequency of the a-c supply voltage. Thus, its speed remains constant with variations in load, until overload occurs. At overload, the synchronization is lost and the motor will stop. The actual speed of the motor, of course, is related to the number of poles, and the speed is not exactly the same as the line frequency, but rather related to it. This was also the case with the induction motor, even though the latter was not synchronized with the a-c line frequency. For the induction motor, the speed under normal load is always less than synchronous speed. A four-pole motor, for instance, runs at approximately 1740 revolutions per minute (rpm)—hence less than the synchronous speed of 1800 rpm. Similarly, the two-pole induction motor has a speed of approximately 3450 rpm, also less than the synchronous speed of 3600.

The construction of the synchronous motor is similar to the a-c generator (see Chapter 5) with the revolving-field design. At no load, there is virtually no current drawn from the a-c power line. The field rotor revolves in synchronization with the rotating fields established by the stator section. When a load is applied to the motor, the rotor lags behind the stator field but falls into synchronization immediately and more current is pulled from the line. For an increase in load, there is an increase in the momentary lag, but synchronization will be maintained up until the pull-out condition.

Formerly, the synchronous motors were not self-starting, but lately additional windings have been included in the rotor section, which is similar to the squirrel-cage rotor induction motor. In consequence, the synchronous motor now has sufficient starting torque for use in various commercial applications and is often used to do work which was once done only by the a-c induction motor.

The synchronous motors are used in industry to furnish the mechanical power necessary for blowers, high-speed compressors, crushers, exhaust and ventilating fans, band and other type saws, centrifugal water, oil, and sewage pumps, steel rolling, and in many other applications. A typical paper-mill installation of eight 350-horsepower, 400-rpm synchronous motors is shown in Fig. 9-7.

The synchronous motors have field magnets which must be excited by d-c; the units providing d-c are termed *exciters*. The necessary direct current can be obtained from any d-c source available in the plant or factory, or separate d-c generators can be employed. Separate motor-generators are usually employed for exciting low-speed synchronous motors. Sometimes a single motor-generator is employed as the exciter for a number of synchronous motors. The d-c can also be furnished from electronic power-supply sources using thyratrons, ignitrons, or silicon rectifiers.

In many synchronous motors the stator winding is of the squirrel-cage type, and initially the motor starts like the conventional squirrel-cage motor. In some motors, the problem of bringing the

Fig. 9-7. Eight 350 horsepower, 400 rpm, open-pedestal-bearing synchronous motors in a paper mill installation (Courtesy Westinghouse)

device up to proper speed is solved by use of external resistors connected to the starter-winding circuit, as described earlier for the wound-rotor motor. The resistance is gradually decreased as the motor speed increases until synchronous speed is obtained. In the Westinghouse H. S. Simplex motor, for instance, the starter winding in the pole faces is so arranged that a three-phase winding is produced and the latter is brought to three slip rings. This permits decreasing the resistance in steps while the field circuit is open until the motor has been brought up to proper speed. By keeping the field circuit open at the time the motor is coming up to speed, the normally high starting current is held to a low value.

Power-factor Correction

One very important advantage of the synchronous motor is its ability to correct the power factor in appliance and commercial installations. Because it acts as a synchronous capacitor with leading current, it will counteract the inductance (lagging current) which occurs when induction motors and lightly loaded transformers are in the line. To correct the power factor, the synchronous motor is often used at the end of the line which feeds the various electric components. Because power-factor correction is important in industrial electronic applications, a brief summary of the theory of cause and correction of power factor will follow.

In Fig. 9-8, an a-c power main is shown feeding three types of devices. The first one exhibits the characteristics of a pure resistance. This could be a heater element, or other resistance unit which con-

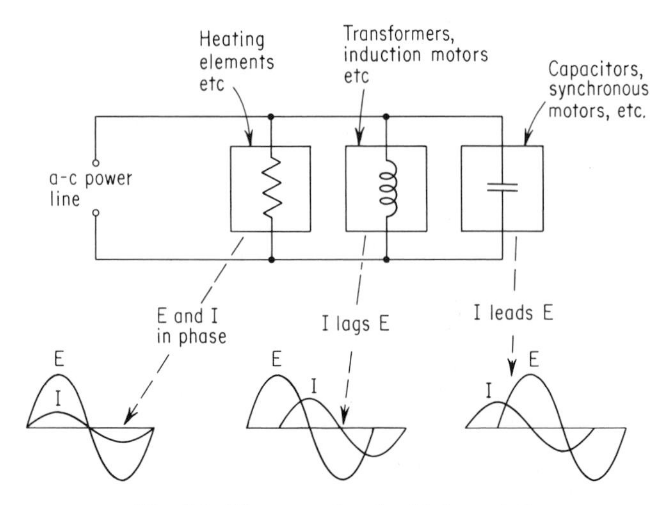

Fig. 9-8. Phase angles for R, L, and C

sumes electric power. The current and voltage applied to a purely resistive circuit will have both the voltage and current in phase, and under this condition the power factor is considered to be 100 per cent. The next unit in the line is represented as an inductance. This could be a transformer, an induction motor, or other type of reactor having primarily inductive characteristics. An inductance in its pure form does not consume electric power, but current does circulate in the device and this current is returned unused to the generator. When an inductance alone is in a line furnishing a-c, the current will lag the voltage by 90 degrees, as shown by the sinewave drawings beneath the schematic in Fig. 9-8. If there is some resistance in the line in addition to the inductance, the lag will be less than 90 degrees but still will not be zero until the line is purely resistive.

When the current lags the voltage, the power is no longer a function of the voltage multiplied by the current, the usual expression for power:

$$P = EI$$

This formula, which solves for the total power consumed by multiplying the effective voltage by the effective current, must now be changed to the following formula when there is a phase angle involved with respect to voltage and current:

$$P = EI \cos \phi$$

In this formula the cosine of the angle is known as the *power factor* and it is a value by which the product of EI must be multiplied to get the correct power in watts.

From the foregoing, it is evident that the true power is a function of the voltage multiplied by the current and the product multiplied by the cosine of the angle. Thus, the simple multiplication of voltage by current is only the *apparent power* and is not the *actual power* used. The true power will be less than the apparent power. For instance, assume that the current through the inductance is 30 amperes, and the current through the resistance is 40 amperes. When these values are set down in a vector triangle as shown at A of Fig. 9-9, the right-angle function of the current in the inductance with respect to the current through the resistance gives an impedance (hypotenuse) current of 50 amperes. Thus, the resistive device is using 40 amperers of current, but 50 amperes circulate in the line and hence 10 amperes is flowing in excess of that utilized by the resistance. If the current through the inductance were 50 amperes and the current through the resistance were also 50 amperes as shown at B, the total current would be slightly more than 70 amperes, and in this case there are approximately 30 amperes of current which must circulate in the line in excess of that utilized by the resistance.

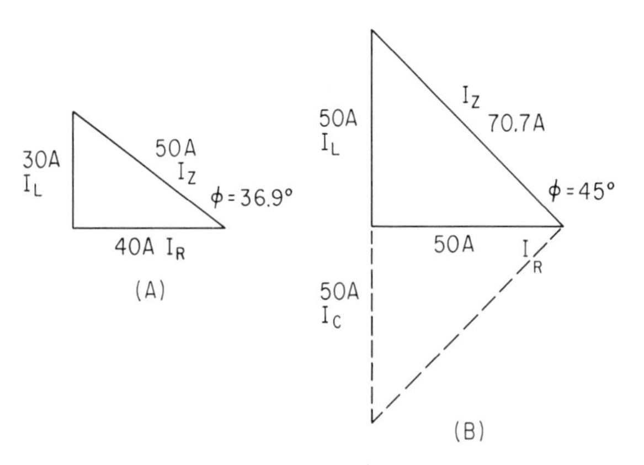

Fig. 9-9. Vector diagrams of current

For the condition shown at A, the angle is shown to be 36.9 degrees. Its cosine is 0.7998, which means that the apparent power is reduced by almost 0.2 to produce the true power. Similarly, for the condition shown at B, the angle is 45 degrees, and its cosine is 0.707. Thus, the true power would be only approximately 70 per cent of the maximum power indicated by the simple formula of E multiplied by I.

If the phase angle were 60 degres, the cosine would be 0.5, and the true power would thus be only one-half of the apparent power. With a phase angle of 60 degrees and a cosine of 0.5, there is a considerable difference between the apparent power and the true power, because as mentioned, one-half of the total power is involved and this can make a considerable difference in high-power devices:

$$P_{\text{apparent}} = 240 \text{ v} \times 50 \text{ amp} = 12{,}000 \text{ watts (12 kw)}$$

$$P_{\text{true}} = 240 \text{ v} \times 50 \text{ amp} \times 0.5 = 6000 \text{ watts (6 kw)}$$

As shown in the earlier drawing (Fig. 9-8), a capacitor can be employed for correcting the power factor. A pure capacity will cause a 90-degree phase difference between current and voltage, with current leading. Thus, an inductance which has an inductive reactance of a certain value can be nullified by a capacitance having a capacitive reactance equal to the inductive reactance. Thus, where one device causes a lagging current, the other will cause a leading current, and in combination the current and voltage will again be in phase. Power correction is important, since many motors have only a 40 per cent power factor and in consequence they draw more current and load down the line circuits more than normal. When an a-c line is thus loaded with inductive motors and other types of reactors, this combination could be such that the current drawn from the power main is almost at a maximum value. Now, the installation of additional motors would not be feasible, since line overload would occur. However, synchronous motors can be installed, which will furnish the additional mechanical power necessary without an increase in the total amount of current drawn. This is because the synchronous motor, with its d-c field excitation, acts as a capacitor because it produces a lead in current. This characteristic is so highly regarded in industry that often a synchronous motor is installed to correct power factor even though no load is connected to the synchronous motor—it runs just to furnish the leading-current characteristics of capacitance.

The function of current to a capacitor is exactly opposite to that of current to an inductance. The dotted-line area at B of Fig. 9-9 shows the vector diagram of the current through the capacitor. If the current through the capacitor is also 50 amperes as shown, it will be opposite in terms of the inductive current and will cancel out the angle established by the current through the inductance. Thus, only the resistive current remains, and the angle becomes zero with the cosine of the zero angle equal to one. When the numeral 1 is inserted in the power-factor formula given earlier, it does not alter the value of the apparent power, and the apparent power then becomes the true power.

The amount of electric power used in industry and the home is measured by a *watt-hour meter,* and the user must pay on the basis of the amount indicated on the watt-hour meter. When there is an inductive reactance in the line which causes an additional current to flow, this does not register on the meter, since the meter only indicates actual power utilized and not the amount of current drawn for such utilization. This is evident from the vector diagram at B of Fig. 9-9. If the resistor device is drawing 50 amperes, and the inductive device is drawing 50 amperes, the impedance formed by the inductive and resistive combination will draw a total of 70.7 amperes, and this means an excess of 30.7 amperes over that actually needed by the resistive (power-consuming) device. In consequence, a watt-hour meter would register the amount of wattage indicating the power consumed by the resistor device, but it would not indicate the fact that this a-c line must furnish over 70 amperes of current, whereas the same resistor device in a line without the inductance would require only 50 amperes. Thus, the power company is obliged to furnish a greater amount of current for the low-power-factor load without receiving additional compensation. The disadvantages of low power factor create problems for the consumer as well as for the power company. With installations where there is low power factor, the a-c power mains are more easily overloaded because of the extra current carried, which increases the frequency of circuit breakers opening or fuses blowing. The low power factor also increases voltage drops across the resistances and loads, and in consequence, generators and transformers are likely to work under overload conditions.

Because industrial users are more apt to have low-power-factor devices in their commercial installations, the power companies distinguish between home and industrial users when charging for power. Hence, instead of the watt-hour meter, volt-ampere-hour meters are installed; or if the watt-hour meters are employed, the actual power factor is determined and penalty rates are paid by the industrial consumer so that the power company does not suffer by supplying the additional current for low-power-factor devices. For correction of power factor other than by use of synchronous motors, large capacitors can be installed in the line to counteract the lagging current characteristics established by inductive loads.

Review Questions for Chapter 9

1. Briefly describe the principles of a basic motor.
2. What are the essential differences between the series-type motor and the shunt-type motor?
3. What are the basic characteristics of the differential-compound motor?
4. Explain briefly how a transformer reaction occurs in the basic a-c motor.
5. How does the wound-rotor motor differ from the shaded-pole induction motor?
6. What are the advantages of the synchronous motor in industrial electronics usages?
7. Why is power-factor correction essential in industrial electronics?
8. Explain briefly what is meant by *true power* and apparent power.
9. How does a synchronous motor correct for undesirable power factor effects?
10. In addition to the use of a synchronous motor, what other means can be employed to correct the power factor in industrial plants?

10

Servomechanisms and Circuits

INTRODUCTION

Certain combinations of electric, electronic, and/or mechanical devices, called *servomechanisms,* are encountered frequently in industrial electronics with respect to control. The term *servomechanism* does not refer to a circuit, machine, or other such unit, but instead refers to a system. The servomechanism can be basically electrical, but it may use as a sensing or detecting device some mechanical, thermal, hydraulic, or optical principle, or a combination thereof.

Essentially, what a servomechanism does is compare the operational characteristics of an installation with a desired or preset standard operational characteristic; when a deviation (error) occurs, it is detected and a signal is produced which is used for correction purposes. The servomechanism category includes a variety of commercial control devices, and comprises an important adjunct to the study of industrial electronics.

SERVO DEVICES

Servomechanisms have two basic classifications, *open-loop* and *closed-loop.* The distinguishing feature of the open-loop type is that manual control is employed to initiate a particular process. There are

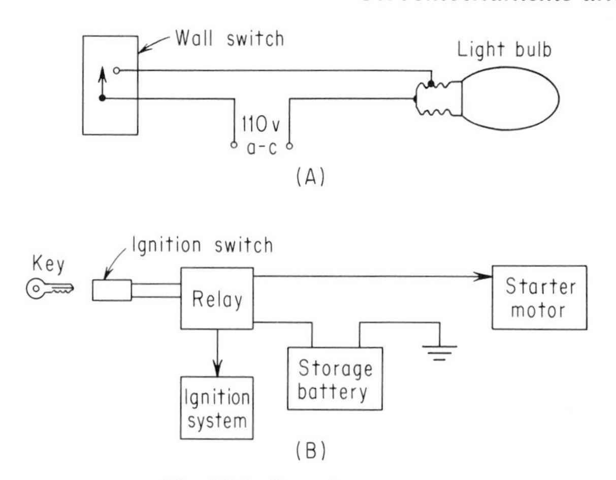

Fig. 10-1. Open-loop servos

a number of the open-loop servo devices, two of which are illustrated in Fig. 10-1. At A is shown the simple switch which turns on a light bulb. Here, when someone decides that a light should be lit he throws the switch which then closes the circuit and applies power to the light bulb. This is a basic open-loop servomechanism. If a photoelectric cell were employed to sense the failing of the natural light source and then initiate the turning on of the light bulb automatically, it would be a closed-loop servo device.

Another basic servo device is the automobile ignition system turned on by a key as shown at B. Here, again, manual operation is involved. When the ignition is turned on, relay contacts apply the power from a storage battery to the ignition system and also, in many cars, to the starter motor. The process is initiated by manual control, not by some detecting device which regulates the turning on and off of the system by a preset standard.

The closed-loop servomechanism system is sometimes known as a *closed-cycle* or a *closed-circuit* system. Closed-loop operation implies a complete closed circuit which initiates or terminates a process automatically when a certain preestablished set of conditions occurs. The circuits used in a central heating system, for instance, constitute a servomechanism because they initiate the heating-cycle process automatically under the direction of a thermostat. Some of the basic components are illustrated in Fig. 10-2. Here, the sensing and controlling device is the thermostat which is placed at some location in the home or factory where it will not be subject to artificial temperature changes such as would occur if an electric fan, radiator, or other device affecting temperature were in the vicinity. The thermostat is,

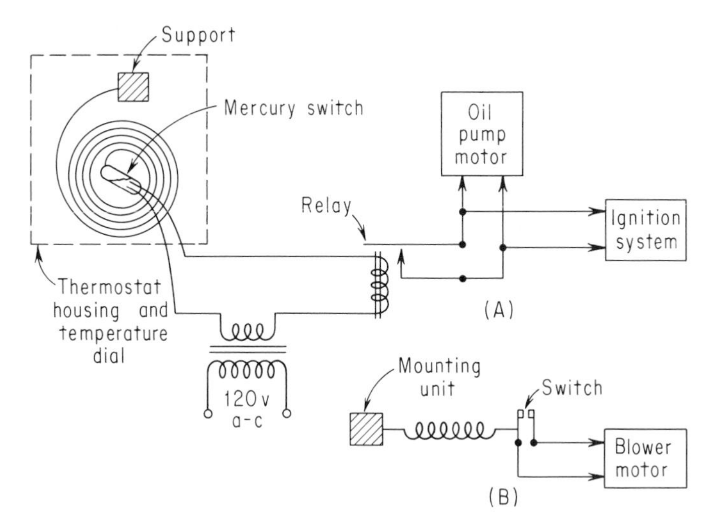

Fig. 10-2. A typical closed-loop system

of course, sensitive to temperature changes; it employs a spiral or helical bimetal strip composed of dissimilar metals. The dissimilar metals, such as brass and steel, are welded together to form a single strip. Because of the difference in the coefficient of expansion between the two metals, when the strip is subjected to temperature changes it bends. This transducer characteristic can be used to control the turning on or off of the heater.

In some thermostats a mercury switch is employed as shown in Fig. 10-2. As the spiral bimetal strip bends under the influence of a temperature decrease, it tilts the mercury switch and the mercury flows down the small vial, and since it is a liquid metal, it will close the switch contacts. When the temperature increases, the bimetal strip reverses its bending process, and the mercury flows to the other end of the housing, opening the switch. The standard or reference is set by a dial which indicates the temperature at which the mechanism is to operate. When the temperature in the building drops to a value which is sufficient to actuate the thermostat, the mercury switch is closed and a low voltage (approximately 24 volts a-c) is applied to a relay from the secondary of a transformer as shown. The relay is a *normally open* unit. When current flows through the solenoid the relay armature is pulled down and closes the circuit for the oil-pump motor and the ignition system. The ignition system of the heating device produces a spark across a gap, and the oil-pump motor forces the oil through the aperture of the nozzle which sprays the vaporized oil into the heat chamber where it is ignited by the spark.

Inside the heat chamber is another heat-sensing device. This is illustrated at B of Fig. 10-2, where a helical bimetal strip is employed. (See also Fig. 7-12.) As the heat builds up within the chamber, the helix expands until finally a switch is closed which applies a-c to the blower motor. The latter then forces the hot air through various ducts into the building. The application of power to the blower motor is delayed with respect to the application of power to the oil-pump motor and the ignition system, to make sure that the heat chamber comes up to temperature before the blower system forces the air through the building. If there were no delay, the air forced through the ducts initially would be cold.

In a complete home or industrial heating system other servomechanism devices are included for safety purposes. One temperature-sensing device, for instance, is utilized in the heat chamber to make sure the oil-pump motor is shut off if the ignition system fails to ignite the oil vapor. Thus, when the relay is closed which actuates the oil-pump motor and the ignition system, if the proper temperature is not reached within a certain time interval, a safety relay opens and shuts off the power to the heating system. On the other hand, if the heat from the heat chamber rises to an excessive value (owing to failure of the blower motor or for other reasons) another thermo-sensing device will shut off all power. The thermostat which senses the temperature in the building will, of course, also turn off the entire system as soon as the temperature has reached the proper level. Since there is still considerable heat in the heat chambers after the ignition system and the oil-pump motor have stopped, the blower motor continues to blow the hot air throughout the building until the heat chamber has dropped to a temperature sufficiently low to open the blower-motor switch.

Thus, the closed-loop system is employed in the thermostat section for turning on the oil-pump motor and the ignition system. Another closed loop is employed to sense the temperature increase and turn on the blower motor. Other closed-loop servos are utilized for safety purposes by sensing incorrect temperatures.

In department-store, factory, and other such larger installations, there is so much gas vapor employed in the large chambers that additional safety measures are usually taken. Reliance is not placed solely on bimetal temperature-sensing strips. Instead, the light which is released by the spark gap is sometimes focused by a lens system on a photoelectric cell so that the absence of the spark can result in shutdown of the system. Often, also, a gas flame is utilized as an auxiliary ignition for safety purposes in case of failure of the arc, since if the spark is delayed, the injection of a considerable amount of oil vapor into the heat chamber can be dangerous.

ERROR DETECTION AND CORRECTION

In the foregoing example, a thermostat was utilized to sense the deviation from a preset reference or standard; hence the thermostat can be considered as an error-detecting device. When the thermostat detects a deviation from the preset reference, the deviation is construed as an error. Thus, a decrease in the temperature in the building causes the thermostat to turn on the heating system and bring the temperature to normal or slightly above normal, within a preset range, which is considered to be the correct or the reference temperature range.

The thermostat is a thermal error-detecting device. Other error-detecting devices may be electrical, electronic, hydraulic, and so on. One method (electrical) for ascertaining deviations from normal is by use of a bridge circuit. When the bridge circuit is balanced, there is no error voltage produced. When the bridge is unbalanced, however, because of deviations from normal in the controlled device, an error voltage is present which can be utilized for error correction.

The basic resistive-bridge circuit is shown at A of Fig. 10-3. It is

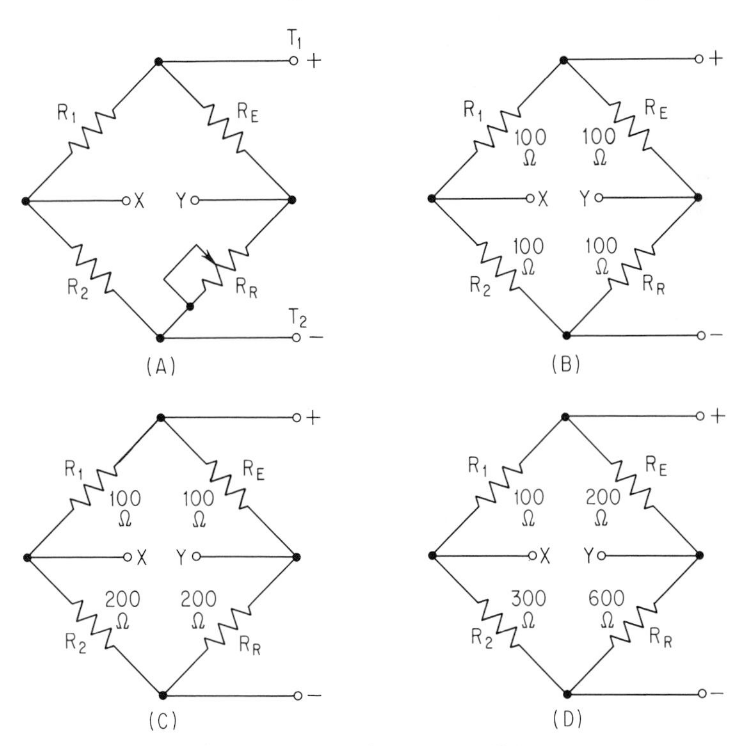

Fig. 10-3. Bridge balance conditions

sometimes known as the wheatstone bridge, after Charles Wheatstone (1802–1875), the English scientist and inventor. The basic bridge circuit consists of four resistors, marked R_1, R_2, R_E (for the error-detecting resistor), and R_R (for the reference resistor) shown in Fig. 10-3. Resistors R_1 and R_2 are in parallel with resistors R_E and R_R as shown. A voltage is impressed across terminals T_1 and T_2, either d-c or a-c, depending on the type of detecting circuits which are to be utilized at terminals X and Y. Resistors R_1 and R_2 are of a fixed value, while resistor R_R is adjusted to establish the reference resistance or the standard which will be utilized in conjunction with the error resistor for producing an error voltage across terminals X and Y. The three conditions of bridge balance are shown at B, C, and D of Fig. 10-3.

If all resistors are of equal value such as shown at B, no voltage will exist across terminals X and Y; X is neither more negative nor more positive than Y because there is as much of a voltage drop across R_1 as there is across R_E. Also, the voltage drop across R_2 equals that across R_R. At C, the bridge is again balanced, that is, no voltage occurs across terminals X and Y, even though resistors R_1 and R_2 are of different value, as are resistors R_E and R_R. The reason for the zero voltage across X and Y is that the voltage drop across R_1 is equal to that across R_E and again terminal X is neither more positive nor more negative than terminal Y. The same bridge-balance condition exists at D of Fig. 10-3. Again, unequal resistance values exist, but the ratio of the resistance of R_1 with respect to R_2 is equal to the ratio of the resistance of R_E with respect to R_R. Thus, if the voltage impressed across the bridge circuit is, for instance, 40 volts, 10 volts would develop across R_1 and 30 across R_2. Since the resistances R_E and R_R have the same ratio as R_1 and R_2, 10 volts will also develop across resistance R_E and 30 across resistance R_R. Thus, zero voltage again exists across terminals X and Y.

Resistance R_R is adjusted to have a value which is the reference with respect to resistance R_E. Thus, as long as resistance R_E is equal to that of R_R, the bridge is balanced and no voltage exists across terminals X and Y. Should the resistance R_E change, however, the bridge will be unbalanced and in consequence a voltage will develop across terminals X and Y. Such a voltage can then be employed to correct the error which resulted in the deviation of resistance R_E from its standard ohmic value.

The variation of resistance R_E can be accomplished in several ways. Resistance R_E will vary if it is subject to temperature changes, since the ohmic value of a wire-wound resistor will increase as it becomes hotter. R_E could also be a variable resistor, the variable arm of which is connected to a shaft so that a mechanical change (rotation) can be translated into an electric change for error-detecting purposes.

The voltage drop across resistance R_E could also be changed by photoelectric devices and by other means as more fully detailed subsequently. When the bridge is balanced, the ohmic value of R_E can be ascertained by the formula:

$$R_{\mathrm{E}} = R_{\mathrm{R}}\frac{R_1}{R_2}$$

When all resistors are of equal value during bridge balance, the formula, of course, has little value. For the condition shown at B, however, the formula would be convenient for ascertaining the value of the resistance R_{E}. In this instance, the value of 200 ohms for R_{E}, if the latter were unknown, would be solved for as follows:

$$R_{\mathrm{E}} = 600 \times \frac{100}{300} = 600 \times \frac{1}{3} = 200$$

Bridge circuits can also be designed using either inductances or capacitances as shown at A and B of Fig. 10-4. At A, an inductance bridge is shown, with the standard or reference inductance replacing the reference resistor. The error-detecting inductance, L_{E}, replaces the former R_E shown earlier. Since the inductances have a specific value of inductive reactance which depends on the frequency and the amount of inductance, there will be voltage drops across L_E and L_R which are proportional to the inductive reactance of the two coils. Again, three conditions of balance can be obtained, as shown earlier for the resistance bridge. Thus, when the values of L_E and L_R are equal to the resistive values of R_1 and R_2, the bridge is balanced and no voltage occurs across terminals X and Y. (Alternating current must be employed for the actuating voltage, because the inductive reactance of the coils is established only for a-c and not for d-c. If d-c were employed, the inductance value could not be found, since the bridge would measure only the d-c resistance of the individual coils.)

If the ratio of the resistances of R_1 and R_2 equals the ratio of inductive reactances of L_E and L_R, the bridge is again balanced. Thus,

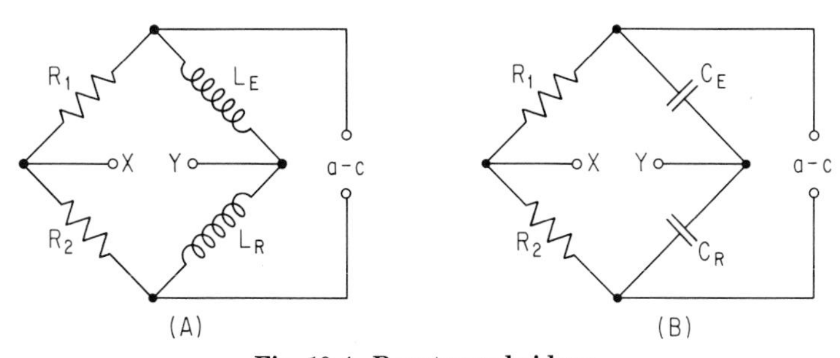

Fig. 10-4. Reactance bridges

resistance R_1 could have a value of 1000 ohms, and R_2 a value of 2000 ohms. A balance is achieved if the inductive reactance of L_E is 1000 ohms and of L_R is 2000 ohms. A balance would also be procured if the resistance R_1 were 1000 ohms and R_2 were 3000 ohms, with inductance L_E having a reactance value of 2000 ohms and L_R 6000 ohms. When the various components have different values of opposition, the inductive value of L_E can be found by use of the formula:

$$L_E = L_R \frac{R_1}{R_2}$$

A reactance bridge employing capacitors is shown at B of Fig. 10-4. Here, two capacitors replace the reference resistor and the error resistor, or the reference inductance and the error inductance. Voltage drops occur across the capacitors because of the capacitive reactance established when alternating current of a specific frequency is applied to the capacitors. Three conditions of balance again prevail, as for the resistive and inductive bridges discussed earlier. For the inductances, the inductive reactance increases as the number of turns of a coil is increased. That is to say, the inductive reactance is a function of the amount of inductance, increasing as the latter increases. For a capacitor, however, the inductive reactance *decreases* as the capacity increases. Hence, the formula for finding the capacity of the error capacitor C_E is different from the formulas previously used, since the ratio of R_1 and R_2 must be inverted to find a correct capacitance:

$$C_E = C_R \frac{R_2}{R_1}$$

To illustrate the foregoing, assume that resistor R_1 is 10 ohms and resistor R_2 is 20 ohms. If the inductance of L_R is 20 henrys, the inductance of L_E must be one-half this value, because only then would the inductive reactance of L_E be one-half the value of that for L_R and hence provide the same ratio as the resistances of R_1 and R_2. Thus, the formula indicates the value for L_E to be 10 henrys as follows:

$$L_E = 20 \times \frac{10}{20} = 20 \times \frac{1}{2} = 10 \text{ henrys}$$

For the capacitance bridge shown at B, again assume that resistance R_1 is 10 ohms and resistance R_2 is 20 ohms. Thus, there is a two-to-one ratio of resistance present, and for a balanced bridge, the ratio of the capacitive reactances of C_E and C_R must coincide. Thus, if C_R has a value of 20 microfarads, the capacitor C_E would have to have a capacitive value twice that of C_R in order for its capacitive reactance to be one-half that of C_R, because it requires more capacity to get a decrease in capacitive reactance. Thus, the 40 microfarads for C_E is

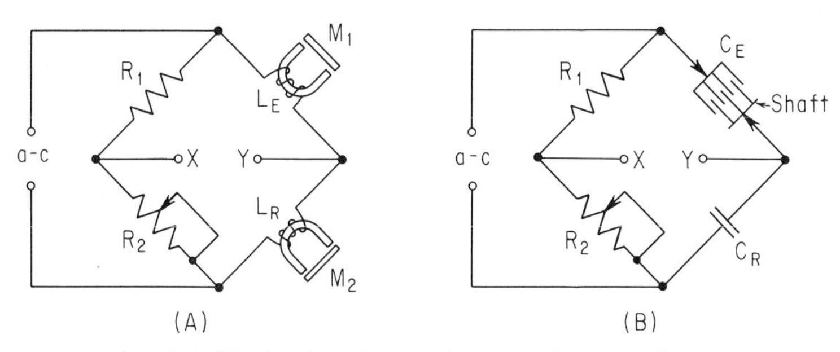

Fig. 10-5. Mechanical factors in error-detecting bridges

indicated by use of a formula, where the R_1 and R_2 symbols are inverted as follows:

$$C_E = 20 \times \frac{20}{10} = 20 \times 2 = 40 \text{ microfarads}$$

As with the resistive bridges, various mechanical or electrical devices can be utilized with respect to the error-detecting sections of the bridge. At A of Fig. 10-5, for instance, the coil is shown wound around a horseshoe-type core, with a bar of metal near each inductance core. For L_E, the metal bar is indicated as M_1 while for L_R, the metal bar is indicated as M_2. When a metal bar is brought within the field of the core, it will alter the inductance, because it alters the air gap between the core and the bar pole piece. Thus, bar M_2 is set at a fixed distance from the core of L_R, to establish a fixed value of inductance. Bar M_1 could be a portion of some device such as a shaft or other mechanical device. When a mechanical change occurs which would bring bar M_1 closer to or farther away from the core of L_E, the inductance value of the latter would change and an error voltage would then be present across terminals X and Y. The moveable-plunger core-type transducer described and illustrated previously can also be used. Whatever means are employed for altering the inductance of L_E, however, a change in the latter will establish a correction voltage across terminals X and Y. For the circuit shown at A, resistance R_2 is also indicated as a variable device. This variable feature with respect to R_2 is often adopted so that the ratio of R_1 to R_2 can be changed to conform to the ratio which exists with respect to L_E and L_R, so that the bridge can be balanced when no error is indicated by a given inductance for L_E.

For the capacitance bridge, capacitor C_E can be made variable, with the stator of the variable capacitor connected to the upper side of the bridge, and the rotor connected to a shaft. Thus, a rotation of the shaft will move the rotor plates within or else out of the stator plates. An increase or a decrease in the mesh of the stator and rotor plates will result in establishing an error voltage across terminals X

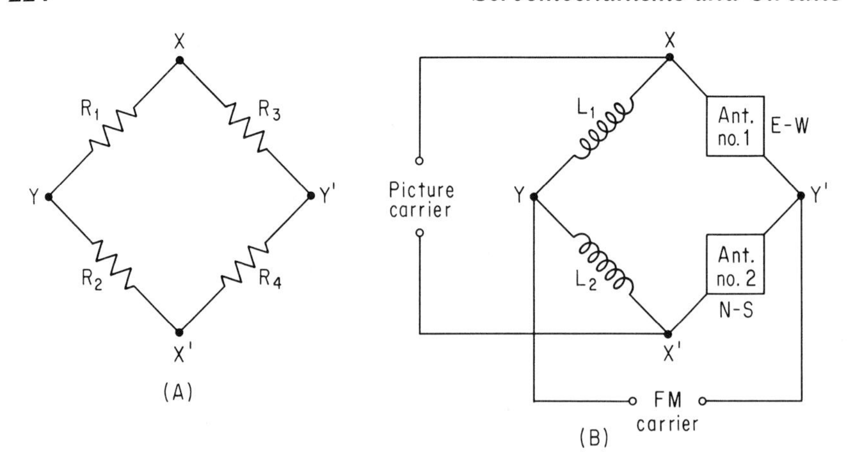

Fig. 10-6. The bridge circuit in diplexer application

and *Y*. A large fixed plate could be used for the stator of C_E, with another plate adjacent to it as a movable section for establishing the error indication.

The bridge circuit actually can have two zero-potential terminals, in its balanced condition. This is illustrated at A of Fig. 10-6, where it is assumed that each resistor is of equal value. Now, if the voltage is impressed across the *X* terminals, there will be zero voltage across the *Y* terminals. If another voltage is impressed across the *Y* terminals from an external source, there will be no voltage across the *X* terminals for the voltage applied at the *Y* terminals. This factor is utilized in some industrial applications, particularly in what is known as the *diplexer* device used in broadcasting practices. In television transmission, for instance, the picture-signal r-f carrier must be transmitted simultaneously with the sound carrier. If both are fed to the same antenna, however, the output circuits of the picture-signal Class C amplifier will load down the output circuits of the FM audio-signal Class C output amplifier, and vice versa. To eliminate interaction between the final stages of the picture and sound transmitters, while still using the same antenna, a bridge network is utilized, such a bridge circuit being known as a diplexer.

At B of Fig. 10-6, a typical bridge-circuit diplexer such as utilized for the transmission of television is shown. A bridge is formed by fixed inductances L_1 and L_2, in conjunction with one antenna which transmits signals in an east-west direction, and another antenna which transmits signals in a north-south direction. The FM audio carrier signal from the transmitter is applied across the *Y* terminals as shown. The r-f energy circulates throughout all inductances and antennas, and thus the energy will be sent out by both antenna no. 1 and antenna no. 2. Across terminals X, however, there is no potential difference for the FM carrier signal. The picture carrier signal is impressed across the X terminals, and also circulates through both inductances and antennas, and in consequence is radiated by the antennas and transmitted. For the television carrier, however, no potential difference appears across the Y terminals. Thus, each transmitter sends its energy to the antenna systems, yet there is no voltage from one transmitter induced into the other transmitter. Consequently, excellent electrical isolation is achieved by the diplexer bridge system and the necessity for using separate antennas has been eliminated.

The basic bridge circuit is also utilized in tests and measurements, and many commercial meters employ the bridge circuit. As indicated by the formulas given previously, the value of an unknown capacitor, inductance, or resistor can be ascertained by placing it in a bridge circuit and creating a balanced bridge, then utilizing the formula. A galvonometer or some other voltage-indicating device is employed across the terminals X and Y shown in the earlier illustrations. For the inductive and capacitive bridges, however, the meter must be an a-c type.

FREQUENCY COMPARATORS

Error-detecting devices can be constructed of vacuum tubes, crystal diodes, and other similar signal-handling units in addition to the thermal-sensing devices or photoelectric devices. Basically, error detection consists of sensing the difference in a motion, temperature, or electrical signal as compared to a standard. Some device must then be utilized to generate an error voltage which may in turn be used to correct the deviation from normal.

A vacuum-tube device for comparing a frequency deviation with respect to an electric signal is the diode frequency comparator shown in Fig. 10-7. This circuit could also be constructed using crystal diodes. The basic circuit shown in Fig. 10-7 is also known as a *phase discriminator* or *FM discriminator detector* and is used both in transmitting and in FM receiving circuitry, in addition to error detection in industrial electronics. In transmission it is utilized to stabilize certain signals, while in the reception it is a common detector circuit for frequency-modulated signals.

As shown, the signal which is to be controlled is applied to the inductance L_1, and by transformer action the signal voltage is induced across the secondary of the transformer, consisting of inductances L_2 and L_3. Here, capacitor C_1 in conjunction with the secondary inductance is made resonant for the frequency of the signal input. The ref-

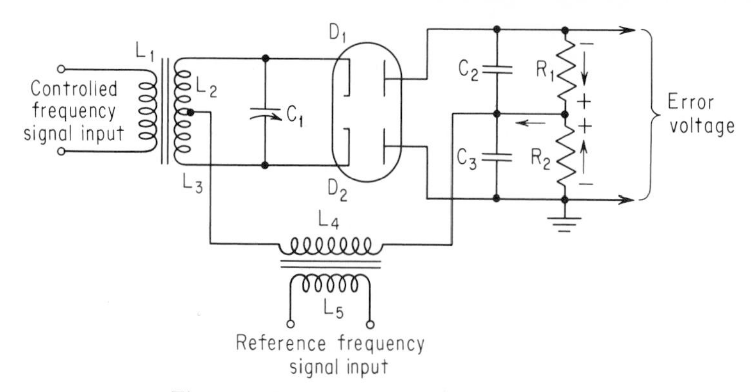

Fig. 10-7. Frequency comparator circuit

erence or standard signal is applied to the primary L_5, and induced across the secondary L_4 which center-taps inductances L_2 and L_3 as shown. The output circuit of the two diodes consists of capacitors C_2 and C_3, which bypass resistors R_1 and R_2 respectively. Conduction for diode D_1 is in the direction shown by the arrow beside resistor R_1 and establishes a voltage which is negative toward the plate and positive toward the junction of resistors R_1 and R_2. Diode D_2 also conducts as shown by the arrow designation beside resistor R_2, again establishing a negative polarity toward the plate. When the amount of current which is flowing through each tube is equal, the voltage drop across resistor R_1 will be equal to the voltage drop across resistor R_2. Consequently, the total voltage or error voltage across the output terminals is *zero*.

For an understanding of how the circuit functions, an analysis must be made of the phase relationships between the various voltages which are established in the circuit. For this purpose, a vector diagram of the voltages as shown at A of Fig. 10-8 is useful. Here, the secondary current is shown by the vertical arrow pointing downward, as is the induced voltage. The secondary current, I_S, is indicated as being in phase with the induced voltage (E_{ind}). The in-phase condi-

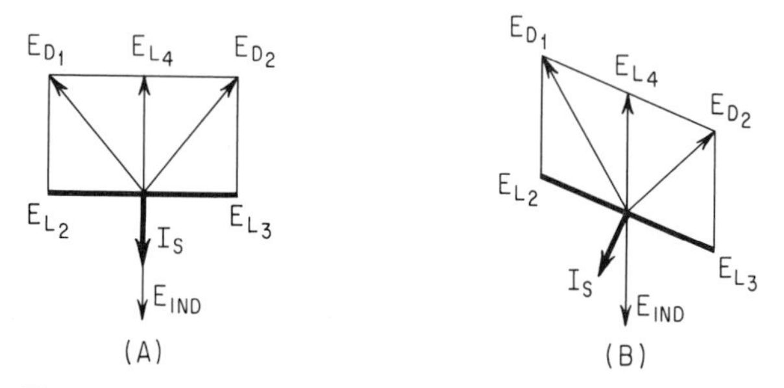

Fig. 10-8. Vector diagrams of voltages for comparators

tion results because of resonance, and at resonance the inductive reactance is nullified by the capacitive reactance, leaving only resistance. The signal voltage which develops across inductance L_4 is 180 degrees out of phase with the induced voltage, and hence the voltage across L_4 (E_{L4}) is shown as a vertical arrow pointing upward.

An inspection of the circuit for the frequency comparator will indicate that each diode receives two signals, the control-frequency signal and the reference-frequency signal. The total voltage of the signal for either diode, however, is not the simple addition of the two voltages, but instead is the vector sum of the two voltages, because of the phase difference. As shown in the vector diagram at A of Fig. 10-8, the signal voltage which develops across inductance L_2 is 90 degrees out of phase with the induced voltage. This comes about because the voltage which develops across inductance L_2 will be displaced with respect to the secondary current by 90 degrees, because there is a 90-degree phase difference between voltage and current in an inductance. The voltage across L_3 is 90 degrees out of phase with the secondary current, but 180 degrees out of phase with the signal which develops across L_2. Hence, the voltage for L_2 (E_{L_2}) is shown in the vector diagram in the opposite direction from the voltage across L_3 (E_{L_3}). Because the voltage impressed across diode D_1 is the sum of the voltages across L_4 and L_2, this voltage will be as shown at *A*, consisting of the vector sum of the voltage across the two inductances. Similarly, the voltage across diode D_2 consists of the vector sum of the voltages across L_3 and L_4, and again the voltage for diode D_2 is shown by the arrow from corner to corner of the parallelogram at A of Fig. 10-8.

This is, then, the vector drawing of the various voltages which exist when both frequencies are identical for the signals applied at the two inputs. Because each diode conducts equally (each receiving the same amount of signal voltage) the voltage drops across resistors R_1 and R_2 are equal and opposite, hence no error voltage exists. Capacitors C_2 and C_3 filter out the signal-frequency ripple component which results from rectification of the signal by diodes D_1 and D_2. (These diodes only pass one alternation of each cycle of the signal applied.) Hence, the voltage appearing across the output resistors consists of pulsating d-c. Capacitors C_2 and C_3, however, filter the ripple frequency and produce a fairly acceptable d-c. Capacitors C_2 and C_3 can also be considered as typical "bypass" capacitors which have a low reactance for the signal frequency and hence shunt it to ground and prevent the appearance of the ripple frequency across the output resistors.

When the frequency of the signal applied to inductance L_1 deviates from the reference frequency, phase relationships of the voltages in the circuit change, and one diode will then conduct more than the other. The consequence is the production of an error voltage across the output terminals. When the signal frequency changes, the circuit composed of inductances L_2 and L_3 and capacitor C_1 no longer is resonant for the new frequency. Hence the secondary current will either lag the induced voltage or lead it, depending on whether the circuit becomes inductive or capacitive. If the current lags the induced voltage as shown at B of Fig. 10-8, the vector diagram is altered as shown. The lagging secondary current also shifts the horizontal vector arm designated by E_{L2} and E_{L3}. This horizontal arm tilts by the number of degrees by which the secondary current lags the induced voltage. The reason is that the individual voltage across inductance L_2 will still be 90 degrees out of phase with the current through the coil, because inductance L_2, analyzed by itself, still presents a 90-degree phase difference between voltage and current. An identical situation exists with respect to the inductance L_3. Here, there is again a 90-degree phase difference between voltage and current; this must be shown in the vector diagram.

Because of the tilt which occurs for the voltage vector arm, the arrow which indicates the voltage for diode D_1 is now longer and indicates an increase of voltage across diode D_1. The arrow indicating the voltage for D_2 is now shorter, indicating a decrease in the voltage present for diode D_2. Because diode D_1 conducts more current, there will be a greater voltage drop across resistor R_1 than across R_2. The voltage across the latter resistor is reduced below normal because of the decreased conduction through diode D_2. If, for instance, prior to the change in the frequency of the control signal, the voltage across each resistor had been 5 volts, the new voltages may be 8 volts across R_1 and 2 volts across R_2. Since the 2 volts across R_2 opposes a similar voltage across R_1, the error voltage which is developed is 6 volts. If the frequency deviates from normal to a greater extent, diode D_1 will conduct proportionally more and diode D_2 will conduct proportionally less, developing an even greater error voltage. The error voltage can then be applied to the proper corrector circuits, and the frequency of the control signal brought back to normal. When the latter occurs, diodes D_1 and D_2 again conduct equal amounts of current, and the voltages across R_1 and R_2 become 5 each. With 5 volts across R_1 opposed by 5 volts across R_2, the error voltage again becomes zero.

If the frequency deviates from normal in the other direction, the secondary current will lead the induced voltage instead of lagging it. The result is that diode D_2 conducts more than diode D_1, and the voltage drop across R_2 becomes greater than that across R_1. An error voltage is again developed across the output terminals, except that the polarity of this error voltage will be opposite to that developed for the earlier deviation.

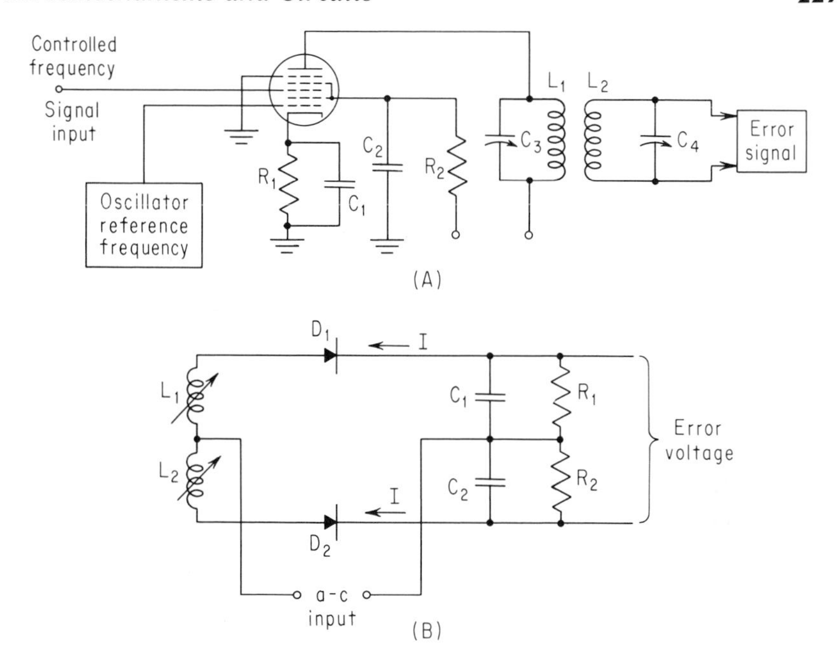

Fig. 10-9. Heterodyning comparator and null indicator with transducer

Diodes D_1 and D_2 in Fig. 10-7 can be crystal diodes as mentioned earlier, without altering the manner in which the circuit functions. The error voltage which is developed can be applied to a reactance tube of the type described elsewhere herein. The reactance tube can then be controlled with respect to the value of its specific reactance and it, in turn, can alter the frequency of an oscillator and provide correction.

In the frequency-comparator discriminator type of circuit just discussed, a comparison was made between two signals of the same frequency. The circuit can be utilized to compare two signals having different frequencies, except that a constant voltage will appear across the output terminals which then must be considered as the reference error voltage. For instance, if the voltage which is created because of the difference in frequencies of the two signals is 6 volts, then a deviation above or below such a voltage would indicate a change in the frequency of the signal applied to inductance L_1.

A circuit often used for comparison of signals having different frequencies is the heterodyning comparator shown in Fig. 10-9A, also known as a *mixer* circuit. It is extensively employed in superheterodyne receivers for heterodyning together a carrier frequency from the station and the frequency of a local oscillator, to produce an intermediate frequency (i-f). Both the carrier signal from the station and the oscillator signal are tuned by resonant circuits to maintain the same difference in frequency, in order that a high degree of selectivity may be maintained in the i-f stages. The circuit can be utilized for comparing two frequencies for industrial electronic purposes, so that an error voltage can be obtained for a deviation from normal. In such an application, the circuit shown in Fig. 10-9A is utilized. A five-grid (pentagrid) tube is employed, and the control-frequency signal as well as the reference signal developed by the local oscillator are injected to the grids as shown. The grid of the control-frequency signal input is surrounded by the screen grid which is bypassed for signal ground by use of capacitor C_2. The result is that the signal inputs are electrostatically shielded from each other to minimize interaction.

The circuit functions somewhat as a Class C amplifier, hence has severe nonlinear characteristics. The nonlinearity means that when two signals are applied to the circuit, they are not only amplified in the usual manner, but they combine to produce other signals. Such a process is known as *heterodyning* and the resultant signals which are produced are sometimes known as *beat-frequency* signals.

In the heterodyning process, not only are the original signals produced at the output of the tube, but also *sum* and *difference* frequencies. Thus, for instance, if the controlled-frequency signal input is 100 kilocycles, and the oscillator reference frequency is 150 kilocycles, these signals will appear in the anode load circuit, as well as the sum-frequency signal of 250 kilocycles, and the difference-frequency signal of 50 kilocycles. The difference-frequency signal (the intermediate frequency) is usually chosen, and inductance L_1 and capacitor C_3 form a resonant circuit for this intermediate-frequency signal. This signal is transferred by transformer action to the secondary L_2, which also forms a resonant circuit in conjunction with capacitor C_4. Successive resonant circuits might also be employed for additional rejection of all signals other than the desired signal (the intermediate-frequency signal). Thus, the resonant circuits reject the original frequencies as well as the sum-frequency signals. As long as the intermediate-frequency signal is 50 kilocycles (in the present example) no error exists, since the controlled-frequency signal is maintaining the proper difference frequency with respect to the reference oscillator frequency. When the controlled-frequency signal deviates, however, the intermediate-frequency signal will also change; such a change represents an error signal. Thus, if the controlled-frequency signal changes to a higher signal such as 125 kilocycles, the intermediate frequency resulting from the heterodyning process will no longer be 50 kilocycles, but instead will be 25 kilocycles, the result of mixing the 125-kilocycle signal with the 150-kilocycle signal of the oscillator, the difference now being 25 kilocycles.

Variable-L Null Indicator

When two transducers are employed, an error voltage can be produced with a comparater circuit similar to the discriminator previously discussed. Although any electronic transducer can be used for the input, assume for the purposes of this discussion that the differential-transformer type of transducer is employed, where a moveable plunger type of core is present as discussed in Chapters 4 and 7. The basic circuit, plus the differential reactors L_1 and L_2, are shown in Fig. 10-9 at B.

For balancing the circuit to produce zero output, both variable cores are midway within the coils so that each produces the same amount of inductive reactance as the other. As with the previous circuit (Fig. 10-7), diodes D_1 and D_2 conduct for positive alternations of a-c, and current flow is in the direction shown by the arrows. (The diodes could be reversed for current flow in the opposite direction, as was the case for Fig. 10-7, but performance is not altered.) The output from the circuit is zero voltage, indicating a balance. (These circuits are sometimes referred to as *null indicators,* or bridge circuits, because of the zero output when a balance prevails.)

The plunger for the differential reactor L_1 can be used to sense curvatures or thickness variations in a continuously moving sheet-metal fabrication process, or both could be used (one above and one below) for curvature-variation measurements. Either one could also be used for edge control of continuously moving belts of materials, as more fully discussed later. Assume, however, that only L_1 is the transducer sensing device. If the material over which the plunger slides causes the latter to move into the coil, inductance (and inductive reactance) increases. The result is less current flow through D_1, and the voltage across R_1 declines, producing a voltage differential across the output in a fashion similar to that described for the discriminator circuit. Similarly, if the plunger moves outward, coil reactance declines, and D_1 conducts more than D_2, again producing a voltage differential, this time in the opposite direction. Thus, a correction voltage is produced to compensate for the variation sensed in either direction.

In cases where both differential reactors are employed simultaneously, such as above and below a moving sheet of metal or fabric, both reactances vary. Assume, for instance, that the function of the control device is to indicate variations in the curvature of the material. As the material bends upward, the core plunger for L_1 (assuming this reactor is above the material) moves into the core and the plunger for L_2 moves out of the core at the same time. Thus, the reactance for L_1 increases, but the reactance of L_2 decreases. Again, voltage differences are produced at the output of the circuit, such voltages having a polarity dependent on whether the sensing devices indicate an upward bend or a downward bend.

PHOTOSENSITIVE COMPARATORS

Photosensitive devices can be used to sense change in light intensity between two light sources, for producing an error voltage or control voltage. At A of Fig. 10-10, two photosensitive devices are shown feeding two resistors as in the discriminator principle discussed earlier. Photosensitive device no. 1 is attached to resistor no. 1 in such a way that current will flow through the resistor as shown, making the top of the resistor negative and the bottom positive. The second photosensitive device is wired to resistor R_2 as shown, so that the resultant voltage has a polarity which is negative at the bottom and positive at the top. Thus, if the light sensitivity of each device is adjusted so that both are equal, and both light sources have equal intensity, the current flow through each resistor will be the same in value. In consequence, the two voltages are opposite in polarity and hence no error voltage is produced across the output terminals.

When a change occurs for one of the light sources, an error voltage is produced. If the light rays striking photosensitive device no. 1 become less intense, current flow through resistor R_1 will decrease and hence there will not be complete cancellation of the voltages at the output terminals. If, for instance, the voltage across resistor R_1 is 3 volts and that across R_2 is 10 volts, a 7-volt error signal will be present across the output terminals.

The ground connection shown at the center is for reference purposes only; it indicates the relative connections of the two photosensitive devices. The ground can be removed from the center tap and

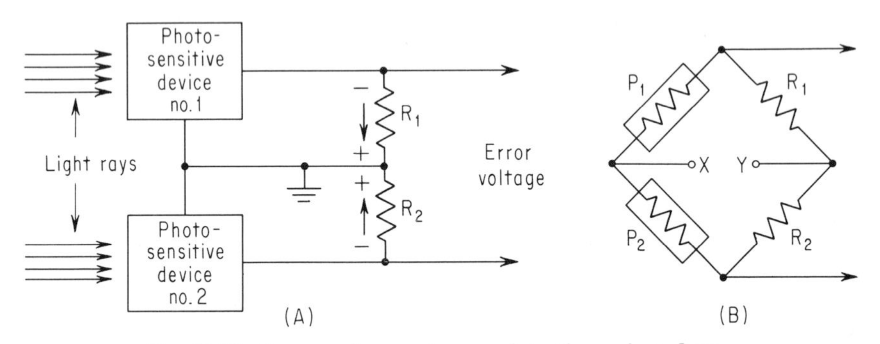

Fig. 10-10. Comparators and error detection using photosensitive devices

placed at the bottom of resistor R_2, so that the error voltage will be present with respect to common ground.

The photosensitive devices are useful in a number of ways, since light rays can be directed through two fluids, and hence a check maintained on the characteristics of one liquid which is to be controlled in viscosity, density, or some other property with respect to that of a standard. The light rays striking the first photosensitive device, for instance, could be directed through a Lucite or Plexiglass tube through which liquid is flowing. The light rays striking photosensitive device no. 2 could be directed through a container which holds a liquid of standard characteristics.

The photosensitive devices can also be used with a bridge circuit as mentioned earlier. Each photosensitive device acts as one resistive leg of the bridge as shown at B. The error-sensing device, meter, or other instrument is connected at terminals X and Y. As discussed earlier, an error voltage is ascertained when the bridge is unbalanced by either less light or more light striking one of the photosensitive devices. In a bridge circuit, a null or zero reading can be obtained even though the ratios of resistances or voltage drops differ.

REACTANCE CIRCUIT

A reactance circuit is one which exhibits the characteristics of an inductance or of a capacitance, depending on design. Since it has such characteristics, it also has a specific reactive *value* established by the circuitry involved. A voltage impressed on the grid of the tube will vary the value of the reactance produced, and hence will also alter the inductive or capacitive characteristic, whichever is present. Because of this circuit behavior, the reactance-tube device lends itself to error-voltage applications, since an error voltage applied to the reactance circuit controls the amount of reactance represented by the circuit, and hence the reactive value can be utilized to modify a subsequent circuit for corrective purposes.

In Fig. 10-11 a typical reactance circuit is shown, with application to the correction of an oscillator's frequency. Here, the error voltage is applied across the input terminals and hence appears at the grid of the tube used. Capacitors C_2 and C_4 have a large value so that the resulting low reactance will provide a path for the signals to be transferred, while blocking the d-c of the plate supply from the grid circuit and also from the ground through the resonant circuit of the oscillator. The plate circuit, as shown, is coupled directly across an oscillator's resonant circuit so that it may control the frequency of the oscillator by varying the reactance of the oscillator's resonant circuit. The

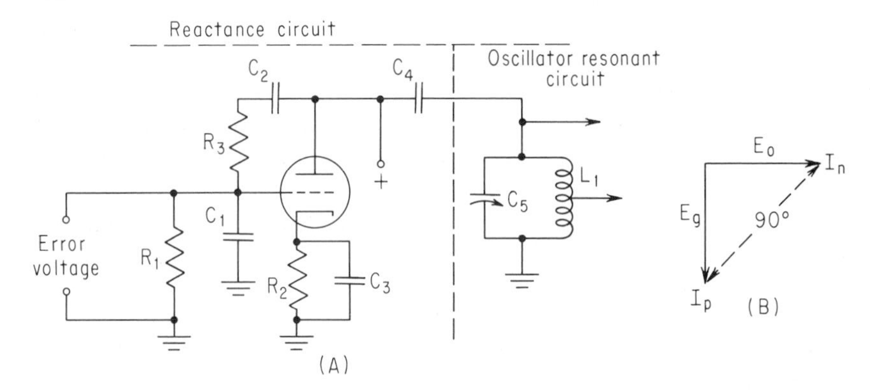

Fig. 10-11. Reactance control circuit

particular reactance is established by the components R_3 and C_1. Here, the value of the resistor R_3 is made approximately ten times the value of the capacitive reactance of C_1. The oscillator, while generating its signal, also impresses such a signal across the resistance-capacitance network composed of R_3 and C_1.

To understand how a reactance is established, consider the vector diagram of the voltages involved as shown at B of Fig. 10-11. Because the oscillator voltage is impressed across a resistive-capacitive network, the oscillator voltage is in phase with the current established in the network. Thus, the oscillator voltage (E_o) is shown as a horizontal line at B, with the network's current (I_n) indicated as an extension of the horizontal line, to show an in-phase condition. Since the resistor is approximately ten times the value of the capacitive reactance, there is very little phase shift in this resistive-capacitive network. Across capacitor C_1, however, there is a voltage lag since there is a 90-degree difference between voltage and current in a capacitor. The signal for the grid is obtained from across the capacitor. Because of the lag in voltage across the capacitor, however, the oscillator signal across the network is delayed by 90 degrees when applied to the grid, as shown by the vertical line marked E_g at B of Fig. 10-11. Hence, the 90-degree phase difference between the voltage applied to the grid and the current in the network is shown at B, and because plate current is in phase with voltage, the plate-current (I_p) line is shown as an extension of the grid-voltage vertical line. Thus, it is evident that the plate current lags the network current (oscillator current) by 90 degrees. A lagging current (or a leading voltage) indicates an *inductive* circuit. Thus the reactance acts as an inductance—and thus as an inductive reactance—across the oscillator resonant circuit. On adjusting the oscillator resonant circuit composed of C_5 and L_1, the inductance presented by the reactance circuit will be a factor in establishing resonance. The amount of inductance which is created is related to the formula:

$$L = \frac{10}{6.28\,(f)\,(gm)}$$

From the foregoing formula, it is evident that the inductance depends on the frequency (f) of the oscillator signal which is employed, as well as on the transconductance (gm) of the tube. Since the transconductance is a factor, a change in plate voltage or plate current will alter the value of the inductance, as well as the inductive reactance. The inductive reactance can thus be altered by changing plate current, the latter being varied by a change of grid voltage:

$$X_L = \frac{E_p}{I_p}$$

Thus, if a signal is applied to the grid and such a signal changes plate current, the value of the reactance (and hence the inductance) will change.

If an inductance is substituted for the capacitor C_1, the circuit will act as a *capacitance*. It would seem, at first glance, that the substitution of an inductance would create an inductive circuit, but this is not so. The determining factor for establishing whether the circuit acts as an inductance or as a capacitance is the lead or lag of the plate current which results with respect to the oscillator signal current.

COMMERCIAL SERVOS

A number of electronic manufacturers market servo kits or servo packages to provide uniformity and a matching of component parts. Such unified assemblies can then be adapted by industrial users for process control, metering, and other applications. Many closed-loop servos, however, are integral devices of the unit as a whole, one example being the temperature-control and safety-protection units associated with oil heater installations.

A typical servo kit is that shown in Fig. 10-12. This is the Atcotran Servo-Kit furnished by the Automatic Temperature Control Co., Inc. The unit shown at the upper left is the servo device itself, which has a mechanism for driving the pen of a strip-chart recorder for graphing on a running strip of paper variations which occur in a particular process. The units shown at the bottom left comprise the transducer mounting bracket and the transducer itself for sensing variations. At the lower right is shown the terminal block and connecting cable, while at the upper right the servo amplifier is shown. A close-up of the servo mechanism is shown in Fig. 10-13, which more clearly indi-

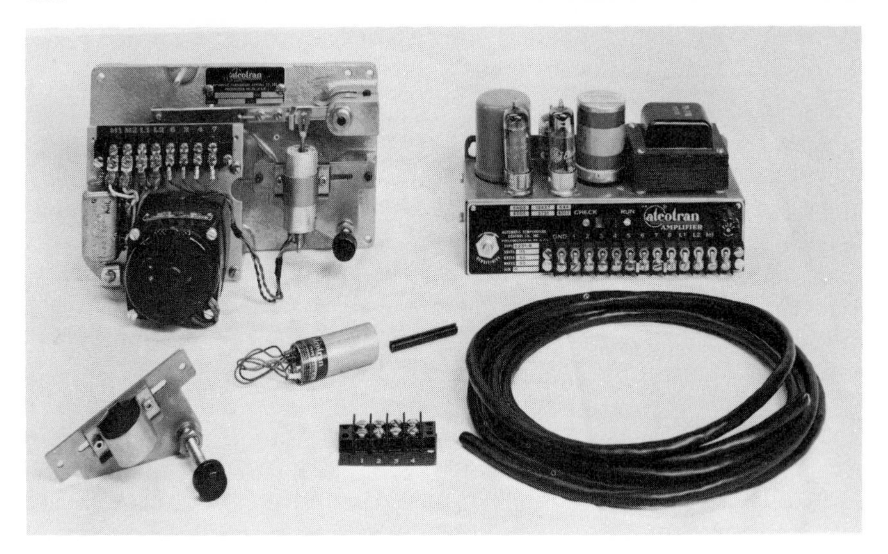

Fig. 10-12. Atcotran Servo-Kit (Courtesy Automatic Temperature Control Co., Inc.)

cates the terminals, the variable inductor with its core mounted on a swivel arm, and the adjusting knob immediately beside it. The servo will also pulse accumulative counters in addition to graphing (see Chapter 12) to record the number of units tested.

The package type of servomechanism eliminates the need for pur-

Fig. 10-13. Servo mechanism (Courtesy Automatic Temperature Control Co.)

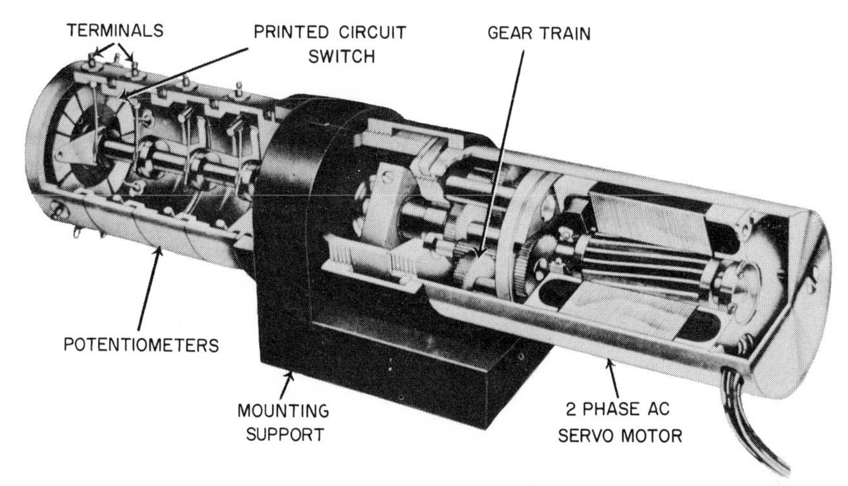

Fig. 10-14. Spectrol position servo

chasing and assembling the units individually, and again, as with the kit-type servos, uniformity and a matching of parts can be closely maintained. The Spectrol Electronics Corporation furnishes servo packages designed from system specifications; a typical unit is that shown in Fig. 10-14. This comprises a position servo device, shown schematically in Fig. 10-15. A potentiometer serves as the transducer for converting a physical change (such as a shaft rotation) to an electric signal. This potentiometer (marked *command potentiometer*) has an excitation voltage applied to it, as well as to the feedback potentiometer shown at the right of the schematic. The moveable arm of the command potentiometer is applied to the error-signal circuit (such as previously described) and marked *difference senser* in the drawing. The error voltage is amplified and applied to the motor and gear train.

The two potentiometers act as a resistive "selsyn" system, similar

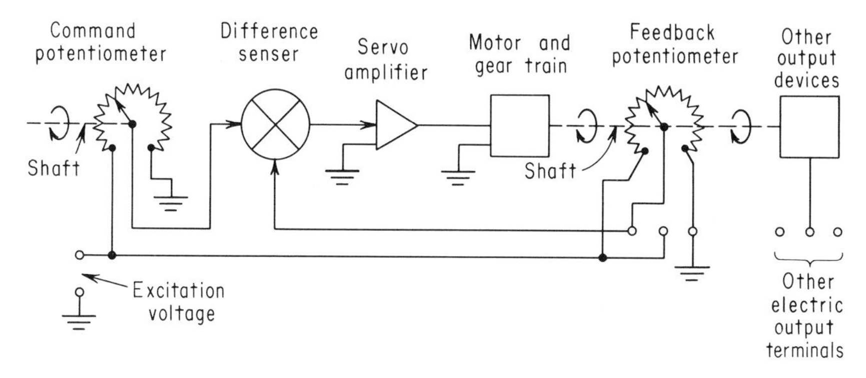

Fig. 10-15. Position servo circuit

in basic function to the motor types discussed later in this chapter. If both potentiometer arms are at the same relative position, the voltage picked up by each is the same, and the difference-senser circuit will have zero output. When the command-potentiometer arm moves, it will pick up a different voltage than the feedback potentiometer. This error voltage, when applied to the motor, rotates the shaft which corrects the error, and at the same time rotates the feedback potentiometer until the voltage from the latter coincides with that of the command potentiometer. At that time no voltage output is present at the difference senser and motor rotation stops. As shown, the motor shaft can also be utilized to turn other devices to produce other output signals.

SELSYN SYSTEMS

A basic selsyn system has already been described using two potentiometers, one as the sensing potentiometer, the other as the correcting potentiometer. Although the two were shown in an integrated package form, the potentiometers could be separated a considerable distance and correction would still take place. This process defines the word "selsyn." It is basically a device which senses a physical change and translates it by electric means to an identical physical change at some remote point.

Selsyns are formed not only from potentiometers, but also from units which resemble small motors. As with the resistive types, two or more may be used in error-detecting and control applications. As a contrast, in vacuum-tube circuits the variations in signal frequency or intensity can be utilized for error correction or for control purposes, whereas with selsyn devices, shaft rotations are generally employed.

The basic selsyn system in block diagram form is shown in Fig. 10-16. Here, a shaft (no. 1) is connected to a selsyn motor which is nearby. Selsyn no. 1 is connected to another selsyn unit at some remote place, with three interconnecting wires as shown. The remote selsyn is connected to shaft no. 2. Now, when shaft no. 1 rotates a specific number of degrees, shaft no. 2 will also rotate the same number of degrees in synchronization with the first shaft. It is from this "self-synchronous" principle that the name "selsyn" is derived. The rotation of shaft no. 1 can thus be utilized to rotate another shaft at

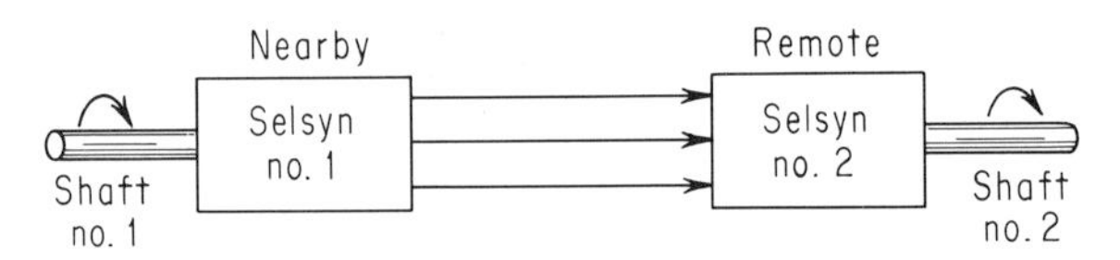

Fig. 10-16. Selsyn system of control

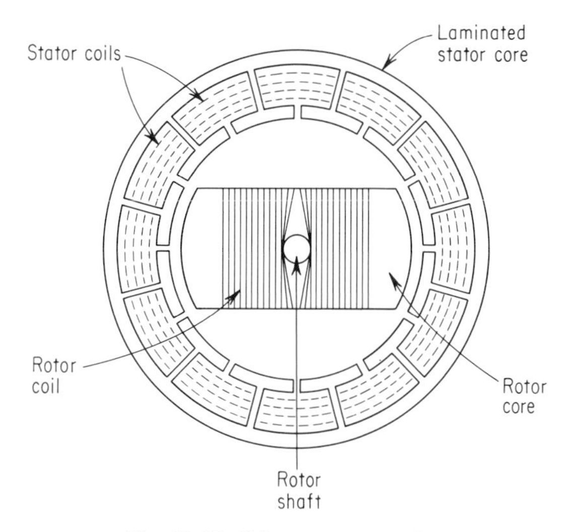

Fig. 10-17. Selsyn cross-section

a remote place, or the rotation of shaft no. 1 could be indicative of an error and the rotation of shaft no. 2 by the same degree can be employed for corrective purposes.

Even though the two selsyn devices shown in Fig. 10-16 are identical, the nearby selsyn which initiates the voltages which actuate selsyn no. 2 is known as the *master unit* or the *generator.* The second selsyn at a remote distance is known as the *motor* or the *slave unit.* Generator or master unit therefore refers to the sensing selsyn, while the motor or slave unit refers to the control selsyn.

The cross section of a selsyn motor is shown in Fig. 10-17. A series of coils which are fixed and not rotating are located around the center moveable coil. The collection of stationary coils is called the stator, while the coils in the rotor section comprise the rotor of the selsyn. The coils in the stator are wound inside the slots of the laminated iron core material as shown. The stator coils consist of three separate groups so arranged that they are spaced 120 degrees apart. There is an overlapping with respect to the field of the coil, so that a uniform motion is generated for the rotor as more fully detailed subsequently. The three coils have a common connection, and three wires emanating from the stator section. The three wires from the stator section, plus the 120-degree spacing of the inductances, would tend to indicate a three-phase device. Actually, however, only a single-phase voltage-current signal is employed. The three sets of stator coils are necessary for the selsyn function, as will be evident subsequently in this discussion.

The single rotor coil is also wound on a core material, which is

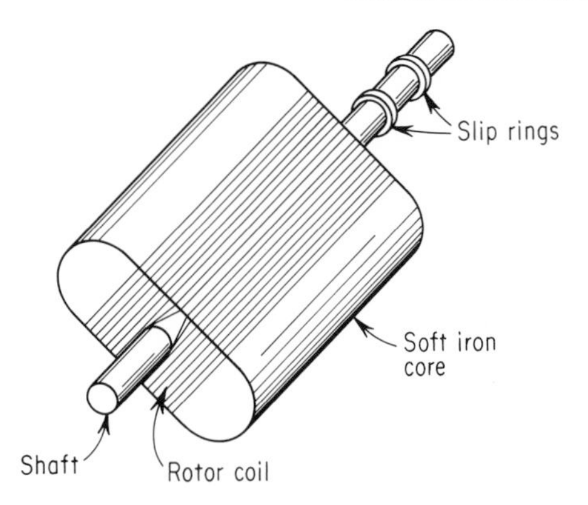

Fig. 10-18. Selsyn rotor

curved at each edge as shown in Fig. 10-18, so that it can be brought as close as possible to the magnetic lines of force of the stator coils during rotation.

The electrical hookups of the selsyn generator and the selsyn motor are shown in Fig. 10-19. In the generator section, the inductance marked L_7 is the selsyn rotor. The stator coils for this selsyn are indicated as L_1, L_2, and L_3. For purposes of explanation they are shown in the angular placement, to indicate the influence of the magnetic fields which are generated. The second selsyn, the motor, has for its rotor inductance L_8. The stator coils consist of inductances L_4, L_5, and L_6.

For purposes of discussion, assume that a-c of 110 volts is employed. This is applied to both the rotor coils as shown in Fig. 10-19. When current circulates through the rotor coil (L_7, for instance) the latter acts as the primary of a transformer and induces a voltage in each stator winding. When the rotor, L_7, is in the "zero" position as shown in Fig. 10-19, it will induce approximately 50 volts in L_1, and approximately 25 volts across L_2 and also 25 volts across L_3. (For purposes of analysis, we will assume instantaneous values and polarities, as though only one alternation of the a-c signal were present.)

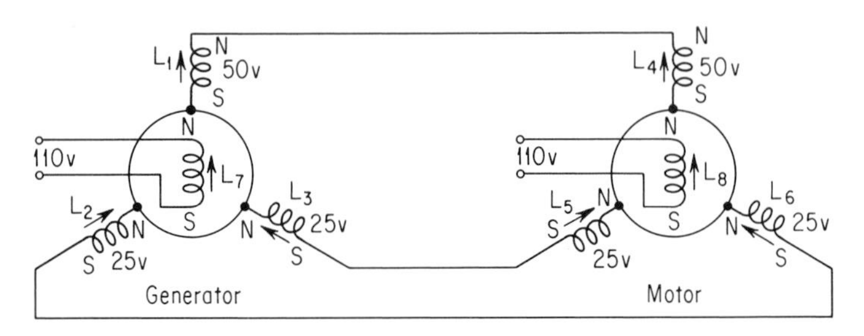

Fig. 10-19. Generator selsyn and motor at zero

The interconnection between two selsyns is as shown in Fig. 10-19, though as will be described later, the leads can be reversed for altering the indication on the calibrated dials of the selsyns. When both generator and motor are in the zero position, the voltages induced across the stator coils will be as shown, and hence the relative positions of the south and north magnetic poles of each coil are also as indicated.

It is also assumed, as indicated in the block diagram of Fig. 10-16, that a shaft is connected to the rotor (L_7) of the generator, and that a shaft is connected to the rotor of the motor (L_8). With the interconnections as shown, the voltages developed across the individual coils of the generator selsyn are similar to those of the motor selsyn. Because of the relative polarity of the voltages, they are in opposition to each other and hence prevent current flow between them. Coil L_1, for instance, has a voltage drop across it which opposes the voltage drop across L_4. Similarly, the voltage drop across inductance L_3 opposes that of inductance L_5, and so on. Because no current flows in any of the stator coils, no magnetic field is built up around any one of the stator coils and hence there is no magnetic interaction between the stator coils and the rotor coils. Thus, both rotors will retain their zero position indication because of the symmetrical voltage drops which occur. The same symmetrical condition of circuitry would also prevail if both rotors were at the 5-degree rotation, 25-degree rotation, or any other degree of rotation so long as both were identical. An unbalance occurs only when the two rotors are at different positions with respect to degree of rotation, as discussed next.

In Fig. 10-20, the rotor of the generator selsyn is shown at the 30-degree angle instead of the zero position. When the rotor shaft of the generator selsyn causes the inductance L_7 to turn to this angle, the balance of voltages between the generator and motor is disturbed as shown. Now, approximately 43 volts is induced across L_1, and 43 volts across L_3 because of the angular position of inductance L_7 with respect to L_1 and L_3. No voltage is induced across inductance L_2. On the motor side, however, the zero position of the rotor L_8 causes the

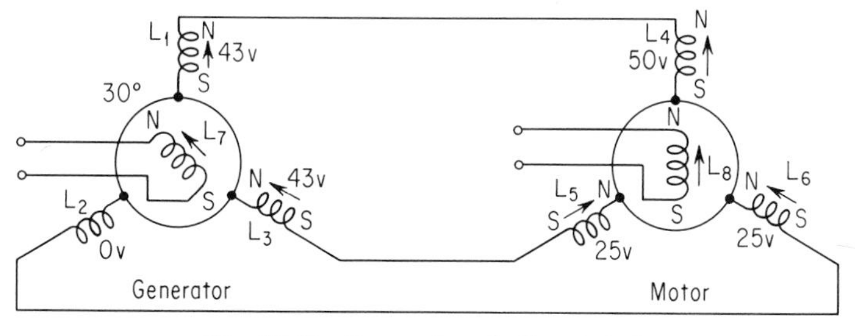

Fig. 10-20. Generator shaft, rotated

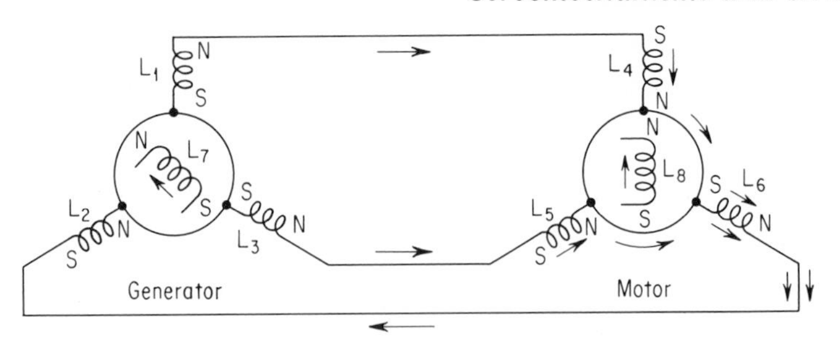

Fig. 10-21. Magnetic fields acting on motor rotor

voltages to exist as shown, recalling the previous illustration where both generator and motor were in the zero position. As a result of the unbalance, the magnetic fields in the motor are now such that the rotor will turn and align itself up with the rotor of the generator. When both generator and motor rotors are aligned, equal and balanced voltages will again prevail as was the case for the zero position. Actually, the voltage unbalance between generator and motor would also tend to cause the rotor of the generator to turn additionally. In standard applications, however, the shaft of the generator is turned only by the device which develops the error and is not free to turn under the influence of the fields existing in inductances L_1, L_2, and L_3.

The relative magnetic fields which are established by the voltage unbalance are shown by the next illustration, Fig. 10-21. Since the voltage across L_4 is greater than that across L_1, the direction of current flow is determined by the voltage drop across L_4 and becomes as shown in Fig. 10-21, with the south pole at the top and the north pole toward the rotor. Similarly, the larger voltage drop across L_3 with respect to that across L_5 causes the former to determine the direction of flow, which is as shown in Fig. 10-21, with the south pole away from the rotor and the north pole toward it. Inductance L_6 had 25 volts across it as compared to the zero voltage for L_2, hence L_6 is the polarity determining inductance; the direction of flow is as shown in Fig. 10-21, with the south pole established near the rotor. Note that the current through L_4 and L_5 flows through the common circular connection and combines through inductance L_6. Thus, the magnetic lines of force across inductance L_6 are greater than those across L_4 and L_5. The south pole of L_6 repels the south pole of the rotor and attracts the north pole. The south pole, if positioned between the north poles of L_4 and L_5, will be repelled with equal force. Thus, the inductance L_8 assumes the 30-degree angle to conform to the angle of rotation which had occurred in inductance L_7. Once the rotor L_8 is also at 30 degrees in conformity with L_7, the balance of voltages shown earlier in Fig. 10-19 will again prevail, even though both rotors are not at zero position. The relative direction of rotation of the motor can be determined by interchanging the connections between L_2, L_3, and L_5, L_6. Also, the connections to the rotor of L_8 can be reversed.

The generator selsyn can actuate more than one motor if desired. Because the selsyn motors in themselves do not develop much power, any translation of the rotation of the motor into the turning of a shaft requiring considerable torque would require the use of a special amplifier to step up the power. (Such amplifiers are discussed more fully later.)

THE AMPLIDYNE

Selsyn motors do not develop sufficient torque to be used as work motors. Thus, when the master selsyn moves, and the slave selsyn also rotates to the same angle change, it is necessary to convert this movement into an amplified torque, by amplifying the change which occurred in the slave motor selsyn, to furnish the necessary change of power to some industrial d-c motor or other application. On other occasions the power applied to machinery or to welding devices must be amplified for precise control purposes. For such purposes, besides vacuum-tube and magnetic amplifiers, *amplidyne* amplifiers are often employed.

The amplidyne amplifier is basically a d-c generator hooked up in such a manner that it has high amplification characteristics. The word "amplidyne" stems from the words "amplifier" and "dynamo." Basically, the d-c generator is an amplifier because it only requires a small amount of power in the field coils for control of hundreds of times as much power in the output of the generator. The additional power is, of course, procured from the mechanical power which is applied to cause the armature to rotate. This mechanical power applied to the armature can be compared to the battery or power-supply voltage which must be furnished to the anodes of vacuum-tube amplifiers, so that signal-power amplification can be procured. In a generator 4 amperes of current may be circulating in the control field, but the output current furnished to the load may be as high as 100 amperes. The high output power is developed by the turning of the armature which is under the control of a motor. The motor, of course, is the actual power source as mentioned, just as the B supply is the actual power source in a vacuum-tube amplifier. If the field current is now reduced by a few amperes, the output current from the armature may change from 100 amperes to 50 amperes. Thus, for a few amperes change in the field current, there is a 50-ampere change in the output current.

In the amplidyne, however, the special circuit used causes a much greater amplification to occur than in an ordinary d-c generator. Like

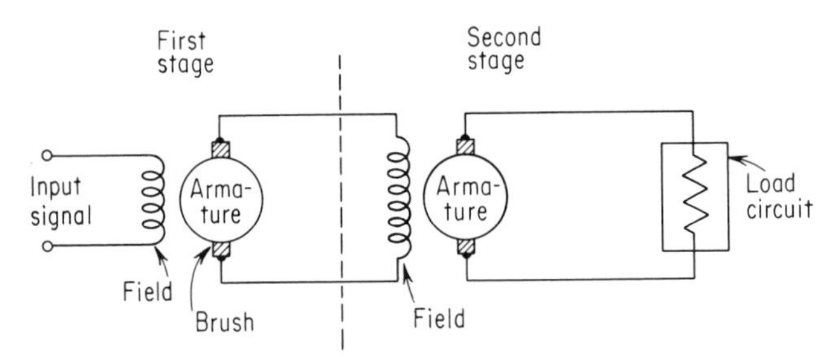

Fig. 10-22. Two d-c generators acting as a cascade amplifier system

an ordinary vacuum-tube amplifier, the d-c generator can be hooked up in cascade, the output from one applied to the second generator as shown in Fig. 10-22. This becomes a two-stage cascade generator system. The input signal, perhaps only a few amperes, is applied to the field of the first generator. The armature of this first-stage generator must, of course, be turned by a motor to furnish the necessary power for conversion. The high current flowing in the output circuit of the armature is applied to the field of the second-stage generator. This generator is now a larger type, since the field current will be much higher than in the first generator. In turn, the field current for the second generator is amplified an additional amount and then applied to the load circuit as shown. The amplidyne functions in a fashion similar to the two-stage d-c generator system, except that two-stage amplification is accomplished by use of only one armature. The manner in which this is done is shown in Fig. 10-23. Here, the two brushes which are normally used with the generator are short-circuited as shown; consequently a large amount of current will flow in this winding. If the output current before short-circuiting was 100 amperes, with a field current of 4 amperes, 100 amperes can be procured in the short-circuited section of the armature with an input of only about 0.2 ampere.

The high current flow in the short-circuited armature establishes a very strong cross-field (known as armature reaction). This strong field is cut by the revolving armature coils and in consequence a voltage is set up which is at right angles to this field. The voltage produced by the coil of the armature cutting the field is at right angles to that voltage which is created by the magnetic lines of force set up by the excitation. Thus, two additional brushes are placed on the armature, at right angles to the brushes which are short-circuited, as shown in Fig. 10-23. These new brushes are shown in the horizontal plane; it is these brushes which are attached to the load circuit. Thus, in the illustration where it is assumed that 100 amperes of current

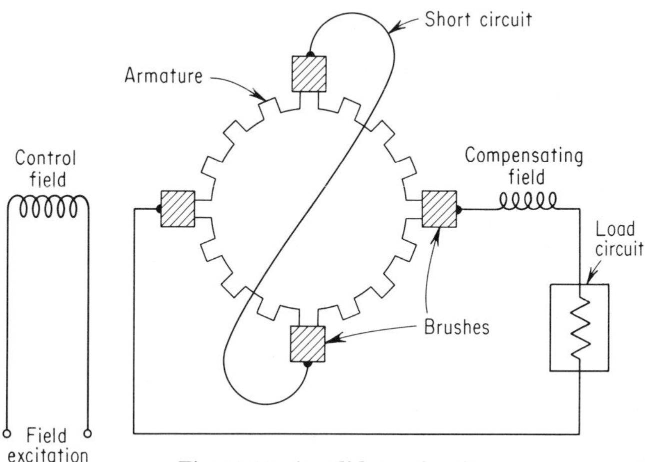

Fig. 10-23. Amplidyne circuit

flows in the short-circuited section, such a current is not permitted to circulate to the load circuit.

The power gain of the amplidyne is quite high, and in practical applications may be of the order of 25,000 or 50,000 to 1 as compared to the gain of an ordinary d-c generator which may be from approximately 25 to 100. Thus, the input power to the field coil may be approximately 0.5 to 1 watt, and it will cause an output power variation ranging from 200 to 25,000 watts or more. As with magnetic amplifiers, the speed of response is not as fast as that accomplished by the vacuum-tube and transistor amplifiers. The speed by which the output power is changed as the input power is altered depends on the time constants which are established in the relationship of field and armature coils to the inductance. In most instances, the time lag of 0.1 second is normal.

There is a 90-degree difference between the magnetic field caused by the armature reaction and the magnetic field which produces the reaction. The reaction field of the load armature is 180 degrees out of phase with respect to the control field, and this phase difference tends to cause cancellation. Unless compensated for, the result would be to reduce considerably the application of the amplidyne, because of the degeneration factor. This degeneration factor can be compared to that which can be established in a vacuum tube by using either current or voltage feedback. To minimize the cancellation factor a compensating winding is employed as shown in Fig. 10-23. The compensating windings are usually wound on the individual poles, and have a sufficient number of turns that the fields which are built up in the compensating winding have the right amplitude for cancelling the reaction flux established in the load armature.

As mentioned earlier, the time constant is a factor with respect to response speed, hence the design of the amplidyne circuit is such that the time constant is considerably lower than that which would be found in the standard d-c generator. The smaller time-constant value makes the amplidyne particularly suitable for furnishing the d-c excitation for high-output a-c or d-c generators which must be controlled with respect to the output procured from them. Because the amount of voltage applied from the exciter to the field of a generator regulates the amount of output which is procured, the amplidyne can be employed for improving the regulation of the large a-c or d-c generators. Since the amplidyne requires only low power for excitation, the problem of stabilization of the voltage to the amplidyne is lessened, hence the latter can be employed for voltage regulation of the large-sized unit.

Besides using the amplidyne as the exciter for generators, its output power can also be applied directly to a motor. Thus, the amplidyne drives the motor directly, and hence the latter is under control with respect to the amount of torque developed. In turn, the excitation to the field of the amplidyne may be controlled by vacuum tubes. This lends itself to a variety of applications, since the vacuum tubes themselves require only low voltage signal at the grids to produce voltage or power amplification. Thus, very small signal voltages can be employed for controlling the amplidyne power output, and the latter, in turn, can be used to supply the power for large motors. In consequence, the system can develop a high order of mechanical torque with considerable power under the direct control of the very feeble signals which are utilized at the grids of vacuum tubes.

Review Questions for Chapter 10

1. Briefly explain what is meant by a servomechanism.
2. Explain the essential differences between the open-loop and the closed-loop servo device.
3. Briefly explain the basic circuits used for temperature control.
4. Briefly explain how a bridge circuit can be employed as an error-detecting device.
5. Briefly explain on what principles the inductive- and capacitive-type bridges function.
6. Show how a bridge circuit can be used for isolation of two different types of signal.
7. How can a bridge circuit be utilized in test and measurement procedures? Illustrate your explanation with a schematic of the device.

8. What are the applications for the phase-discriminator type of frequency comparator?
9. In the discriminator circuit, what output voltage—if any—is present when the frequency and phase of both input signals are alike?
10. How is an error signal developed in the discriminator circuit when one of the input signals has a change in its frequency?
11. What circuit other than the discriminator can be employed for comparing signals having frequencies which differ from each other?
12. Briefly explain how a photosensitive device can be used as a signal comparator. Use simple illustrations.
13. How is a photosensitive device useful for checking the characteristics of liquids?
14. Reproduce the schematic of a reactance circuit and summarize its function.
15. Briefly explain the purpose for a selsyn system.
16. What essential differences—if any—are there between the motor and generator of a two-unit selsyn system?
17. What are the practical applications of an amplidyne?

11

Magnetic and Dielectric Amplifiers

INTRODUCTION

Magnetic amplifiers are extensively used in industrial electronic applications. These amplifiers are in a category all their own with respect to the amplification process. A magnetic amplifier will use a low power to control large amounts of power. Thus, *changes* in a low-power source will create amplified versions of such changes in a high-powered source. This is different from the servomechanism principle. In the latter, a small electric power change or a mechanical change will control the turning on or off of a high-powered device. A servomechanism does not amplify a *change* of power. The magnetic amplifier also differs from the conventional audio or radio-frequency signal amplifiers used in other branches of electronics because magnetic amplifiers are made up basically of a saturable-reactance type of transformer (see Chapter 4, Fig. 4-12) to accomplish the amplification process. Instead of a control grid, a control winding is employed which regulates the degree of saturation within the core of the transformer. By permitting the high power which is to be amplified to flow through another winding on the same core, changes in the power from the high-power source can be produced by the control winding. Thus, if the power applied to the control winding changes from 2 watts to 4 watts, the high-power source can be altered from 5000 watts to 10,000 watts, producing an amplified power change. Hence, the magnetic amplifier is extensively used in industrial electronics for speed control of a-c and d-c motors, voltage and current regulation, temperature control, commercial safety control and servomechanism regulation.

The advantages of the magnetic amplifier over the vacuum-tube types are low cost despite high power-handling capability, indefinite life and ruggedness, plus the advantage of instantaneous usage since no warm-up time is required. The disadvantages are slower response rates and the higher distortion levels encountered in some applications. As the frequency of the power supply is raised above the normal 60-cps rate, better performance is secured because the speed of response increases for a given gain. Often power-supply frequencies ranging as high as 2000 cps are employed.

The magnetic amplifier will operate within wide temperature ranges (approximately -50 to $+100$ degrees centigrade). Abnormally low or excessively high temperatures will alter the characteristics of the core material and hence influence performance.

BASIC MAGNETIC AMPLIFIER

A basic form of the magnetic amplifier is shown in Fig. 11-1. A three-legged core is employed, using laminated sheets for reduction of eddy currents. The core material is of a type producing a rectangular hysteresis loop such as an iron-silicon alloy or a nickel-iron alloy. The iron-silicon alloys have characteristics which result in a high saturation flux density (B) plus low coercive force (H). The trade names for the iron-silicon alloys are Hipersil, Silectron, Supersil, Trancor, and Corosil. These usually contain approximately 97 per cent iron and 3 per cent silicon, with a permeability of 60. The nickel-iron alloys also have a high flux density plus a low coercive force with a very sharp saturation characteristic and hence are particularly adaptable to magnetic amplifier usage. Trade names include Deltamax, Coppernik, Hipernik, Orthonol, and Permenorom. These alloys have approximately 50 per cent nickel and 50 per cent iron, with a permeability ranging between 68 to 125.

The magnetic amplifier core materials are primarily soft alloys having different characteristics than the hard alloys used for the production of permanent magnets. The latter have high retentivity and greater coercive force than the magnetic amplifier core materials.

For the basic magnetic amplifier shown in Fig. 11-1, a *control winding* is wound on the center leg of a core as shown. The power changes to be amplified are applied across the terminals leading to this control winding. In the illustration, a variable resistor R_c is used for

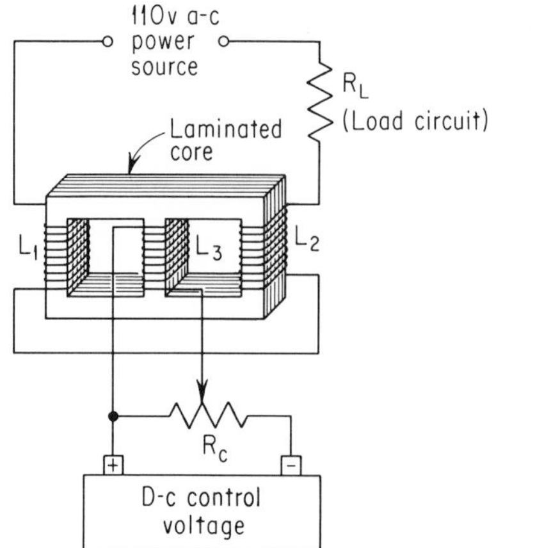

Fig. 11-1. Basic magnetic amplifier

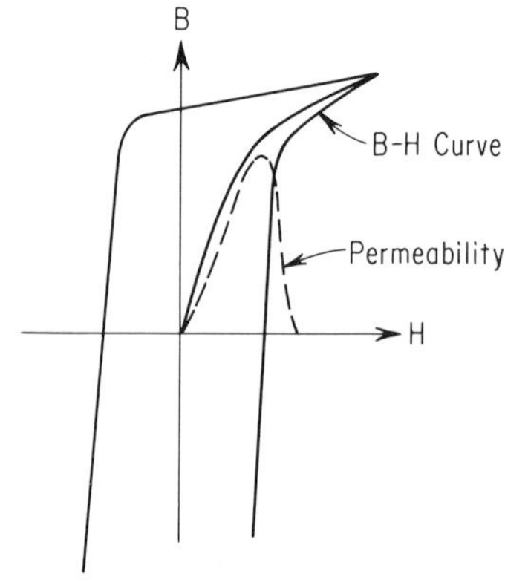

Fig. 11-2. Permeability versus magnetizing force

varying the d-c control potential. The high-power source may be the power mains wherein thousands of watts of power are available. Each line of the power-main source is fed through a coil as shown, one coil (L_1) mounted on the left leg of a core and the other coil (L_2) wound on the right leg of the core. The arrangement of the windings L_1 and L_2 is such that the flux cancels at the center leg of the core and hence there is no induced voltage set up in the control winding by the load windings L_1 and L_2. Also, the relative polarity of the control voltage will not affect the load voltage because the flux of the control winding opposes the flux of one of the load windings while aiding the other at any given instant. The amount of control-winding current, however, will determine the amount of magnetizing force and hence the flux density of the core.

The permeability of core material is not a fixed value, but depends on the degree of flux density. This is shown in Fig. 11-2 where the permeability versus the magnetizing force is graphed for a portion of the *B-H* curve. As shown, the permeability increases from a low value of magnetizing force and reaches a peak at an intermediate level of the magnetizing force (before saturation is reached). For a higher value of the magnetizing force, however, the permeability reduces again and reaches zero at the saturation portion of the *B-H* curve. Since permeability affects the number of flux linkages (see Chapter 4), the inductance of a coil decreases as the permeability is decreased. Hence, the coil inductance will drop to a low value as the core saturates. This is indicated by the formula for the inductance of a coil:

$$L = \frac{N\phi}{I \times 10^8} \text{ henry}$$

where L = inductance in henrys,
N = number of turns of coil linked by flux,
ϕ = number of flux linkages,
I = current in amperes producing the magnetic flux.

As shown by the equation given above, the inductance is proportional to the number of conductors linked by the magnetic flux multiplied by the total number of flux linkages. Hence, because a change of permeability changes flux linkage there is also a change of coil inductance.

Because the control winding can alter the degree of saturation of the core, it will also alter the inductance of the series coils of the power source, L_1 and L_2. The reactance of these coils is dependent on the inductance: $X_L = 6.28fL$. Since the number of turns of the coils as well as the frequency remains fixed, the only change which could occur in reactance would be a change in the coil characteristics established by the core material. Since the core of the a-c supply coils is also common with the core of the control winding, the reactance of L_1 and L_2 can be either increased or decreased by changing the current through the control winding.

A change of inductance (and inductive reactance) will change the power applied to the load circuit because the power factor of the alternating current is affected by an inductance in the circuit. A pure inductance does not consume electric power because there is a 90-degree phase difference between voltage and current. At the peak of the voltage amplitude, the current would be zero; and vice versa. With some resistance in a circuit in series with an inductance, however, the phase angle between voltage and current would be less than 90 degrees depending on the relationship between the inductance and resistance. Thus, the actual power delivered to the load resistance will depend on the amount of inductive reactance which is present in relation to the load-resistance value. The formula for the power calculation in an a-c circuit takes into consideration the phase difference which is established by basing the formula on the cosine of the angle of phase difference existing in the circuit (as was explained in Chapter 9):

$$P = EI \cos \phi$$

If there were no inductance in the circuit, there would be no phase difference between voltage and current, and with no phase angle the cosine is 1. Hence, if the voltage is 100 and the current is 50 amperes, the amount of power equals

$$P = 100 \times 50 \times 1 = 5000 \text{ watts}$$

If, however, only an inductance were in the circuit, the phase angle would be 90 degrees; and the cosine for the latter angle is zero. Thus, there is zero power delivered to the load, since the product of the voltage times the current equals zero when multiplied by zero.

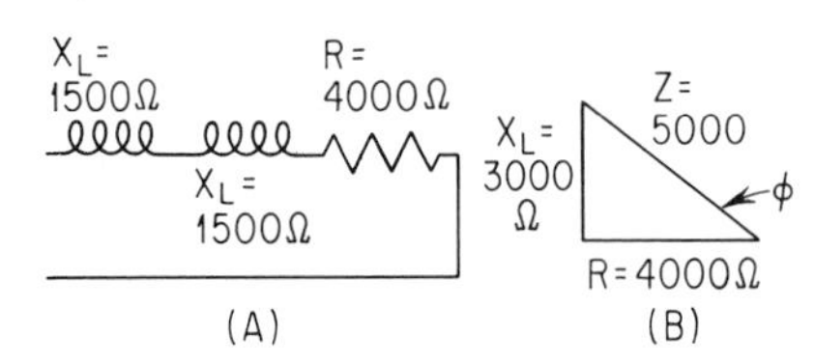

Fig. 11-3. Vector analysis of load circuit

Between the extremes of zero power and full power are various degrees of power, depending on the phase angle. In A of Fig. 11-3, for instance, the two inductances of the magnetic amplifier are shown, each having a reactive value of 1500 ohms. The load resistance is given as 4000 ohms, and when a vector diagram is constructed for this circuit it appears as shown at B. The total impedance is equal to the hypothenuse of the angle and is equal to 5000 ohms as given by the following calculation:

$$Z = \sqrt{R^2 + X_L{}^2}$$
$$= \sqrt{3000^2 + 4000^2}$$
$$= 5000 \text{ ohms}$$

As shown at B, the angle is formed where the impedance line and resistance line meet, and the cosine of this angle may be found by dividing the value of resistance by the value of impedance as follows:

$$\cos = \frac{R}{Z} = \frac{4}{5} = 0.8$$

Using the same values of voltage and current which were given in the previous illustration, the power for this circuit will now be 4000 watts:

$$P = 100 \times 50 \times 0.8 = 4000 \text{ watts}$$

If the voltage applied to the control winding of the magnetic amplifier is now increased, the current flowing through the coils increases and the core approaches more nearly the saturation point. Permeability declines, and in consequence the inductive reactance in series with the load resistance decreases appreciably. The phase angle between voltage and current now decreases, and the cosine value becomes nearer 1 and power output is almost the full value which could be obtained by the 5000-ohm load circuit. If the voltage applied to the control winding is decreased, the decrease in current through the control winding brings the core appreciably below the saturation level and hence the inductance and inductive reactance increase. The phase angle increases, and the cosine becomes a value much less than 1, with a consequent decrease in power. The change in power appearing at R_L will be proportional to the change of power at the control winding.

Hence, a change of the relatively low power applied to the control winding L_3 is influential in causing a change of the relatively higher power applied to R_L. Thus, by use of the saturable-reactor principle, power amplification occurs.

The control signal can also be a-c instead of d-c. As shown at A of Fig. 11-4, a d-c bias is placed in series with the control winding L_3. This d-c bias establishes an operating point on the *B-H* curve as shown at B of Fig. 11-4. When this is done, an a-c signal applied to the control winding will alternately increase and decrease the inductive value of the series load coils. If, for instance, the first alternation of the control signal is positive as shown in A, it makes terminal T_1 positive and terminal T_2 negative. Under this condition, the total voltage appearing at L_3 is increased, because the first alternation of the control signal has a polarity such that it aids the bias potential. Consequently, the operating point approaches closer to the saturation level causing an increase in the power applied to the load. Such an increase will be gradual to conform to the gradual increase of the control signal, and as the control-signal alternation drops to zero, so would the power-source signal also drop to the value established by the d-c bias. This is shown at C, where the power-source signal is shown at the level established by the d-c bias and the change which occurs for the control signal. For the second alternation of the control signal, terminal T_1 is

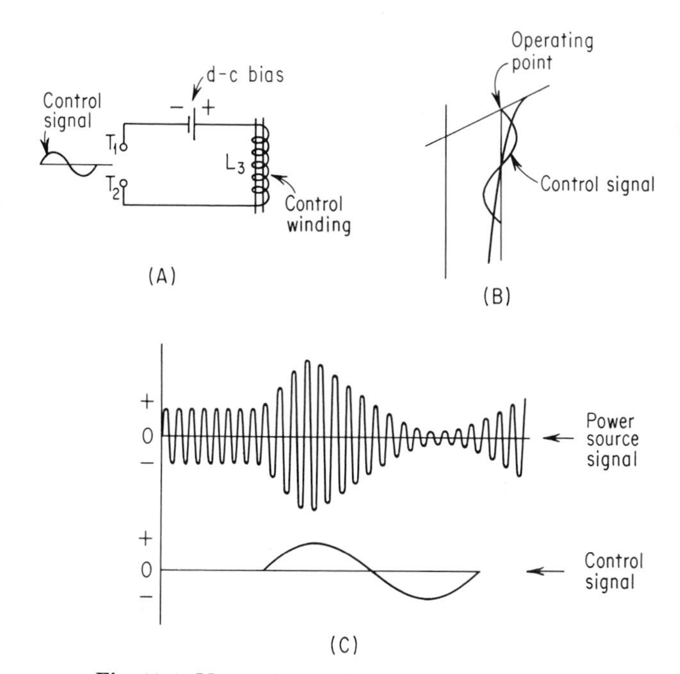

Fig. 11-4. Magnetic amplifier bias and a-c control

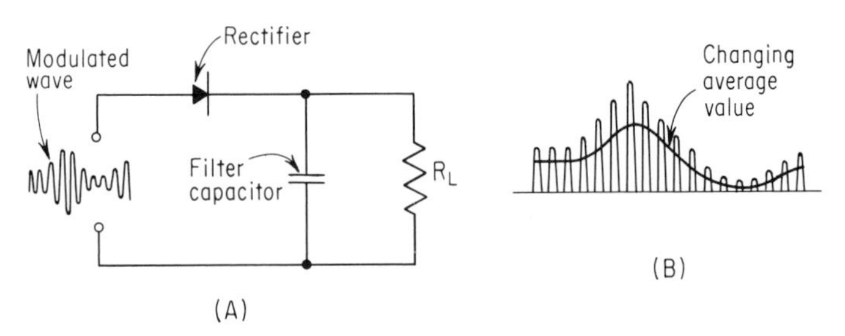

Fig. 11-5. Detection of amplified signal

minus and terminal T_2 is positive. Under this condition the control-signal alternation opposes the bias potential, and the operating point drops lower on the *B-H* curve as shown in B. In consequence, the inductive reactance of the series coils increases and power to the load decreases as shown in C of Fig. 11-4. Thus, the power-source signal is, in reality, amplitude-modulated by the control signal.

By a detector (demodulator) circuit such as shown in A of Fig. 11-5, an amplified version of the control signal can be obtained. The half-wave rectifier produces pulsating d-c, and the filter capacitor provides a low-reactance shunt for the ripple frequency. The charge on the filter capacitor also follows the average value of the pulsating d-c which is established in typical power-supply-filter fashion. In contrast to a power supply, however, a steady-state d-c is not produced, but rather a changing average value occurs as shown in B. This changing average value represents the amplified control-signal power.

Additional types of basic magnetic amplifier circuits are shown at A and B of Fig. 11-6. At A a four-legged core is shown; the coils in series with the power source as well as the control coil are wound on the center two legs. The a-c supply coils are also wound series-

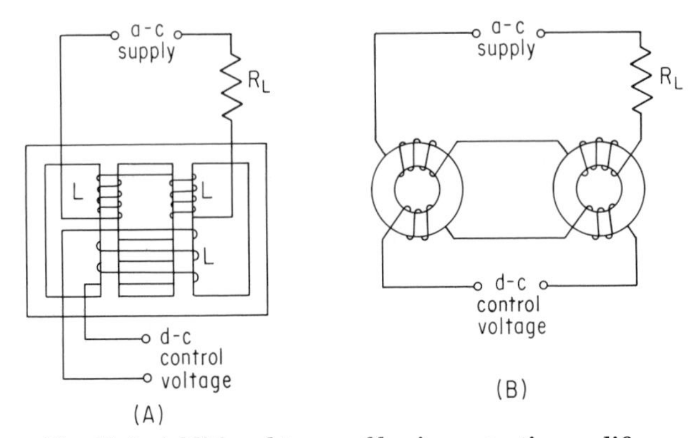

Fig. 11-6. Additional types of basic magnetic amplifiers

opposing so that no induction of voltage occurs between the a-c supply coils and the control-voltage coil. The load circuit can be in a lead of the a-c power source or else can be inserted between the two coils L_1 and L_2, because in any case the load circuit is in series with the load coils. At B of Fig. 11-6 the circuit for a magnetic amplifier using twin-ring toroid cores is shown. Here, two control-voltage coils are used in addition to the two a-c power-source coils as shown.

FEEDBACK AMPLIFIER

The four-legged type of core shown at A of Fig. 11-6 is also useful with magnetic amplifiers employing feedback. Feedback consists of feeding a portion of the amplified signal back to the magnetic amplifier to alter its performance characteristics. The feedback is accomplished by use of an extra feedback coil as shown in Fig. 11-7. As with standard vacuum-tube amplifiers, the feedback can be either positive or negative, depending on the direction of the winding employed for the feedback coil L_4. With positive feedback, regeneration occurs, raising the sensitivity of the magnetic amplifier and increasing over-all gain. When negative feedback is employed, degeneration occurs which improves the amplified signal waveform though it decreases over-all gain. By inclusion of the bridge-rectifier circuit shown n Fig. 11-7, the amplified output power is d-c, though a-c can be procured as for the former types, by omitting the rectifier circuit, while still feeding back a portion of the amplified output signal to the L_4 winding.

To understand the operation of the feedback amplifier of Fig. 11-7, assume that the instantaneous value of the a-c supply is negative at

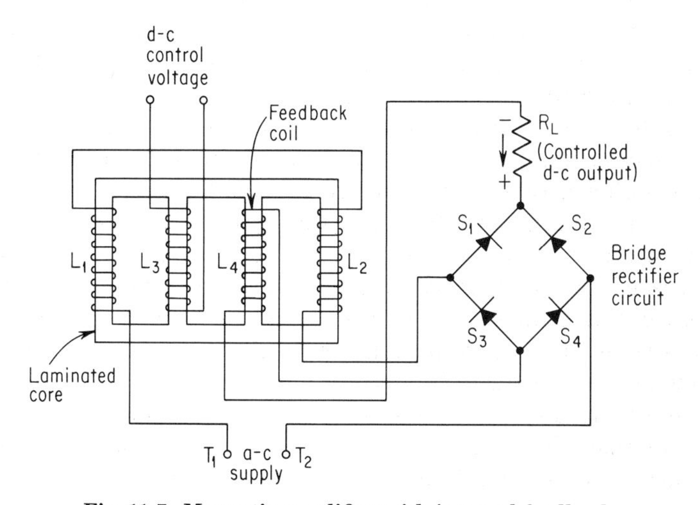

Fig. 11-7. Magnetic amplifier with internal feedback

terminal T_1 and positive at terminal T_2. Under these polarity conditions, current flows to terminal T_1 and through coil L_1 and through coil L_2, to the junction of rectifiers S_1 and S_3. The current flow must complete the circuit by reaching terminal T_2, hence the current will flow through rectifier S_3 and then through the feedback coil L_4 to the top of the load-circuit resistance R_L. The current then flows through R_L and completes the circuit to T_2 by flowing through the rectifier S_2. When the polarity of the a-c signal at T_1 and T_2 changes, a negative potential appears at T_2 and a positive potential at T_1. Now, current will flow to terminal T_2 to the junction of rectifiers S_2 and S_4. In order to complete the circuit to terminal T_1, the current flows through rectifier S_4, through control winding L_4, and again to the top of R_L. The current flow through R_L is again in the same direction as before, as shown by the arrow beside R_L in Fig. 11-7. The current now flows through rectifier S_1 and through coils L_2 and L_1 to terminal T_1 (the current flowing through S_1 will not flow through S_3 since the current seeks a return path to terminal T_1 because of its flow from the negative to the positive terminals of the a-c power supply).

The feedback current flowing through L_4, if regenerative in nature, will augment the current flow through the control winding and hence will add to the change of current which occurs in the control winding L_3. If, for instance, the current through the control winding increases and raises the flux density to the near-saturation point, the current fed back and flowing through L_4 will increase the flux density by an additional amount. Hence, the saturation level is increased over and above that which would prevail for the current flowing in the control winding alone. If the current through the control winding decreases, the energy level across the load circuit resistance decreases and hence the current through L_4 also decreases, causing a reduction in flux density by an amount greater than would occur for the change of current in the control winding L_3 alone.

If the feedback coil L_4 is wound in the opposite direction to that of L_3, regeneration occurs. If the current through the control coil L_3 increases sufficiently to cause core saturation, the current flow through L_4 would set up magnetic lines of force which would tend to oppose those of winding L_3. In consequence, the core saturation level would be decreased below what it would be for the current through the control winding L_3 alone. For a decrease in the current through L_3 the flux density of the core would tend to decrease to a certain level. The feedback current through L_4, however, also decreases, with the result that the flux density would not decline to as low a level.

The rectifier shown in Fig. 11-7 can be of the silicon type or of the diode vacuum-tube type. In either case, it should have a high forward-to-back resistance value so that very little current flows in the reverse direction through the rectifier. As with all magnetic amplifiers, the resistance of the load circuit must have such a value that maximum output power is obtained. The impedances of the input and output windings of the magnetic amplifier are related also to the internal resistance of the coil windings. Generally, magnetic amplifiers, unlike vacuum-tube amplifiers, have a low input impedance.

SELF-SATURATING AMPLIFIERS

For increased gain and better performance, an improved type of magnetic amplifier is used instead of the basic types previously discussed. These superior types are known as the *self-saturating* magnetic amplifiers. The self-saturating amplifiers are also known as the *internal feedback types.*

Figure 11-8 shows the basic self-saturating magnetic amplifier circuit. Instead of illustrating the core as in the types previously discussed, the standard schematic symbols are shown, with N_c indicating the control windings, and N_{L1} and N_{L2} designating the load-circuit windings. As shown, a silicon or other high front-to-back resistance-ratio rectifier is employed in series with the load-circuit resistance and the a-c supply source. Again, core material having a rectangular hysteresis loop is employed, and in the self-saturating magnetic amplifier circuits of this type, power gains of over 500 kilowatts are possible.

The self-saturating magnetic amplifier has the additional advantage over the external-feedback type because a more simple core structure can be used and the feedback winding eliminated. The absence of the feedback coil provides a greater output as compared to the external-feedback types of equal size, because of the absence of the series resistance which the load supply encounters in the feedback winding, as well as the fact that the series-load coils have a greater core area.

The rectifier S_1 in series with the a-c supply line and the load resistance produces a rectified output consisting of single-polarity

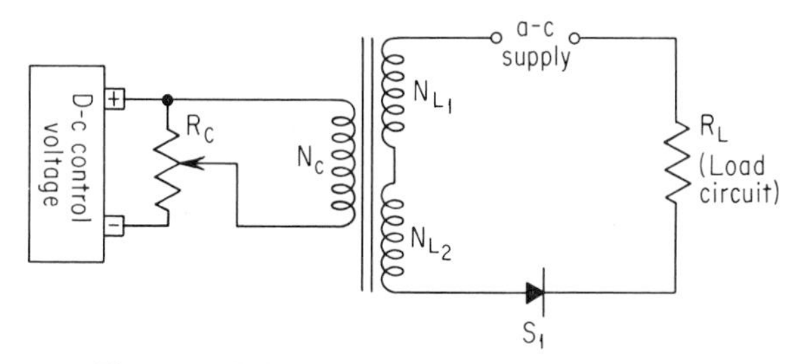

Fig. 11-8. Self-saturating magnetic amplifier

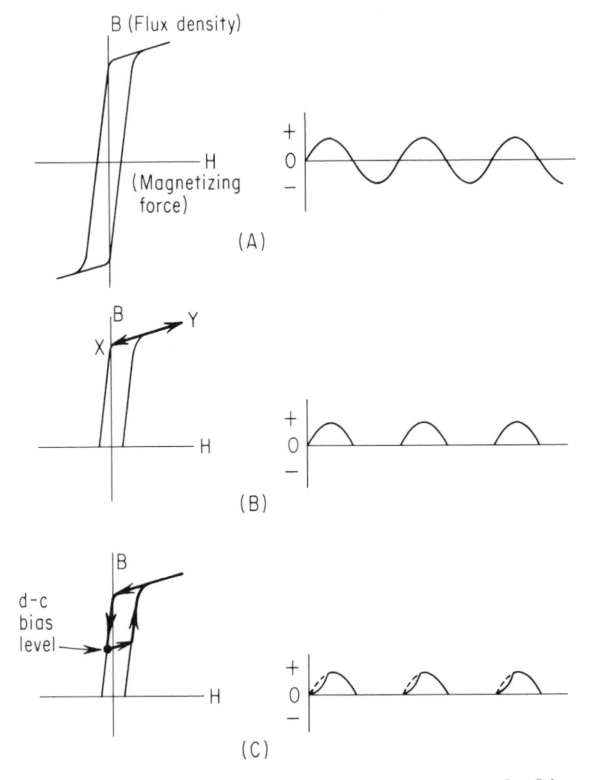

Fig. 11-9. Output waveforms with and without d-c bias

alternations (pulsating d-c). As with the d-c available from the magnetic amplifier with external feedback shown in Fig. 11-7, a filter network consisting of chokes and capacitors would have to be employed for minimizing ripple.

For understanding how the self-saturating magnetic amplifier functions, refer to Fig. 11-9, which shows the *B-H* curves and the output waveforms with and without the control voltage (d-c bias).

If there is no current in the control winding, and with the rectifier removed, the a-c supply current through coils N_{L1} and N_{L2} would vary the flux density above and below the zero level in the positive and negative direction as shown by the *B-H* curve at A. The signal waveform across the load resistance would then be as also shown at A, consisting of positive and negative alternations in typical sinewave form. With the rectifier inserted in series with the load circuit, the results would be as shown at B of Fig. 11-9. The rectifier permits current to flow only in one direction, hence only alternate halves of the a-c flow through the windings. In consequence, the unidirectional current flow through the coils saturates the core in one direction only during the half-cycles. With the rectangular type of hysteresis curve, the point X is reached. When the half-cycle is zero, the flux density is at the residual magnetism level during the absence of any magnetizing force. As the half-cycle starts from zero and reaches a maximum peak value, the flux density rises from its residual magnetism level to the saturation level marked Y at B of Fig. 11-9. Thus, there is no reversal of the flux density, and the operating point of the curve is along the saturation level at the top. The core remains in a virtually saturated condition because the rectifier does not permit the negative half-cycles to flow in the windings, hence the polarity of the flux density is not reversed. The output voltage, in the form of pulsating d-c, has each alternation reaching the peak level of the supply voltage, because at saturation, the reactance of the coils is very low and the only voltage drop across the coils would be by virtue of any internal d-c resistance.

The illustration at C of Fig. 11-9 indicates what occurs when current is permitted to flow in the control winding. If the control current is such that it would tend to build up a flux density having a polarity opposite to that produced by the half-cycles of the a-c power source, it would tend to establish a fixed voltage level referred to as *control bias*. With such a bias, the control current will be effective in reducing the magnetization of the core during the half-cycle intervals when the rectifier is in a nonconducting state. The reduction of magnetism would be to a fixed level on the negative-going line of the hysteresis loop as shown at C of Fig. 11-9. During the half-cycles when the rectifier conducts, the circulating current in the load windings nullifies the effect of the control current, and core saturation again prevails as illustrated at B.

In resaturating the core, the load-winding current must overcome the d-c bias voltage and in doing this a definite interval of time is required. Hence, voltage which appears at the output is at a low level until full saturation is reached. The time interval of delay then modifies the output waveform as shown at C, as well as reducing the output-power level. The value of the bias can be made sufficiently large to saturate the core in the reverse direction to the saturation produced by the a-c load supply to increase the time interval. Thus, the bias can be set to regulate the amount of output power by controlling the amount of magnetizing force required to reestablish the positive saturation level for each conducting half-cycle of the a-c supply power. Changes and variations in the control current would also appear in the output as proportional changes in the output power. Since the changes in output power represent a higher power level than the input-power variations, amplification again occurs. The d-c bias-level polarity will establish the degree of aiding (regeneration) or opposing (degeneration) of flux density contributed by the control winding. The positive or negative polarities are established not only by the voltage applied to the control-winding terminals, but also by the direction of the control winding.

FULL-WAVE SELF-SATURATING AMPLIFIER

The self-saturating magnetic amplifier previously discussed produces an output waveform of the pulsating d-c type. Pulsating d-c requires a high order of filtering to obtain a smooth ripple-free output voltage. If the system is designed to produce successive output half-cycles instead of alternate half-cycles, the system is then known as a full-wave self-saturating magnetic amplifier. The full-wave type, as with the full-wave power supplies, gives improved performance in terms of regulation and less rigorous filter requirements. The full-wave circuit requires two saturable reactor cores, as well as dual rectifiers as shown in Fig. 11-10. As with the magnetic amplifier with internal feedback illustrated earlier in Fig. 11-8, a bridge rectifier is used so that successive conducting alternations may be fed in such a direction through the load resistance that a unidirectional current flow (d-c) is obtained. The bridge rectifier is necessary because one load coil will conduct on the positive alternations of the supply power and the other load coil will conduct on the negative half-cycles of supply power. As shown, the control coils are in series with the d-c control voltage.

The full-wave magnetic amplifier shown in Fig. 11-10 is sometimes known as the *push-pull* magnetic amplifier. Operation for the individual sections, however, follows that of the half-wave type previously

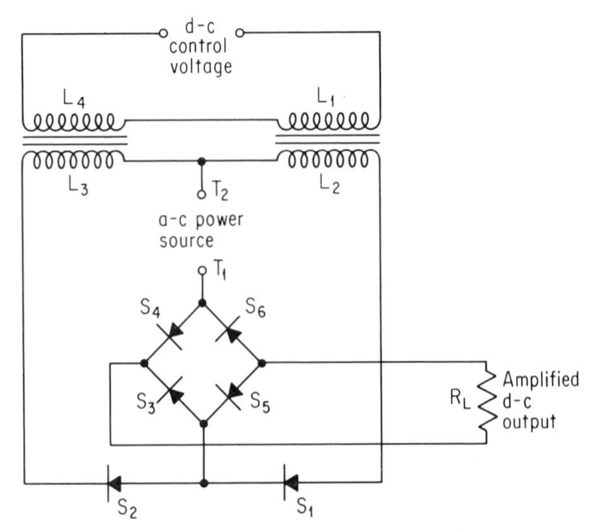

Fig. 11-10. Push-pull magnetic amplifier

discussed. For push-pull type, the individual sections work alternately. Assume, for instance, that the a-c supply potential at a given instant is negative at terminal T_1 and positive at terminal T_2. Current flow from T_1 flows through the bridge rectifier S_6 and so through the load resistance R_L to the junction of rectifiers S_3 and S_4. From the junction, the current will flow through rectifier S_3 in seeking its return path to terminal T_2. At the output of S_3, the current flows toward the junction of S_1 and S_2, and of necessity must flow through S_1, because S_2 is wired for reverse current flow. Hence, the current which flows through S_1 will then complete its path through L_2 and to terminal T_2. For the next alternation of the a-c supply, terminal T_1 would be positive and terminal T_2 negative. Now, current flows from terminal T_2 to the top of windings L_2 and L_3. The current will not flow through L_2, since the rectifier S_1 is in the reverse direction. Thus, the current will flow through L_3 and rectifier S_2 to the terminal between S_3 and S_5. From the latter terminal, current will flow through S_5 and through R_L to the top of the load resistor and to the junction of rectifiers S_3 and S_4. From the latter junction, the current flows through S_4 and to the positive terminal T_1.

The bias current applied to the control input flows through coils L_1 and L_4 in series, hence the bias point is established for either the left or right core simultaneously. Hence, regardless of whether the current is flowing at any instant through L_2 or L_3, the bias point will be fixed by the appropriate control-core coil.

SELF-SATURATING AMPLIFIER WITH a-c OUTPUT

Another version of the self-saturating magnetic amplifier is shown in Fig. 11-11. This differs from the one previously described by virtue of its producing an a-c output. As shown, the d-c control voltage is applied across coils L_1 and L_2, each with its own saturable reactor core. Three-legged cores are again used, with the reactor winding L_3 utilizing the two outer legs of the core as previously described, and L_4 also utilizing the two outer-leg cores of its particular reactor. Rectifiers S_1 and S_2 are in series with the respective control cores as shown.

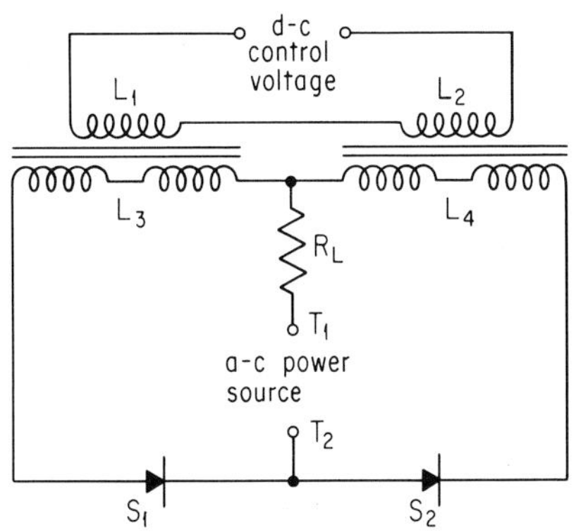

Fig. 11-11. Self-saturating amplifier with a-c output

When an alternation of the a-c power source is such that terminal

T_1 is negative and terminal T_2 positive, current flows from T_1 up through the load circuit represented by resistance R_L. The current flow, in its path to terminal T_2, flows through load winding L_4 and through the series rectifier S_2. (Current would not flow through the load winding L_3, because of the reverse connection of the series rectifier S_1.) At the next alternation of the a-c power source, terminal T_2 would be negative and terminal T_1 positive. Current from T_2 would flow through the series rectifier S_1, and through the load winding L_3. Because the current flow must return to the positive terminal T_1, it flows down through the load-circuit resistance R_L. Hence, successive alternations of the a-c power source will cause current to flow in opposite directions through the load-circuit resistance. Hence, the series rectifiers S_1 and S_2 are not for purposes of rectification for conversion to d-c, but are for internal feedback purposes only.

DIELECTRIC AMPLIFIERS

In addition to amplifiers which can be constructed from vacuum tubes, transistors, and saturable reactors, are those amplifiers built around a *nonlinear* capacitor. Normally, the capacitance of a capacitor is independent of the voltage applied across the capacitor when such ordinary dielectric materials are used such as mica, paper, plastic, or air. With such dielectrics, the value of capacitance in fractional values of farads is established by the cross-sectional area of the capactior plates, the plate separation, and the dielectric material employed. Air is considered as having a dielectric constant of 1, with other materials having a higher dielectric constant and thus increasing the capacitance value. Mica, for instance, has a dielectric constant of from 5 to 10, depending on the quality and characteristics. Glass has a dielectric constant between 5 and 7, while Isolantite has a dielectric constant of approximately 6 and Mycalex a constant of 8.

Certain materials, when used as the dielectric, have a variable effect on the capacitance, depending on the voltage impressed across the capacitor. Materials of this type include titanium dioxide, barium titanate, strontium titanate, and so on. With any one of these materials as the dielectric of a capacitor, the capacitance value can change over 50 per cent when a voltage change across the capacitor occurs from approximately zero to 200 volts. Hence, such materials can be utilized as the dielectric in a capacitor for forming a circuit which has amplifying characteristics.

A dielectric amplifier, unlike the magnetic and transistor amplifiers, has a high input impedance similar to vacuum tubes. The dielectric amplifier also has other advantages. It can be constructed as a compact unit and, like the magnetic amplifier, it is rugged and economical to construct. Like a vacuum tube, it can be operated at higher frequencies than the ordinary magnetic-amplifier types and can be utilized to amplify voltages as well as power. As with the magnetic amplifier, no warm-up time is needed. However, temperature variations have a greater effect on it than is the case with other amplifiers. Another disadvantage is that the dielectric amplifiers require a high-frequency power source, and in practical applications a frequency of over 1 megacycle is usually employed. Dielectric amplifiers operating at signal frequencies of 2 or 3 megacycles have high-voltage and power gains of well over 10,000.

FERROELECTRIC CHARACTERISTICS

Dielectric materials such as those mentioned in the introduction to this chapter and which exhibit characteristic changes upon the application of voltage, are known as *ferroelectric* or *nonlinear* materials. When these materials are used in capacitors the dielectric "constant" decreases as the voltage across the capacitor increases.

When a voltage is applied across the capacitor and the latter becomes charged as shown in Fig. 11-12, the electrostatic fields which now exist between the charged plates influence the electrons, and following the law of unlike poles attracting, the electrons (negative charged) are attracted toward the electrostatic fields of the positively charged plate, creating an atomic distortion within the dielectric. For materials having a high dielectric constant the atomic distortion is greatest. In the ordinary dielectric such as air or a plastic, the distortion is constant, while the non-linear dielectrics, the distortion varies in proportion to the voltage which establishes the charge.

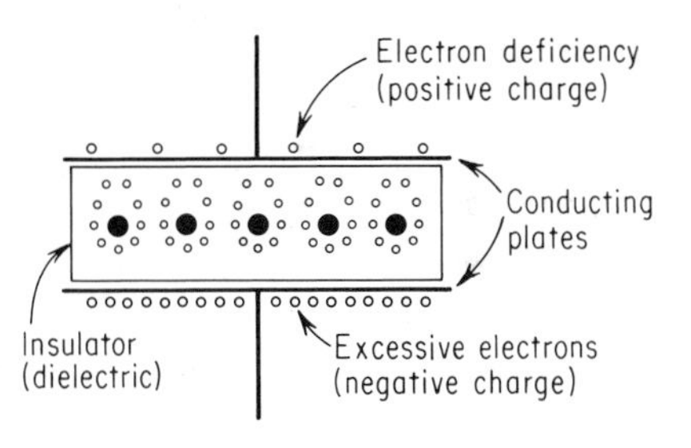

Fig. 11-12. Electron displacement in a charged capacitor

When the dielectric material is distorted under the stress or strain of electrostatic lines of force, each strained atom is known as an *electric dipole* or an *induced dipole* and is then comparable to the magnetic dipoles or domains existing in magnetized material. The induced dipoles are all aligned symmetrically by the electrostatic lines of force of the charged plates just as the magnetic dipoles in ferromagnetic material are aligned. Under the distortion existing during the presence of electrostatic fields, the dielectric is also referred to as being *polarized.* As the capacitor is discharged, the electrostatic fields collapse and the atoms revert to their normal symmetrical arrangement.

Polarization of the dielectric material results in the establishing of *surface charges* on the flat sides of the dielectric material in contact with the charged capacitor plates. These surface charges oppose the electrostatic fields which are established between the charged plates and hence reduce the electric field of the latter to a value lower than would be the case in the absence of the dielectric material. Thus, the *permittivity* between the capacitor plates is also decreased. (Permittivity is that characteristic of a capacitor which relates to the degree by which it can accommodate lines of force. Thus it is an indication of how well the dielectric material of the capacitor can carry the electric lines of force established when voltage is applied and a charge produced.)

Since the amount of distortion or polarization in the ferroelectric materials is not constant, but changes with a change of the voltage impressed across the capacitor, the latter exhibits nonlinear characteristics which make it particularly suitable for amplifier applications.

Besides showing voltage sensitivity, the nonlinear dielectrics are also temperature-dependent, This is indicated in the graph at A of Fig. 11-13, which shows the change in the dielectric constant with a change of temperature. The dielectric-constant factor increases gradually as the temperature rises until a peak level is reached. The peak level is known as the *Curie point*. An additional temperature increase results in a decrease of the dielectric constant. For amplifier applications, the Curie point should be reached at normal operating temperatures. The point is established by regulating the composition of the dielectric material.

At B of Fig. 11-13 the characteristics of the dielectric material are

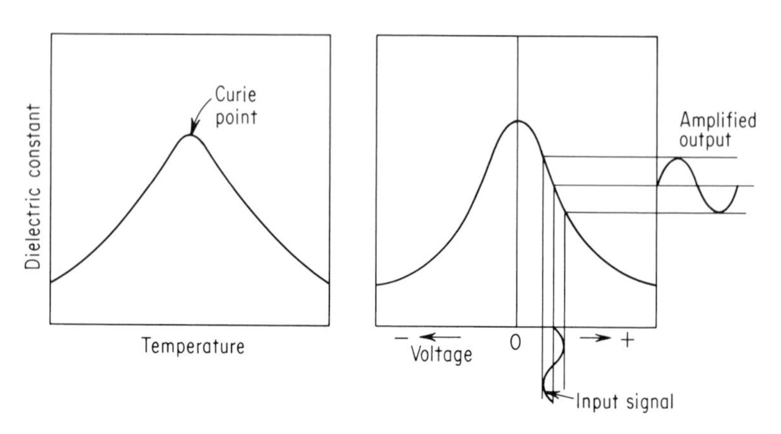

Fig. 11-13. Dielectric amplifier curves

shown with respect to voltage applications. At zero voltage the dielectric constant is high, and it decreases when either negative or positive potentials are applied. The bias point and signal input can be set on either the positive or negative slope either side of center.

BASIC DIELECTRIC AMPLIFIER

A basic dielectric amplifier is shown in Fig. 11-14. A d-c or low-frequency a-c control signal is applied across the nonlinear capacitor as shown. For the dielectric amplifier, a fixed bias voltage must be employed as shown by the battery B_1. The power source to be used in the amplification process consists of a high-frequency signal which is in series with the load-circuit resistance R_L. A radio-frequency choke is placed in series with each line from the low-frequency control signal, to isolate the latter from the high-frequency power-source signal. The r-f chokes (L_1 and L_2) have a low reactance for the low-frequency control signal and hence do not offer much opposition for the entry of the low-frequency signal to the circuit. The high-frequency power-source signal, however, will find a high reactance in each choke, because of the higher frequency ($X_L = 6.28fL$). If d-c rather than a-c is required at the output, a rectifier can be placed in series with one of the output terminals, followed by a ripple-filter section to smooth out the pulsating d-c to the required degree.

The fixed potential of d-c bias is employed for placing the operating point of the amplifier along the steep portion of the dielectric curve for the particular ferroelectric material employed. When the operating point is placed on the steep portion of the characteristic curve, there will be a wide reactance change for a comparatively small

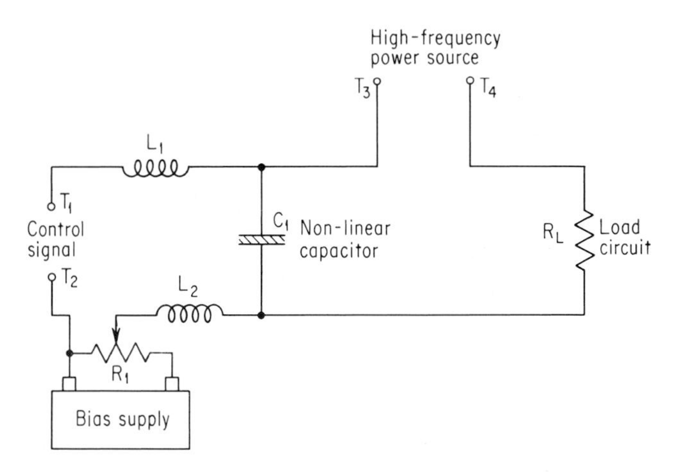

Fig. 11-14. Basic dielectric amplifiers

control-voltage signal change. With a high reactive change, amplification for the input signal occurs, as was shown at B of Fig. 11-13.

With the control-voltage terminals T_1 and T_2 shorted, the bias supply would establish the amount of power presented to the load circuit R_L. Thus, the d-c voltage from the bias supply can be regulated by the variable resistor R_1 and hence a low power source can control a high power and vary the latter as required for application to the load circuit. Thus, d-c can be employed for controlling a-c power. The use of a rectifier circuit and appropriate filter sections preceding the load circuit will convert the high-frequency power source to d-c if required.

With the short across T_1 and T_2 removed, a low-frequency a-c signal can be applied across the terminals for controlling the high-frequency, high-power source applied across terminals T_3 and T_4. The bias supply establishes the initial operating point along the steep portion of the dielectric curve as mentioned earlier, and the control signal a-c will then add or subtract from the bias supply voltage. If a particular alternation of the a-c signal is such that terminal T_1 is positive and terminal T_2 is negative, it will add to the bias supply voltage and hence increase the voltage drop across the nonlinear capacitor C_1. If operation is on the right side of the voltage curve (shown in Fig. 11-13), an increase in voltage will cause a reduction in the dielectric constant and hence will decrease the capacity of C_1. Decreasing the capacity increases the capacitive reactance. The high-frequency power-source signal is applied across the load circuit with the nonlinear capacitor C_1 in series with terminal T_3. Thus, an increase in the capacitive reactance of C_1 will reduce the power of the a-c appearing across R_L. At the next alternation of the control-signal voltage, terminal T_1 becomes positive and terminal T_2 negative. Now, the control-signal voltage opposes that of the bias supply and in consequence there is a reduction of voltage across the nonlinear capacitor with a resultant rise in the dielectric constant. The capacity of C_1 increases and the capacitive reactance decreases. The latter effect will now permit a greater power to appear across the load resistor R_L.

The power variations for the d-c control signal as well as for the a-c control signal are illustrated in Fig. 11-15. At A, a positive d-c control signal is indicated, and this could be the bias supply. The high-frequency power-source signal is shown at B, while the reduced power-source signal appearing across the load resistance is shown at C. An increase in the d-c positive control signal would result in a lower-level power-output signal shown at C. Thus, as the d-c control signal is increased or decreased, it will alter the amount of power appearing across the load resistance.

At D an a-c type of control signal is shown. The latter is much lower in frequency than the power-source signal shown at E. As the low-

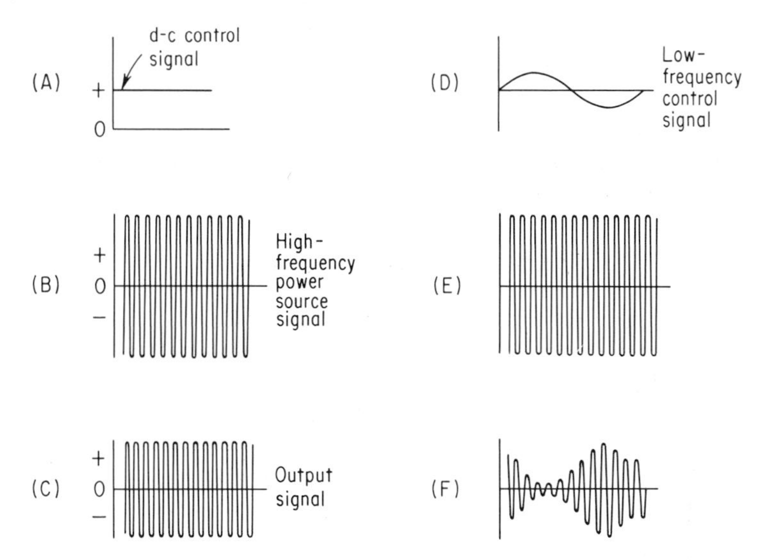

Fig. 11-15. Dielectric amplifier waveforms

frequency control signal goes through its positive alternation as shown at D, the power output is reduced as shown at F. There is a gradual reduction of the output power as the control-signal alternation increases from a zero value to its positive peak value. As the alternation then declines to zero again, the output power would increase to the maximum level permitted by the d-c bias voltage. For the second alternation of the control signal shown at D, the rise of voltage from zero to the negative peak causes a gradual increase in the power across the load resistor. As the second alternation declines from its negative peak value to zero, the output power across the load resistor drops to the level established by the fixed d-c bias-supply voltage as shown at F.

As can be seen from the waveform at F, the signal which appears across the load resistance has amplitude changes which vary at a rate that coincides with the amplitude changes of a low-frequency control signal. In consequence, the waveform as shown at F is an *amplitude-modulated* waveform which resembles the type used in standard amplitude modulation (AM). The average power of this modulated signal is below what it would be if each cycle of the wave were of the same amplitude. The high-frequency power-source signal has thus undergone a power change, the change being controlled by the input signal to the dielectric amplifier. If this high-frequency signal which appears across the load resistance were now demodulated by a detection process similar to that used in AM receivers, the result would be that the diode detector would rectify the signal as shown earlier in Fig. 11-5. The high-frequency portion of the signal would be bypassed by a filter capacitor and the average value of the amplitude changes of the rectified signal would appear across the detector load resistor as a signal having the same frequency as the control signal. The amplitude changes of the rectified signal would follow those of the control signal, hence the output would now consist of an amplified version of the input signal.

MAGNETORESISTIVE AMPLIFIER

An amplifier for industrial power amplification can also be formed using the magnetoresistive slabs for obtaining the Hall effect by using a magnetic field, as described in Chapter 1.

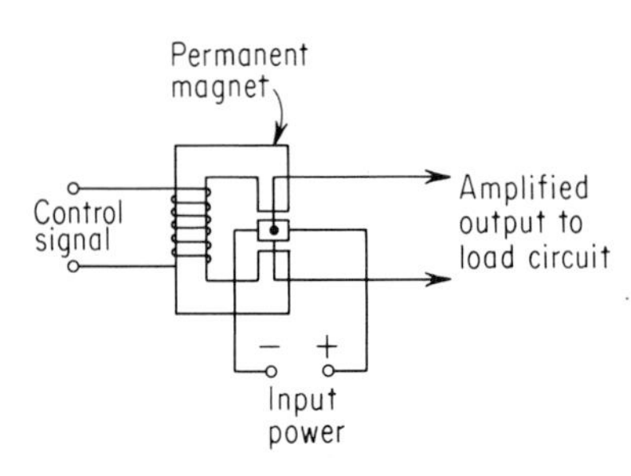

Fig. 11-16. Magnetoresistive amplifiers

A basic magnetoresistive amplifier is shown in Fig. 11-16, and consists of a permanent magnet, a magnetoresistive slab placed in the magnetic field, and a coil wound around the magnet as shown. Under the influence of the magnetic field, the electron stream of the input current flow to the slab is deflected as described earlier, with a resulting output signal.

The magnetic flux between the pole pieces of the permanent magnet can be increased or decreased by the control-signal coil. If the voltage applied to the coil produces a magnetic field which aids that of the magnet, the higher concentration of magnetic flux at the pole pieces will cause a much greater electron deflection within the slab, with an increase in voltage output and in current flow to the load. If the voltage applied to the coil is reversed in polarity, the magnetic field produced by the coil opposes that of the magnet and the magnetic flux at the pole pieces decreases. The result is a decrease in the electron-stream deflection and a decrease in the power applied to the load circuit. Thus, a signal of low power applied to the coil will produce a signal of considerably greater power at the output, and amplification results. The input signal can be d-c and can be changed as required to produce an amplified output change, or the input can be a-c with the result that the output signal will follow the input with respect to amplitude and frequency changes.

Review Questions for Chapter 11

1. Briefly compare the magnetic amplifier to the vacuum-tube type with respect to advantages and disadvantages.
2. Briefly explain why the core material used in magnetic amplifiers should have a rectangular-type hysteresis loop.
3. Why does the permeability change for various degrees of saturation of a core.
4. Explain what factors determine the inductance of a coil with a metal core.
5. What arrangement is made in a magnetic amplifier to prevent the fields of the load windings from inducing a voltage in the control winding?
6. Briefly explain the operation of the magnetic amplifier employing internal feedback.
7. Briefly explain how the self-saturating magnetic amplifier differs from the ordinary internal-feedback type.
8. What is the purpose for using d-c bias with the self-saturating magnetic amplifier?
9. What are the advantages of the push-pull magnetic amplifier over the single-reactor type?
10. Show by a schematic diagram how a-c output can be obtained from a self-saturating amplifier.
11. Compare the characteristics of an ordinary capacitor with those of a nonlinear capacitor.
12. Define the terms *induced dipole, polarized dielectric,* and *surface changes.*
13. When a low-frequency control signal is used in a dielectric amplifier, why should r-f chokes be employed?
14. Reproduce the output waveforms from a dielectric amplifier with a d-c control voltage and an a-c control voltage.
15. In a dielectric amplifier, what is the effect of reversing the bias battery potential? Explain briefly.
16. Explain the basic principles of the Hall-effect amplifier.

12

Counters and Indicators

INTRODUCTION

In industry, testing and maintenance procedures involve the use of ordinary testing and measuring equipment such as the voltmeter, the ammeter and milliameter, the ohmmeter, and the oscilloscope, commonly used in all branches of electronics. In addition to such basic units, however, a number of other instruments are employed in industrial electronics for counting, indicating, and recording. Such devices are necessary to keep a constant check on industrial processes so that accuracy may be maintained with respect to the specifications applying to the items being processed. At the same time, the items manufactured are counted and the count indicated on meter dials or running charts. Fluid flow, pressure, and temperatures must also be sensed and their degree recorded. Variables of any type can also be graphed by special meter devices for tests, design, and maintenance purposes.

Representative types of specialized counting and indicating devices of various manufacturers are described in this chapter so that a practical foundation can be laid for understanding the scope, usefulness, and applications of such items.

COUNTING

Counting devices are used in industry for ascertaining the number of items moving along an assembly line, for the measurement of the number of gallons of fluid passing through a pipeline, and for indicating the number of stamping, shaping, or milling processes completed in certain time intervals.

Often a photoelectric cell is used for counting items on an assembly line; if so, circuits may be used which involve the ordinary decimal counting with which we are familiar. When counting is accomplished by computer devices, the binary-system circuitry is employed as more fully explained in Chapter 15. The binary indications may be in the form of neon lights, but for direct read-out the ordinary decimal indications are employed.

In many indicators, cold-cathode type tubes are utilized which display an indication of the count by ionization of the gas within the tube. One such tube is the Nixie manufactured by Burroughs. This tube has 10 cathodes and one common anode. Each cathode within the tube is an element shaped like a number. When a voltage is present at one of the pins with respect to the anode, the number corresponding to that pin will become visible by the gas ionization glow associated with the pin. If, for instance, the cathode representing the numeral 5 had voltage applied to it, this number would appear as shown at A of Fig. 12-1. The symbol for the Burroughs Nixie #HB106 is shown at B.

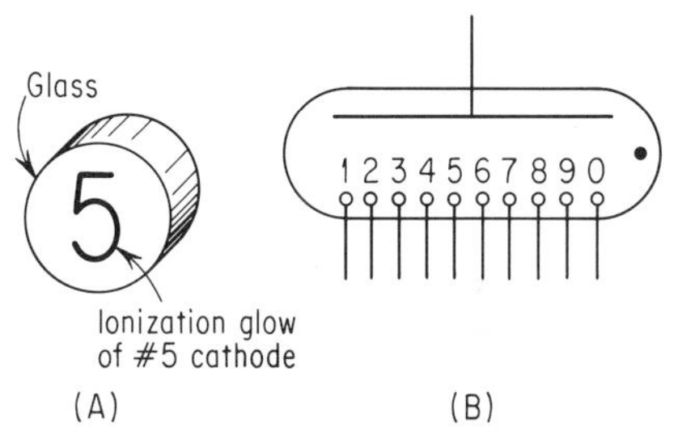

Fig. 12-1. Nixie readout indicator tube

A number of such indicating tubes can be used side by side to read out a number of any proportion desired. The Nixie tubes come in several sizes for production of small visual numbers about a half-inch in size, to larger tubes producing number sizes several times larger.

Another cold-cathode counting tube is the *Dekatron* shown at A of Fig. 12-2. This tube is a product of Ericcson Telephone, Ltd., of Great Britain, and is distributed by Baird-Atomic, Inc. This tube is designed so that when pulses are applied to the input terminals, a glowing spot moves successively around its circumference. The glow moves one segment for each pulse applied, thus progressively indicating the digits 0 through 9 on a faceplate (bezel) surrounding the tube end as shown.

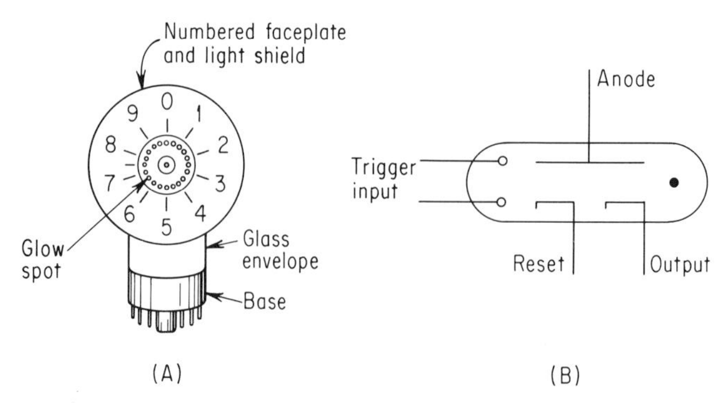

Fig. 12-2. Dekatron indicator and counter tube

The Dekatron is not only an indicating tube, but also a transfer device, because an output pulse is available for each complete revolution of the counting process. Such an output pulse can be applied to a second tube, and since the latter also produces a pulse for one complete decade progression, a number of tubes can be coupled together to form a counter (see Chapter 15) and as many tubes as desired can thus be connected in a string to read a number of any proportion. The symbol for this tube is shown at B.

The transducers described in Chapter 7 can be utilized as sensing elements, including the photocell, the electromechanical switch, or the magnetic sensing devices for counting the passing of ferromagnetic materials.

Another tube with visible ionization-glow numbers is the Digitron illustrated at A of Fig. 12-3. Like the Nixie tube, the Digitron (Baird-Atomic, Inc.) contains elements shaped like numbers, though in the Digitron the numbers are visible from the side of the tube instead of

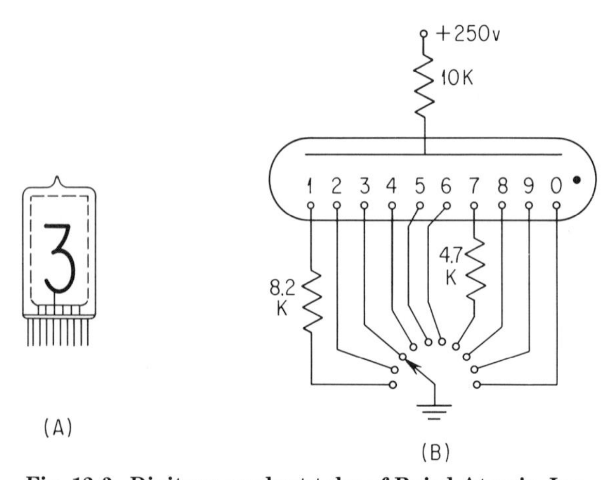

Fig. 12-3. Digitron readout tube of Baird Atomic, Inc.

from the top. Like the Nixie, the Digitron does not advance the indication automatically by the application of pulses to a common input terminal as does the Dekatron. Instead, in the Digitron a particular number is made visible by application of a voltage to the cathode involved. The input switching is shown at B of Fig. 12-3 where the tube symbol is shown.

Commercial Counters

An electronic counter employing the cold-cathode type tube previously described is the Model R counter shown in Fig. 12-4. This unit, by Veeder-Root, Inc., has a speed of 5000 counts per second. This device is easy to operate, and the preset quantity can be established initially through use of the selector knobs on the front panel. The counter circuitry is transistorized to eliminate heat during continuous operation, and to make for a more compact unit.

The Model R is one of a group of such counters available from this company in their 1804 series. Any number of decades can be furnished, plus multiple groups of controls as required for specific industrial applications.

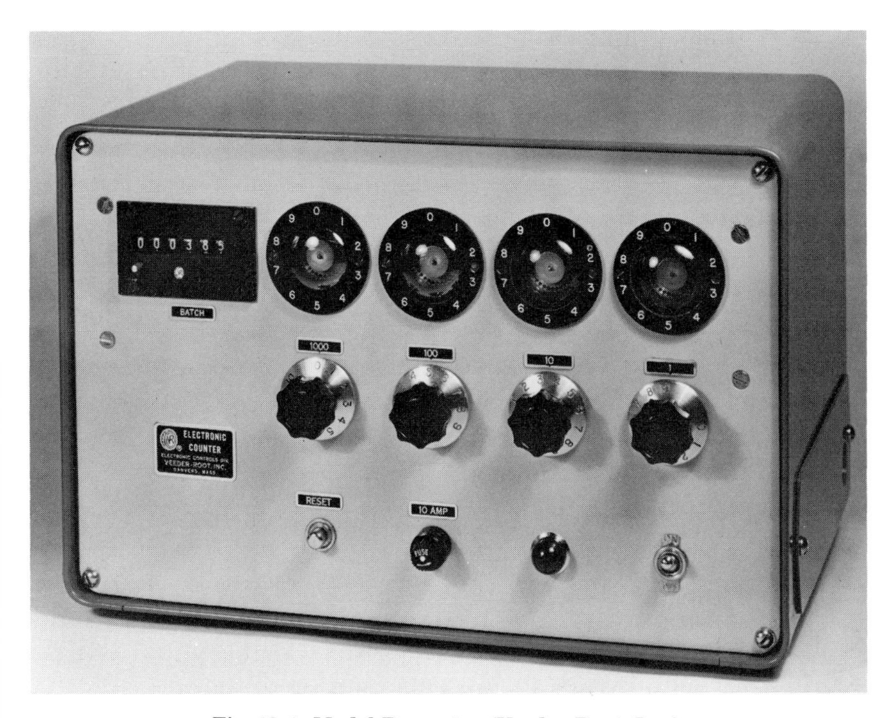

Fig. 12-4. Model R counter (Veeder-Root, Inc.)

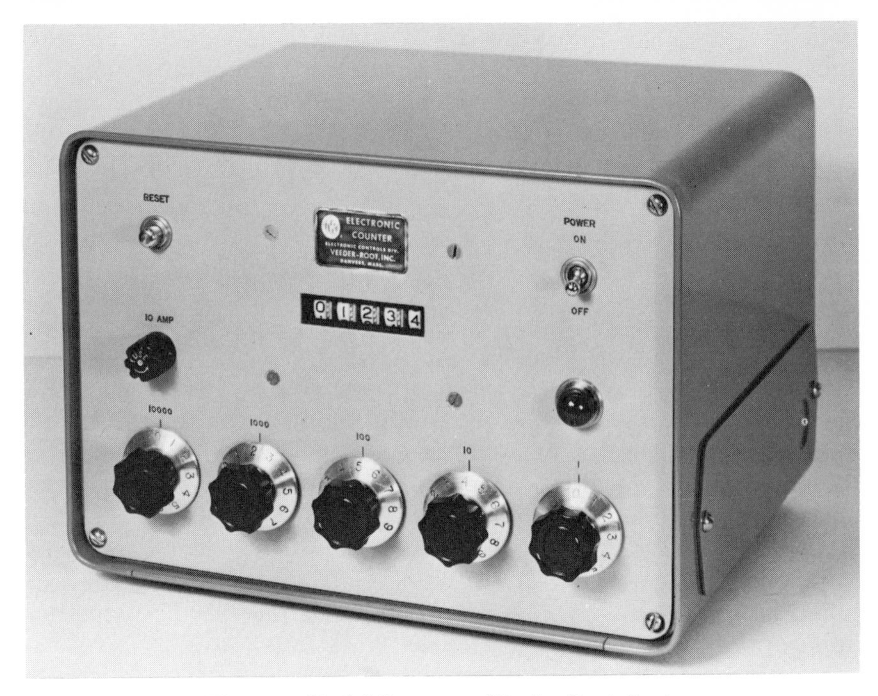

Fig. 12-5. Model S counter (Veeder-Root, Inc.)

Another unit by Veeder-Root, Inc., is the Electric Pre-determining Counter Model E shown in Fig. 12-5. This unit is also designed for industrial control purposes, and it can be preset for the desired count limit. The counting process is visible in the window shown, using mechanical indicators. When the preset number is reached, the unit will actuate any one of four different control functions. The method of counting is electromagnetic, which permits the use of a variety of remote actuating devices such as switches or other sensing transducers. This unit is capable of 1000 counts per minute.

STROBOSCOPE

Stroboscopic devices are utilized in industrial electronics for speed measurements as well as for the observation of rotating, vibrating, or reciprocating machine elements. The stroboscobe is based on the use of flashing lights. When the flashes of light have a frequency which coincides with the rotating or vibrating machine element, the visual effect is to stop the motion so that the moving element can be observed. Thus, the item under observation appears to be stationary and its speed of rotation can be ascertained since it must coincide with the frequency of the flashes of light.

This stroboscopic principle has been used to test the speed of phonograph turntables and other rotating devices by placing on the latter a cardboard disc having black lines around its circumference. In this application a neon or fluorescent light is used since it produces a more pronounced flicker of the 60-cycle line frequency than does the incandescent-type lamp.

The Strobotac

The Strobotac illustrated in Fig. 12-6 is a portable stroboscopic tachometer manufactured by General Radio Company. In industrial applications it is employed for measuring the speed of machine elements and for observing their operational characteristics in apparent slow motion. This device requires no mechanical contact with the unit to be measured, hence the operation of the device tested is not disturbed. This device can be used for measuring the speed of motors, production machine spindles, and any object which has repetitive motion. (See also the discussion on the tachometer transducer in Chapter 7.)

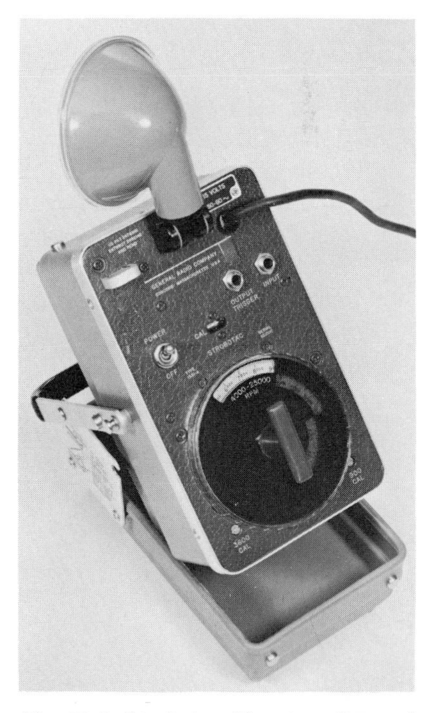

Fig. 12-6. Strobotac (Courtesy General Radio Co.)

Because the rotating elements under observation appear to be standing still or in slow motion, the device is useful for indicating defects in machine operation of such elements as cams, pulleys, governors, gears, fans, sprockets, and so on.

The Strobotac produces a white light flash having a duration of from 1 to 6 microseconds. The light intensity is sufficient for use in highly lighted areas. The flashing range is adjustable from 110 to 25,000 flashes per minute. In direct-reading ranges, speeds up to 250,000 per minute can be measured with flashing rates which are submultiples of the speed of the item under test. The high-intensity flash ranges up to 7 million candlepower per flash. It utilizes a small parabolic reflector, an internal pulse generator, and a power supply operating from the a-c power line.

TEMPERATURE INDICATORS AND CONTROLS

A number of indicating instruments are available for direct reading of temperature, and the control of temperature in industrial processes where stokers, heaters, and other high-temperature devices are used. In conjunction with such indicators and controls, the thermo-transducers are used (see Chapter 7).

For control functions, dials are provided for presetting the required temperature; the unit will thus maintain temperature at the level established by the dial setting, while at the same time giving indication of the temperature on a direct-reading scale.

Commercial Types

An indicating temperature controller is illustrated in Fig. 12-7, the Model T-157M of the Electronic Processes Corp. of California. This is a fully electronic device which uses a precision wire-wound resistance-type temperature-sensing transducer, available in various ranges between 0 and 1000°F. Scale ranges are available between 200 and 600°F. as in the model illustrated, as well as between O and 800°F; 400 and 1000°F; and other ranges.

In operation, the single control knob is set at the desired point and

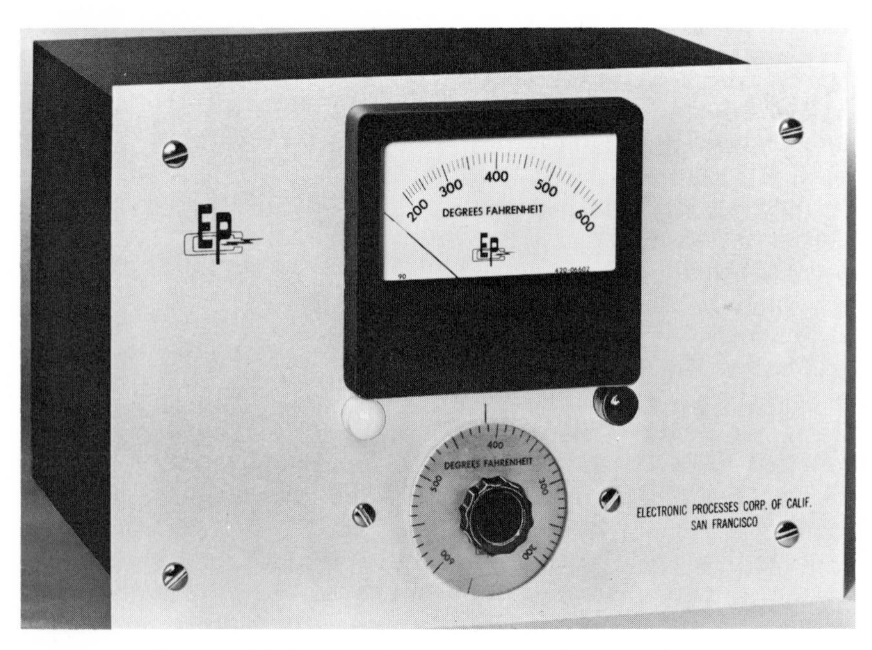

Fig. 12-7. Model T-157M temperature indicator and controller (Electronic Processes Corp. of California)

the internal circuitry compares the setpoint temperature with the temperature of the medium under control. A control signal is produced which is utilized to maintain the temperature at the setpoint. In addition to the indicating dial, a panel light indicates when the temperature has reached the control point. This device is suitable for temperature-control applications in injection molding, extruding machines, vacuum forming ovens, molding dyes, ovens, and heat-treating equipment.

Another indicator-control unit suitable for temperature control in heat treating, baking, drying, and other similar applications is the Model R Indicating-Recording Controller of Leeds & Northrup Co. shown in Fig. 12-8. This round-chart model, which has an automatic-manual switch for selection of either type of operation, is at the lower left of Fig. 12-8. A close–stop–open switch is also included which is used in conjunction with the manual position. The temperature is indicated on the circular scale and the unit provides proportional reset and rate actions. The latter closely regulates temperature by continuously throttling a valve according to the speed, size, and duration of the temperature changes. This device is useful for fuel-fired processes, and for providing uniform heat distribution. It is applicable to recirculation or vertical-bottom furnaces as well as units which heat or cool by steam, refrigerants, or similar liquids or gases.

Fig. 12-8. Model R indicating-recording controller (Leeds and Northrup Co.)

A strip-chart model is also available from Leeds & Northrup Co. and is illustrated in Fig. 12-9. A complete control system is available including the indicators, a drive unit for operating the valves, and the associated sensing devices.

An indicating temperature control of the remote-bulb type is shown in Fig. 12-10. This is the type E36N of the United Electric Controls Company. This device is designed to control and indicate the temperature of gases, liquids, and hot plates over ranges between -100 and $+600°F$. It is particularly suitable for centrifuges, ovens, and other applications where accurate-control must be maintained.

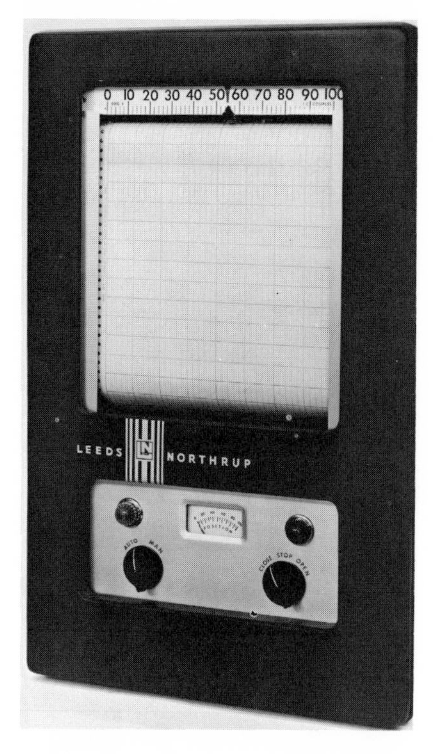

Fig. 12-9. Model S strip-chart recorder (Leeds and Northrup Co.)

Fig. 12-10. E36N indicating temperature control (Courtesy United Electric Controls Co.)

This unit provides both setting and temperature indication on a single dial as shown. A front panel knob adjusts the preset temperature which is to be controlled.

The thermosystem which actuates the movements of the pointer indicator consists of a bellows, capillary, and bulb filled with temperature-sensitive liquids. The bellows expands or contracts with heating or cooling and thus actuates a snap-action switch when the control-point setting is reached.

RECORDERS

As mentioned earlier, recording instruments for industrial applications include those which have a running chart on which a moving pen graphs variables or other data which are to be recorded permanently. Other types of units utilize dials which indicate pressure, rate of flow, temperature, and so on.

Many recorders, like the counters discussed earlier in this chapter, can be preset to initiate new processes at the preset time or to stop certain processes. Recorders can also be used to control temperature, rates, and time intervals.

Commercial Recorders—Indicators

The Brown Electronik Function Plotter shown in Fig. 12-11 is a recording plotter produced by the Minneapolis Honeywell Regulator Company. This type of plotter is capable of recording the results of two variables and hence is essentially a graphing device. It can, for instance, plot a hysteresis loop of magnetic materials when the variable function of the change of magnetic intensity is applied to the plotter in conjunction with the increase in the magnetizing force with respect to the current change flowing in the inductor (see Chapter 4).

The plotter shown in Fig. 12-11 uses a strip-chart single-pen recorder which is actuated by one signal, while the chart drive mechanism is actuated by an independent measuring-system signal. Hence, this device contains two measuring sections, one controlling the recorder pen and the other the chart movement. The chart, like the pen, can respond to either a positive or negative position. For instance, the chart can be driven up or down in response to changes in one variable while the pen moves to the left or right for changes in a second variable.

Both pen and chart circuitry can be energized by any d-c source, though the chart can be controlled with a selsyn motor if desired, with the latter having a direct linkage to a transducer or to a mechanical pickup responding to one variable. The plotter, besides its usefulness in hysteresis-loop graphing, finds applications in speed-versus-torque plotting, stress-versus-strain, temperature-versus-pressure, force-versus-motion, and other X- and Y-axis graph plottings. A wide selection of standard charts and scales is available for use with this instrument.

Another recorder is the Wheelco Series 8000 strip-chart type shown in Fig. 12-12. This device, a product of the Taber Instrument Corporation, has been designed for measurement and control of pres-

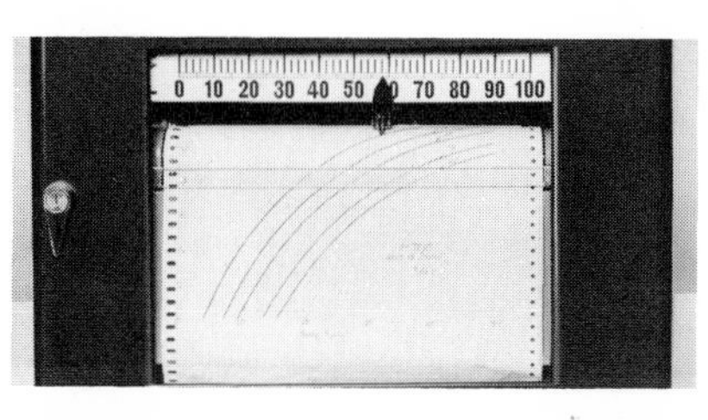

Fig. 12-11. Brown electronic function plotter (Courtesy Minneapolis-Honeywell Regulator Co.)

Fig. 12-12. Strip-chart pressure recorder (Courtesy Faber Instrument Corp.)

Fig. 12-13. Pressure indicator (Faber Instrument Corp.)

sures sensed by the Taber Bonded Strain-gauge Transducer described earlier in Chapter 7. This unit is of the null-balancing type (see Chapter 10) and is available in a wide variety of models for measuring, indicating, recording, and control, while at the same time producing a permanent record of the measured pressure sensed by the transducer. For the Wheelco model shown, the indicating scale is 11 inches wide and the chart speed is from 1 to 4 inches per hour.

A related device by the Taber Instrument Corporation is the Model 216 Teledyne pressure indicator shown in Fig. 12-13. This unit is designed for operation with a 350-ohm strain-gauge bridge as described in Chapter 7. Its usage includes the measurement of fluid and gas pressures, thrust, and torque, where the indication of the measured

Fig. 12-14. X-Y recorder (Courtesy Sanborn Co.)

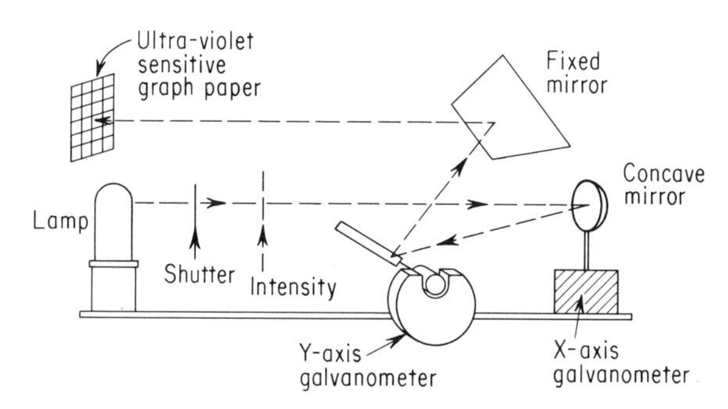

Fig. 12-15. Mirror-galvanometer system of X-Y recorder

force (as well as control) is to be accomplished at a distance from the transducer. The unit is available with dials calibrated for any standard pressure ranges. It operates on standard 110 volts, 60 cycles.

Another graphing instrument is the X-Y Recorder, Model 670 shown in Fig. 12-14. This unit, manufactured by the Sanborn Co., will plot two rapidly changing variables such as acceleration versus velocity of mechanical elements. This device utilizes optical galvanometers and a light beam to produce the recording trace, and it has writing speeds greater than 2500 inches per second. The method by which the mirror-galvanometer system controls the recording light beam is shown in Fig. 12-15. Here, a 100-watt mercury arc lamp provides a light source which is deflected by two mirror-galvanometers, and directed to the chart composed of ultraviolet-sensitive 8 by 8 inch paper which can be loaded in daylight. Traces are visible almost instantly and require no photographic development. As shown, the light beam is reflected by a spherical *X*-axis mirror to a long flat *Y*-axis mirror, and finally to a fixed flat mirror which redirects the light beam to the recording chart. The light beam is controlled by an on-off shutter and by an intensity control which places various field stops in front of the shutter.

RUNNING-TIME METERS

Running-time meters are used to show the elapsed time with respect to a certain process or to record precisely how long a particular machine has been running. Some timers introduce a preset time delay between the closure of one circuit and the operation of another. These are known as *time-delay timers*. Another type of timer is the *interval timer,* which closes a load circuit for a preset interval when energized by a momentary contact. Also used frequently in industrial electronics is the *recycling timer,* which repeats a different continuous on-off cycle. The latter timers can control a program of as many as 20 different functions in time cycles ranging from a fraction of a second to many hours. A running-time meter also finds practical applications in indicating cumulative circuit closures in different units of time, from fractions of a second to a number of hours.

Commercial Timers

A typical time-delay timer is shown in Fig. 12-16, the series TDAB of the Industrial Timer Corp. This has a maximum time cycle of 60 seconds, but is also available in models having a maximum time cycle between 1 second and 3 hours. The timer ordinarily will reset when the circuit is broken, thus it is capable of functioning again immediately. It finds applications in induction heating, plastic molding processes, photography, and packaging processes.

An interval timer, also by the Industrial Timer Corp., is shown in Fig. 12-17. This is specifically designed for process control in industrial electronics, including rubber processing, electrical spot welding, automatic conveyors, and automatic grinders. The series PAB is shown; it is available in various models having maximum time cycles ranging from 1 second to 3 hours. This is an instantaneous reset timer designed to close a load circuit for a predetermined time interval.

The Industrial Timer Corp. series MC Recycling Timer is shown in Fig. 12-18. This timer repeats a continuous on-and-off cycle of operations, and hence can control up to 20 different manufacturing processes in time cycles from a fraction of a second up to 72 hours. A multi-cam timer it has from 2 to 20 switches and from 1 to 15 motor

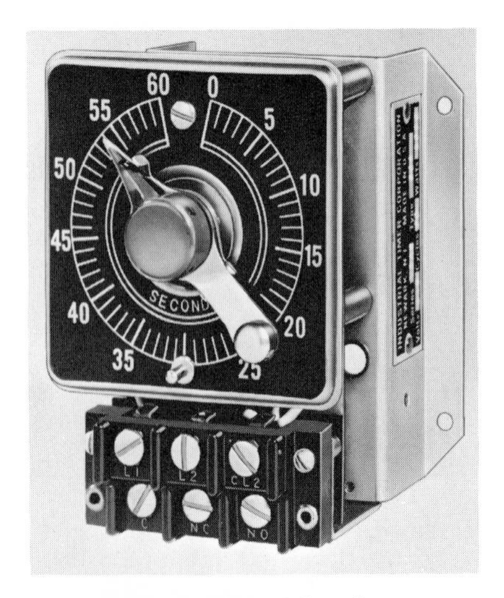

Fig. 12-16. Time delay timer (Industrial Timer Corp.)

Fig. 12-17. PAB interval timer (Industrial Timer Corp.)

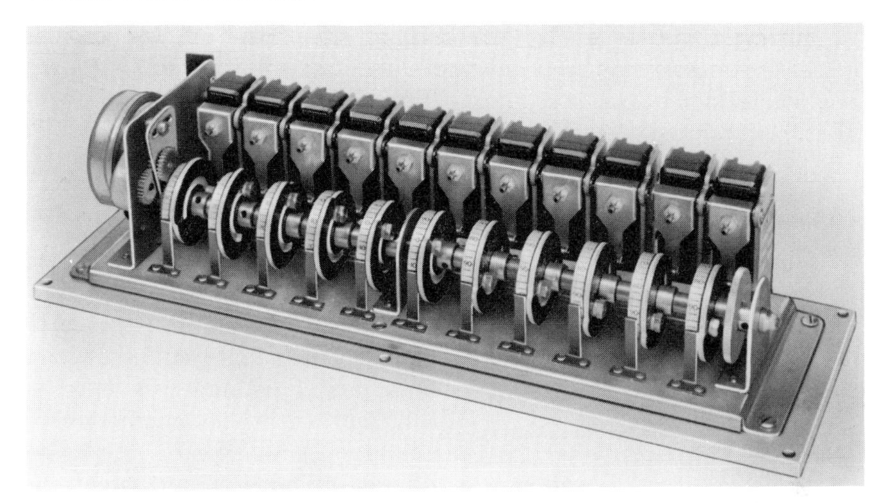

Fig. 12-18. Recycling timer (Courtesy Industrial Timer Corp.)

speeds, for the selection of time cycles required. The timing indications are visible on the circular dials for each cam shown in Fig. 12-18.

A running-time meter is shown in Fig. 12-19 (Model C-5, Industrial Timer Corp.). This one may be reset to zero at any time by the knob at the right. Typical applications are in automatic lubrication systems, chemical flow for water treatment systems, and control for electric ovens, pumps, oil burners, and stokers.

A compact timer is the Atcotrol unit shown in Fig. 12-20. This is a product of Automatic Timing and Controls, Inc. This device is useful in a number of industrial machine and process operations, since is will regulate a process for a predetermined length of time; the

Fig. 12-19. Running time meter (Industrial Timer Corp.)

Fig. 12-20. Atcotrol series 305 timer (Automatic Temperature Control Co., Inc.)

timing cycle is set by the dial at the front of the unit. A number of these controls can be connected together to initiate or terminate operations in continuous sequence. Ten standard dial ranges are available from zero to 15 seconds up to zero to 250 minutes.

SPECIAL VOLTMETERS

Besides ordinary voltmeters, special types are used in industrial electronics to perform special functions. The Speedvolter of Servo-Tek Products Co., Inc., illustrated in Fig. 12-21, is a volt-ohmmeter combination. This meter is used in conjunction with a tachometer (see Chapter 7) to measure the speed of moving or rotating objects. It also has the usual provisions for voltage and resistance checks in common with ordinary meters.

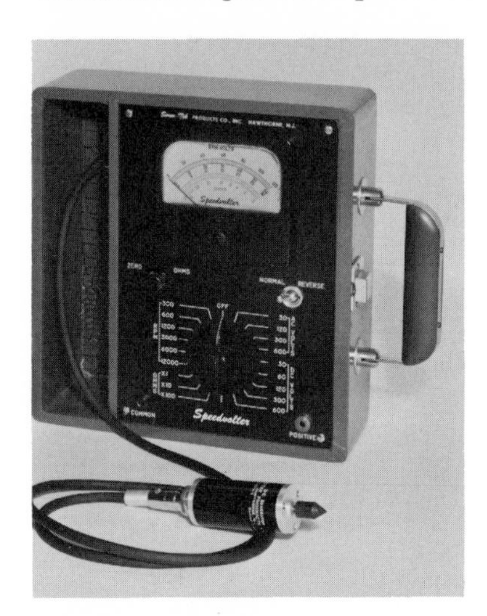

Fig. 12-21. Tachometer speedvolter (Courtesy Servo-Tek Products Co., Inc.)

The linear tachometer generator converts the motion of rotating machinery, conveyor belts, and motor revolutions into a d-c voltage which is proportional to speed. Such voltage is calibrated on the meter dial in terms of rpm.

Another special meter is the digital voltmeter illustrated in Fig. 12-22. This is the model 405AR of the Hewlett-Packard Company. This d-c digital voltmeter automatically displays the measured voltage directly in large numbers as shown. Both positive and negative voltages are displayed visually from 0.1 volt to 999 volts with high accuracy. This device will also measure d-c voltages in the presence of a-c by utilizing a filter for a-c rejection.

The Model 405AR generates a "print signal" each time the measured voltage is displayed. Because of this feature the meter will operate the Hewlett-Packard 506A Digital Recorder illustrated in Fig. 12-23, thus providing a permanent record of the readings. This provision permits voltages to be measured and recorded without an operator. The voltage sampling rate may be varied by a front panel control on the Model 405AR meter, permitting one reading every five seconds to five readings per second. The sampling rate can also be controlled by external signals so that readings may be programmed automatically.

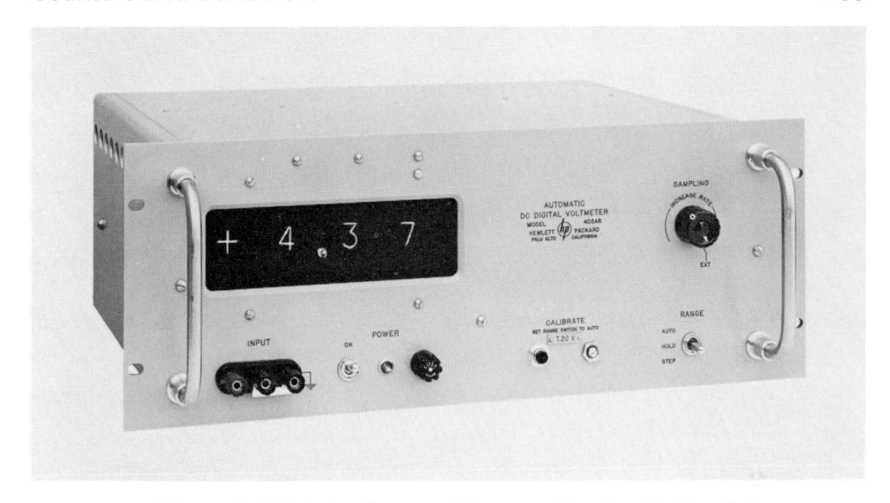

Fig. 12-22. Digital voltmeter (Courtesy Hewlett Packard)

The digital recorder shown in Fig. 12-23 prints readings not only from the digital voltmeter but also from counters. It prints on paper tape, single- or double-spaced. The recorder has an analog output signal (see Chapter 15) which will drive a strip-chart recorder. The analog signal is a current or voltage proportional to the value of any three-digit number printed by the recorder.

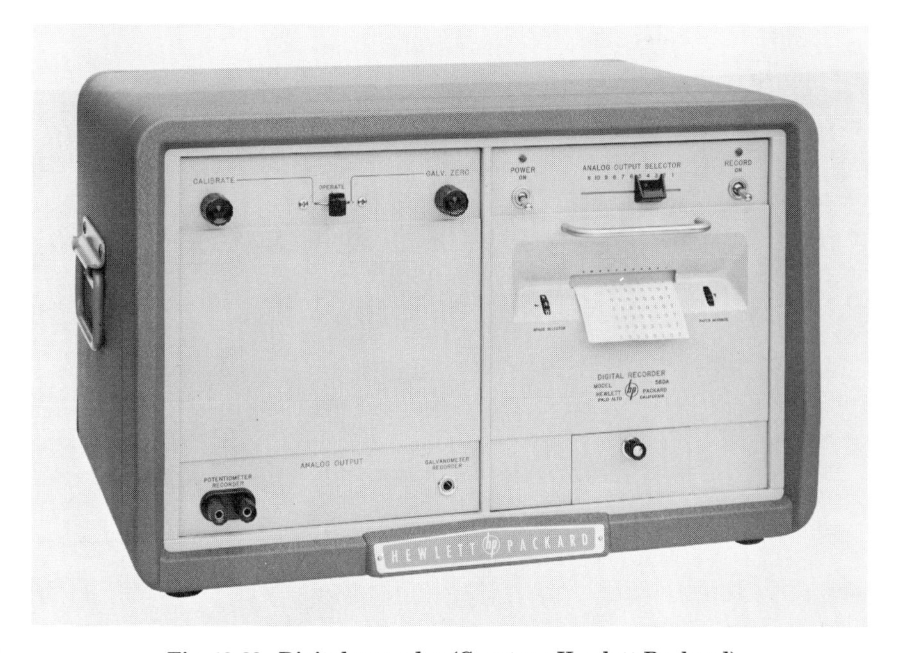

Fig. 12-23. Digital recorder (Courtesy Hewlett Packard)

Review Questions for Chapter 12

1. Explain the basic differences between counting tubes such as the Nixie, the Dekatron, and the Digitron.
2. List some of the features of commercial counters.
3. Briefly explain the underlying principles of the stroboscope type of tachometer.
4. List some of the features of commercial temperature indicators and control devices.
5. Explain briefly what uses recorders and plotters have in industrial electronic applications.
6. What are the differences between time-delay timers, interval timers, and recycling timers?
7. List the features of some typical special-purpose industrial voltmeters.
8. How can voltmeter measurements be obtained without the presence of an operator?

13

Control Circuits and Systems

INTRODUCTION

The miscellaneous circuits and components previously discussed herin are combined in various ways to operate and control industrial and manufacturing processes. Transducers sense changes and other variables and produce signals, which in some cases must be modified and amplified before application to appropriate control circuitry. Alternating-current power must be stepped up or down, and its application controlled. Rectifier circuits convert a-c to d-c for application to regulate variable-speed motors or other devices, and such d-c must also be controlled with respect to its amplitude and time of application. Various reading and recording instruments are employed for obtaining visual and permanent records of signal amplitudes, process variations, and the like.

In this chapter, basic control circuits and processes are covered as well as practical commercial package units. Industrial process applications are covered in the next chapter.

CONTROL APPLICATIONS

Various industrial processes can be regulated and controlled by standard circuit combinations. Where, for instance, considerable power must be applied at certain intervals, or where the amount of such power must be regulated, standard rectifier-filter systems are employed as described earlier in Chapter 6. When sufficient power is available, its application and amplitude can be controlled by use of thyratrons, ignitrons, silicon-controlled rectifiers, and similar devices, using appropriate phase-control methods and magnetic amplifiers, such as have been described earlier. Automatic regulation of industrial processes can be employed using transducers and null-indicating circuits to produce error-correction voltages, which in conjunction with selsyn and servo devices will maintain proper fabrication or processing. Such combinations are also capable of direct manual control, as shown later. Once controlled power of specific type and amplitude is available, it can be used for welding control, motor control, inducting heating, and numerous other industrial requirements.

Welding

One welding process is that known as *spot welding,* and the basic circuit set-up is as shown at A of Fig. 13-1. This is a type of resistance welding, because the two metal plates to be welded provide sufficient surface-contact resistance to generate heat when passing current from the welding electrodes. The heat causes a fusion of the sheets at the spot to be welded. In large welders the contacting electrodes are cooled by a continuously running stream of water through the electrode piping as shown at B. Both electrodes apply force during the fusion process.

As shown at A, the line voltage (through the gated thyratron

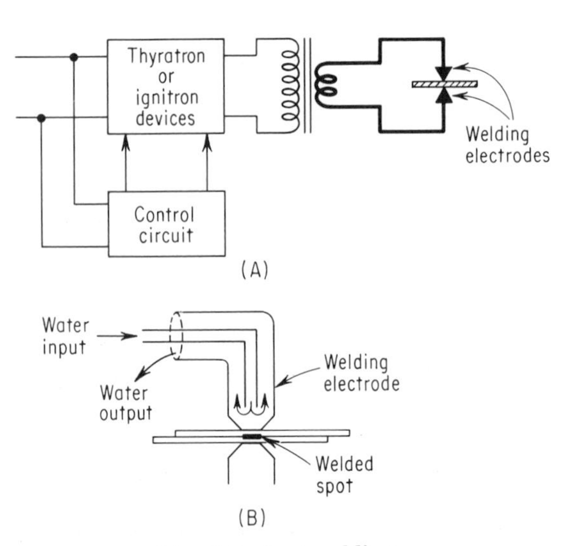

Fig. 13-1. Spot welding

circuits) is stepped down by a transformer to deliver approximately 2 to 10 volts at a current rating ranging anywhere from a few thousand amperes to well over 50,000 in some of the larger welders. Precise control must be maintained to assure proper welding without burn-through or the making of a bond of insufficient holding characteristics.

Seam welding is another form of spot welding, though instead of electrodes of the type shown at B of Fig. 13-1, rollers are used. As the material passes between the rollers, the control circuits apply bursts of power to the roller electrodes, and a series of spot welds are formed in a running seam. Again, thyratron-controlled circuits are employed to apply the proper amount of power at the right intervals for just the right degree of welding.

In *arc welding,* the process consists of producing a concentrated high-intensity arc between two electrodes, and applying the heat so produced to the metal to be welded. The electrodes are made up of special welding rods which melt during the arc, so that a portion of the melted electrode material can flow onto the metal being welded. For arc welding, either d-c or a-c can be employed. The arc-welding process has been used primarily for manual operation where portability is required, though in some special industrial electronic applications automatic control has been employed.

Induction and Dielectric Heating

Another instance where control circuitry applies to industrial processes is in heating. Temperature-control devices are sometimes included in the reading instruments for ovens, heat chambers, kilns, and so on as discussed in the preceding chapter. Control, however, also applies to the application of heat when it is produced by either the induction or dielectric heating process (Fig. 13-2). For high-frequency induction heating, the circuitry is required as shown at A, consisting of a power supply for obtaining d-c voltages for the high-frequency oscillator circuit. The r-f output signal from the oscillator circuit is applied to the material to be heated by use of a large, high-power-handling coil as shown. The radio-frequency fields generated heat the material to the required degree under direct control by the regulating circuits employed.

For high-power induction heating, the power can be obtained directly from the power mains, using motor-driven generators (Chapter 5) having signal frequencies of several thousand cps, and ranging from a few kilowatts to about 1000 kilowatts. Applications include heating metals for shaping or annealing and other similar processes where heating speed is important to minimize the effect of gases generated by other processes, and to prevent scaling and the oxidizing

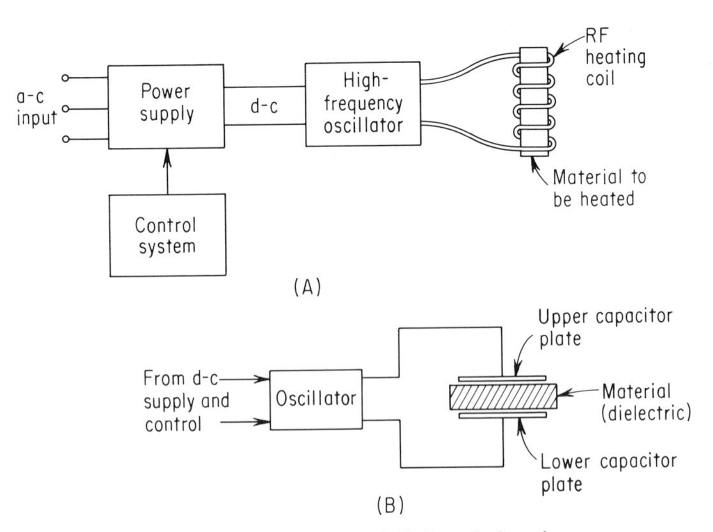

Fig. 13-2. Induction and dielectric heating

of metal surfaces. Induction heating is also important where only a portion of the material is to be heated. The coil shown at A is usually composed of copper tubing—for two reasons: the larger diameter can handle greater power, and the hollow center can be used for circulating water through the coil for cooling.

Induction heating finds applications in annealing, melting, hardening, and brazing processes. In all these, the frequency of the a-c used must be under control as well as the amount of power. The depth of heat penetration in induction heating of a particular application is related to the frequency of the a-c power. In metal melting, for instance, frequencies as low as the standard 60 cps power mains are often used. For annealing, or for good heat penetration of large objects in surface heating, the frequency may range from 500 cps to approximately 3000 cps. For surface heating and hardening of small (or thin) metals, frequencies ranging from 200,000 cps to well over 750,000 cps are employed.

The dielectric heating system shown at B of Fig. 13-2 finds application in the processing of plastics, textiles, and laminates such as plywood, where heat treatment is required in the curing, drying, gluing, or molding. The advantage of dielectric heating lies in its ability to heat from within, rather than relying on gradual heat penetration from the outside.

The principle involved is that of the heating effect which occurs in some dielectric materials when placed between two conducting plates. In the dielectric materials used for electronic capacitors, the resistive loss factor is kept at a minimum by choosing dielectric materials having low loss, such as ceramics, air, or mica. With most other materials, the power factor is such that some power loss occurs because of leakage current through the dielectric. Thus, considerable heat can be created when such materials are inserted between capacitor plates having high voltages placed on them, as shown at B of Fig. 13-2. Again thyratron-type devices under circuit control are employed.

PHOTOTUBE CONTROL CIRCUITS

Any of the phototubes or phototransistors can be employed to control the firing of a gas tube such as the thyratron. A typical circuit for the high-vacuum type photo tube is shown at A of Fig. 13-3. Tube V_1 represents the phototube, and V_2 is the gas-type thyratron. In this circuit, the gas tube can be made to conduct by an increase in the light striking the phototube V_1. Initially, assume that V_2 is not conducting. The a-c supply source is impressed across terminals T_1 and T_2 and when the switch is closed, this voltage appears across the phototube V_1 as well as across the gas triode V_2.

Assume, for instance, that one alternation of the a-c supply source has such a polarity that terminal T_1 is positive and terminal T_2 is negative. This places a positive polarity at the top of R_1 and a nega-

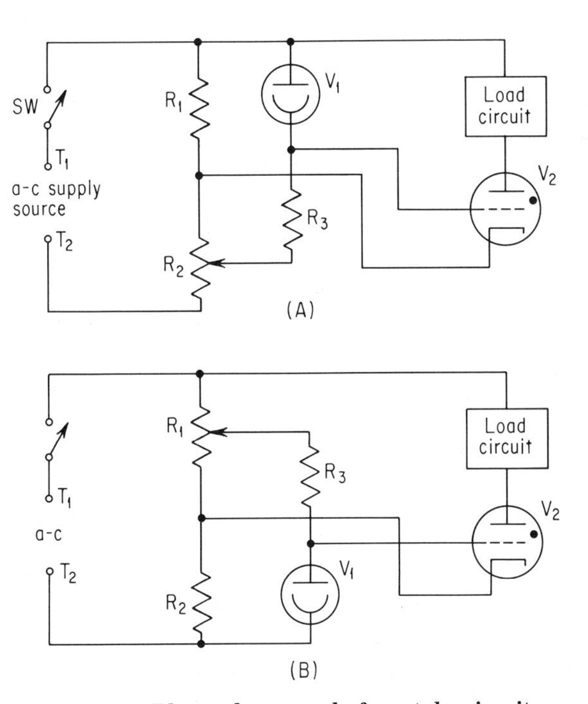

Fig. 13-3. Phototube control of gas-tube circuit

tive polarity at the bottom of R_2. If low light intensity (or no light) strikes V_1, only a small amount of current will flow through the latter. The cathode of V_2, because it is attached to the junction of R_1 and R_2, is more positive than the grid, since the latter is at a lower potential level by being connected to the variable arm of R_2. Thus, the fact that the grid is negative with respect to the cathode of V_2 prevents conduction of the latter. When there is an increase in the light which strikes V_1, the current through the latter increases and the voltage drop across R_3 rises. The increase in current through R_3 makes the bottom of the latter negative and the top positive. Obviously, also, since the internal resistance of V_1 decreases as the latter conducts more current, there is less voltage drop across V_1 and the grid terminal of V_2 is connected to the upper positive polarity through a much lower resistance than heretofore. The decrease in the negative potential of the grid with respect to the cathode causes the gas tube to fire and thus current will flow through the load circuit.

For the second alternation of a-c which appears across the input terminals, terminal T_1 is negative and terminal T_2 is positive. Under this condition, the current flow through the gas tube V_2 ceases because of the negative potential at its plate. Conduction through V_1 also stops, since the latter cannot conduct either when its anode is negative. Thus, this circuit will apply pulsating d-c to the load circuit for an increase in light intensity. As with the thyratron circuits described earlier, the average power of the pulsating d-c can be utilized for the load, or filtering can be employed to obtain relatively ripple free d-c for application to the load if required.

At B of Fig. 13-3 another phototube control circuit is shown which acts in opposite fashion to the one shown at A. For the circuit at B, the gas tube will apply power to the load circuit for a *decrease* in the light intensity which impinges on the phototube V_1. Again, assume that a positive alternation appears across the input terminals, making T_1 positive and T_2 negative. Such an alternation of a-c at the input terminals will make the anodes of both V_1 and V_2 positive with respect to the cathodes. With light impinging on V_1, V_1 conducts current, and since such current flows through resistor R_3 it makes the bottom of R_3 negative with respect to the top. (When V_2 is conducting, its low resistance places the grid of V_2 nearer the negative potential of T_2.) In consequence, the grid of V_2 is sufficiently negative to prevent conduction. For a decrease in the light intensity which strikes V_1, conduction through V_1 decreases and the voltage drop across R_3 decreases. Now, the grid of V_2 becomes positive with respect to the cathode and the tube fires and again applies power to the load circuit.

The variable resistor for either of the circuits shown in Fig. 13-3 adjusts the relative sensitivity of the phototube to establish its control at the exact light intensity desired. The values of various resistors depend on the characteristics of the phototube. For the circuit shown at A, R_1 may be 20,000 ohms, while R_2 may be approximately 1000 ohms. R_3 may range from 1 to 10 megohms. For the circuit shown at B, R_1 is approximately 2000 ohms, and R_2 is approximately 100 ohms. R_3 is also 1 to 10 megohms, depending on the characteristics of the phototube.

COMMERCIAL TEMPERATURE CONTROLLER

A basic package unit for temperature control is the Electrol Unichannel Model 7158-4-PO shown in Figs. 13-4 and 13-5. The sensing device, shown in Fig. 13-4 at the bottom of the drawing, consists of a stainless steel tube which contains the sensing element. A setpoint dial is provided as shown, and the power transformer and amplifier-modulator are mounted on the chassis top, including the tubes. This device automatically controls temperatures of industrial processes. The sensing element continuously measures temperature of the process

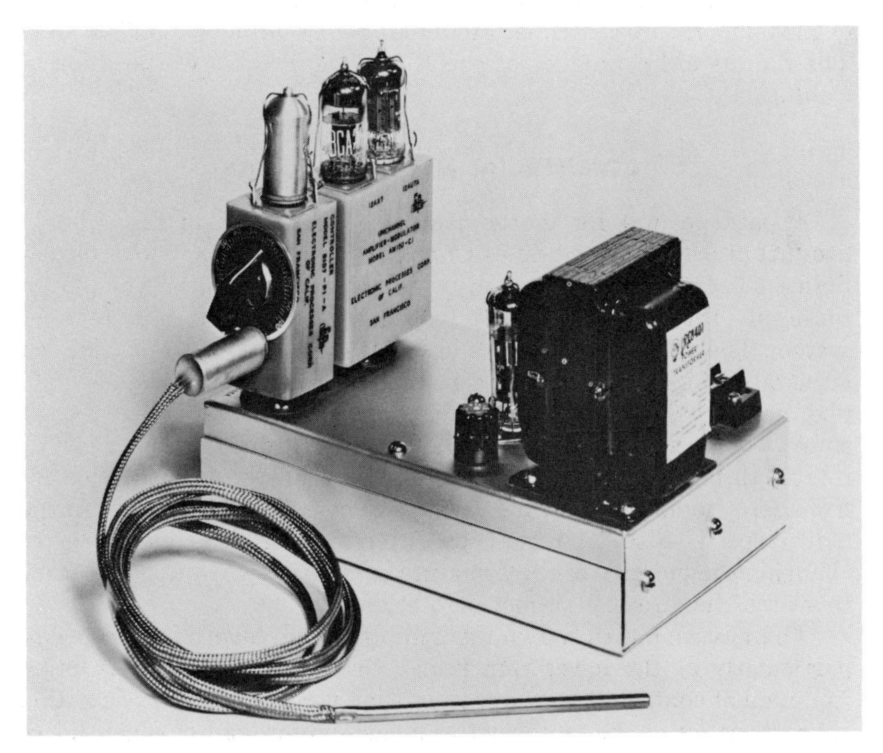

Fig. 13-4. Temperature controller amplifier (Courtesy Electronic Processes Corp. of California)

Fig. 13-5. Controller (Courtesy Electronic Processes Corp. of California)

under control, and the signals generated by the transducer are compared with the setpoint temperature. The controller then automatically turns the heat on or off as necessary. The front and rear panels of the temperature controller Model 7158-4-PO are shown in Fig. 13-5. These units are a product of the Electronic Process Corporation of California.

COMMERCIAL MOTOR CONTROLS

A package unit for motor control is illustrated in Fig. 13-6. A product of Servo-Tek Products Company, it is known as Motorformer Series 400. In these units, an adjustable autotransformer is employed to supply the voltage for a full-wave silicon-diode bridge-rectifier system. The schematic is shown in Fig. 13-7. This system provides an adjustable d-c armature voltage. Similar silicon diodes are used in a plug-in assembly for furnishing substantially constant voltage for the shunt-wound motor.The contact arm of the autotransformer can be rotated through approximately 270° for changing the armature voltage from zero to maximum, thus causing a corresponding change in the motor speed. Also, a drum-type reversing switch is available for changing the polarity of the armature connection when it is necessary to switch the direction of motor rotation.

This system has the advantages of providing smooth motor speeds, particularly at the lower rpm levels. Gradual acceleration is under full manual control and no warm-up time is required. The regulation characteristics of the motor act as a cushion for load changes, hence control of this type is particularly suited where rapid changes in torque or tension are undesirable during the manufacturing process.

Fig. 13-6. Servo-Tek motorformer drive

There are a number of occasions when an adjustable-speed motor is required. It is, however, also desirable that a change in the torque load cause no appreciable change in motor speed. For this reason, thyratron tubes have been used in motor control in a circuit arrange-

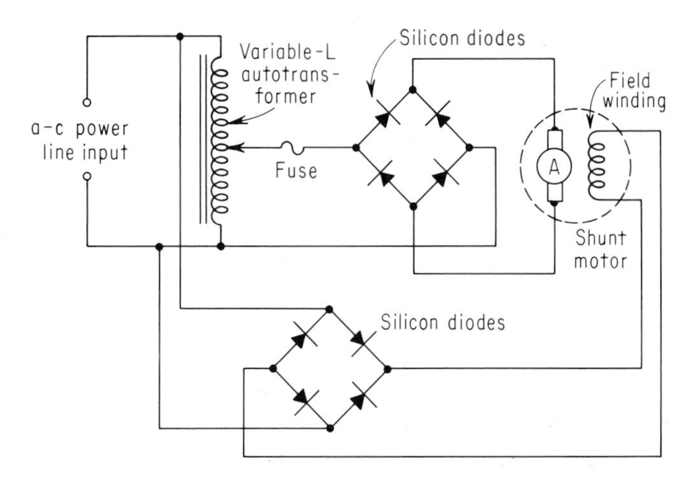

Fig. 13-7. Circuit of series 400 motorformer drive

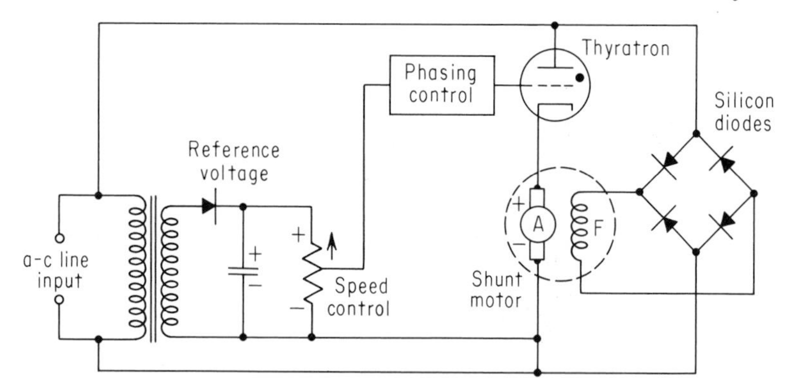

Fig. 13-8. Circuit of Servo-Tek series 300 motor drives

ment such as shown in Fig. 13-8. As discussed in Chapter 9, the armature current in a shunt motor is virtually proportionate to torque. Since the current flows through the armature, increased torque causes an increased amount of input power to be converted to heat by virtue of the armature resistance. The circuit shown in Fig. 13-8 maintains a shunt motor at fairly constant speed with increased torque by using a feedback thyratron circuit for increasing the voltage applied to the armature.

During one-half of each cycle, a positive alternation is presented at the plate of the thyratron. As discussed in Chapter 8, ionization occurs within the tube when a positive grid voltage is present during a positive plate alternation. This initiates current flow through the motor armature, across which voltage is developed with a polarity as shown. The armature rotation is started by moving the slider of the speed-control potentiometer in the direction of the arrow.

The circuit shown in Fig. 13-8 is another package unit available from Servo-Tek, their Series 300 Motor Drive. The speed is determined by the reference or control voltage. This device can be used in conjunction with electric transducers for control purposes.

A third type of motor control package by this company is the Series 100 Precision Drive with Tachometer Feedback, shown in Fig. 13-9. This circuit is illustrated in Fig. 13-10. This unit is of especial advantage in industrial automatic control where the need is for an adjustable-speed drive that can be accurately set to a precisely maintained speed.

This system is basically a servo device. In standard procedures, the true final speed is first measured with an accurate tachometer (see Chapter 7) which is usually mounted in the assembly framework to form an integral part of the motor assembly. The signal voltage obtained from this tachometer may be a-c or d-c, and it is compared

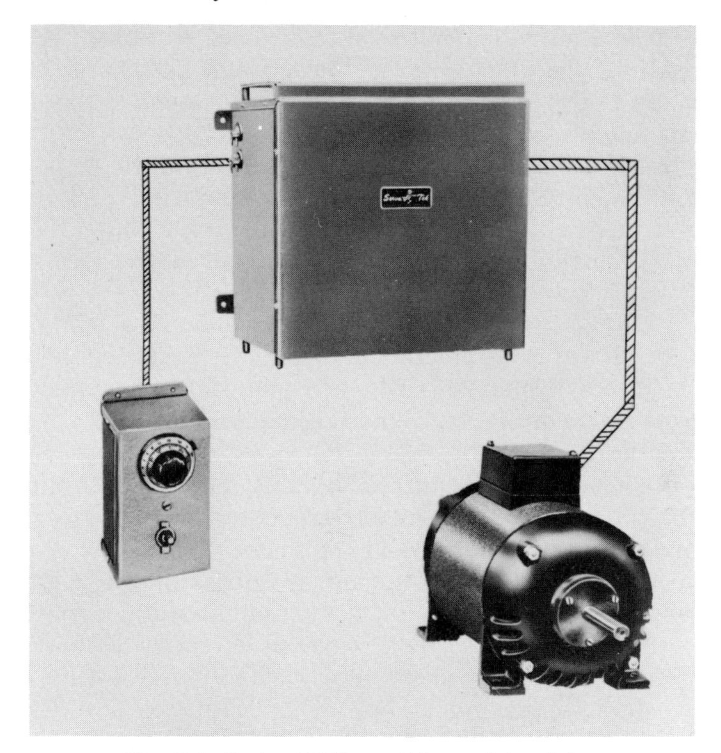

Fig. 13-9. Series 100 Servo-Tek precision drive

with a control voltage that can be adjusted precisely to a desired level. The reference voltage is applied in opposition to the polarity of the tachometer signal, hence any difference in their respective values forms an error voltage in a typical closed-loop servo assembly. The

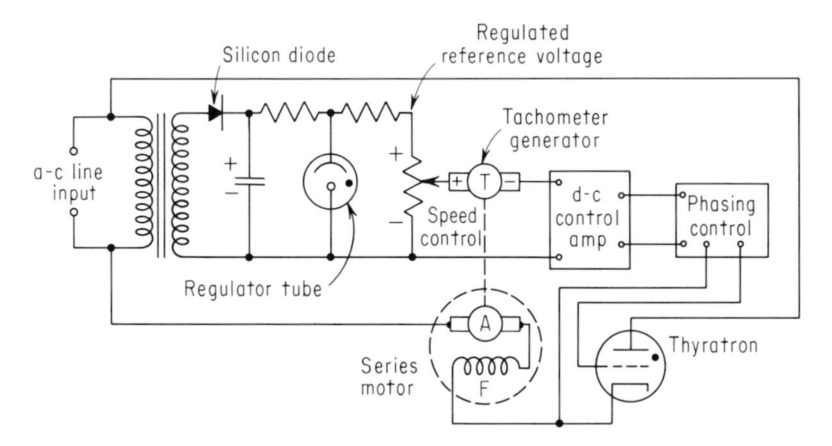

Fig. 13-10. Servo-Tek series 100 motor control system

error voltage is amplified and used to advance or retard the firing of the thyratron tube which supplies the armature current of the motor. The change in the thyratron output results in a motor-speed change to correct any deviation in speed.

Another commercial unit for thyratron grid control is the VecTrol unit shown in Fig. 13-11. This is a phase-shift network for proportional control of thyratrons having outputs up to 20,000 watts, requiring a d-c control signal of only 1 milliwatt. The unit can be used with two thyratrons (full-wave) and the phase shift is linear for a full 180°, with a maximum of 270°. The device uses four isolated d-c control windings with saturable-reactor characteristics for magnetic-amplifier function. Typical applications include regulated power supplies, adjustable-speed motor drives, servo motors, and machine-tool applications in automation.

As with many other commercial package units of electronic devices and circuitry, the company holds patents on the phase-shifting circuitry in the control unit, as well as on some of the associated external circuits. The VecTrol phase-shifting network is shown in Fig. 13-12. Inductance L_3 consists of the a-c windings of a saturable reactor. The latter also contains d-c control windings to saturate the core and thus alter the phase angle of the network. The phase-shifting depends on the values of the inductors and capacitors in a series circuit as shown.

A typical application of the VecTrol unit is that shown in Fig. 13-13. Here, the device is utilized for armature-voltage control of adjustable-speed d-c shunt motors. Self-regulated armature (A) voltage is developed by a feedback circuit without the need for amplification of the

Fig. 13-11. VecTrol thyratron control (Courtesy VecTrol Engineering, Inc.)

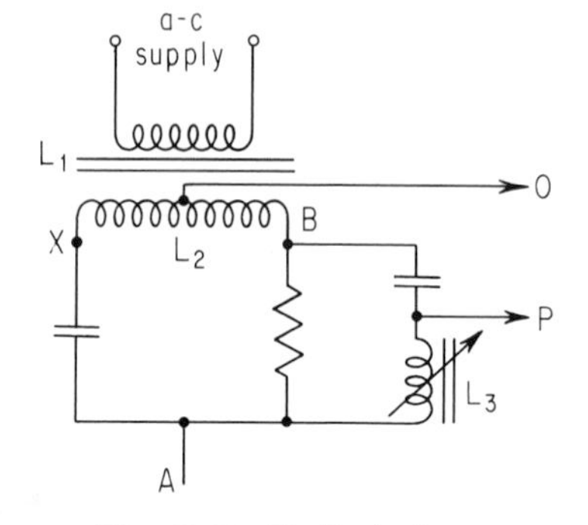

Fig. 13-12. VecTrol phase-shifting network

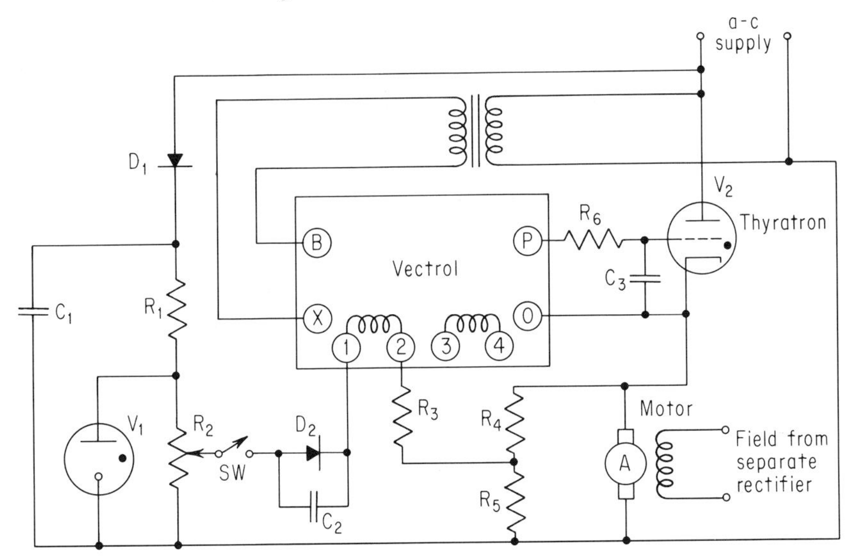

Fig. 13-13. VecTrol motor armature voltage regulator

error signal. In the feedback circuit a fraction (about one-third) of the armature voltage is used for feedback purposes and is obtained from the junction of R_4 and R_5 as shown in the illustration. The feedback voltage is applied to terminal 2 and then transferred through the VecTrol control unit to terminal 1. The feedback voltage is compared to that of a d-c reference voltage procured from the speed-controlling variable resistor R_2. The d-c reference voltage is obtained by rectifying the line voltage with diode D_1. A voltage-regulator tube is utilized (V_1) and a filter capacitor C_1. The difference between the feedback voltage and the reference voltage comprises the error signal, and this appears across the control terminals 1-2 and thus controls the thyratron output.

A small selenium rectifier D_2 prevents accidental reversal of the error signal, and this circuit design is also covered by patents. The capacitor C_2 smoothes out any ripple component across D_2. Resistor R_3 in series with the feedback voltage is used occasionally to reduce the sensitivity of the control winding when necessary for increasing stability.

VecTrol Engineering, Inc., also has a phase-shifting device available for the gate control of silicon-controlled rectifiers. The latter, as described in Chapter 8, also have thyratron characteristics, and are employed in a wide variety of applications where it is necessary to release considerable power to such devices as adjustable-speed motors, servo motors, welding equipment, and so on. The VecTrol unit is known as the Silicontrol and is shown in Fig. 13-14.

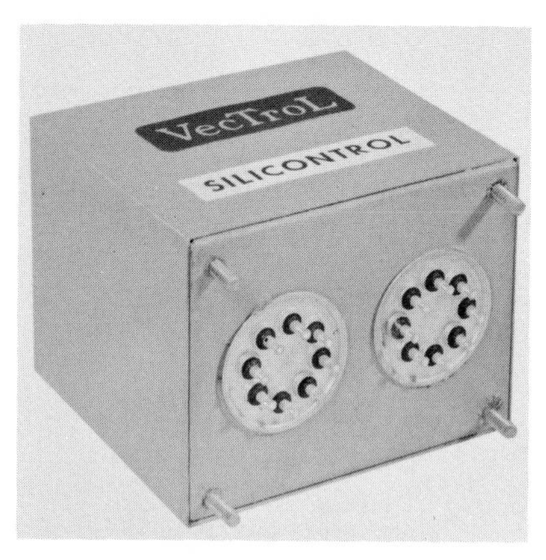

Fig. 13-14. The Silicontrol (Courtesy VecTrol Engineering, Inc.)

Review Questions for Chapter 13

1. What are the essential differences between the spot-welding and the arc-welding processes?
2. Why is electronic control essential in welding processes?
3. What are the basic principles of induction heating?
4. In what fabrication or molding processes is dielectric heating useful?
5. Reproduce a schematic of a photoelectric thyratron control where an increase in light intensity fires the gas-tube thyratron, and summarize its operating principles.
6. What are the essential control differences between the two circuits illustrated in Figs. 13-7 and 13-8?
7. What specific application has the circuit shown in Fig. 13-10?
8. Briefly explain how the circuit shown in Fig. 13-10 resembles a servo device.
9. How is an error signal procured in the circuit shown in Fig. 13-13?
10. How is the feedback voltage procured in the circuit shown in Fig. 13-13?

14

Practical Industrial Applications

INTRODUCTION

The practical applications of industrial electronics may be grouped in three primary categories: error detection, process control, and counting and measuring. Actually the three types are interrelated and overlap to a considerable extent, because in most instances one electronic or electromechanical process depends on the other for completion of the industrial program.

This chapter illustrates the variety and diversity of industrial applications of electronics. At first it discusses in a general way the controls and devices used in various manufacturing and industrial processes, then goes on to some specific practical applications, describing the equipment of companies specializing in industrial electronic control devices. No attempt will be made to exhaust the subject, because new applications of the basic principles described in this book are constantly being devised and applied to error detection, process control, and counting and measuring.

ERROR DETECTION

A variety of processes are included under the broad category of error detection. Among these is the general-alarm system employing electronic means. One such device is a burglar alarm system using photoelectric devices or switches which activate an alarm of audible or visual nature when triggered. This device is shown in A of Fig. 14-1. Another device is designed to protect employees from danger, as shown at B. In the latter case, the machine shuts off if the operator's hands interrupt the light beam in front of the device.

In a broad sense, the alarm system is an error-detecting device, since the standard is the normal condition which prevails, and the error is the interruption of the light beam to the photoelectric cell or the closing of the switch whether it is by an intruder or because some manufacturing process is either endangered or off standard. Thus, error-detecting systems can be employed for giving an alarm if a certain manufacturing process is deviating from a preset standard. The error-detecting devices are also used for ascertaining the relative speed and accuracy of an industrial process such as manufacturing, sorting, labeling, or packaging. When a deviation from normal occurs, the error-detection device must then develop some sort of error signal which can regulate a correcting device. Thus, the correcting device is in essence a process-control since it will correct any deviations from normal during a manufacturing process.

The error-detecting and alarm systems can be applied to a number of commercial and industrial processes. In the chemical field, for instance, error detection could be applied to detect deviations in density or specific gravity of fluids, to determine the rate of fluid flow and liquid levels, and to detect temperature variations or other reactions in chemical mixtures.

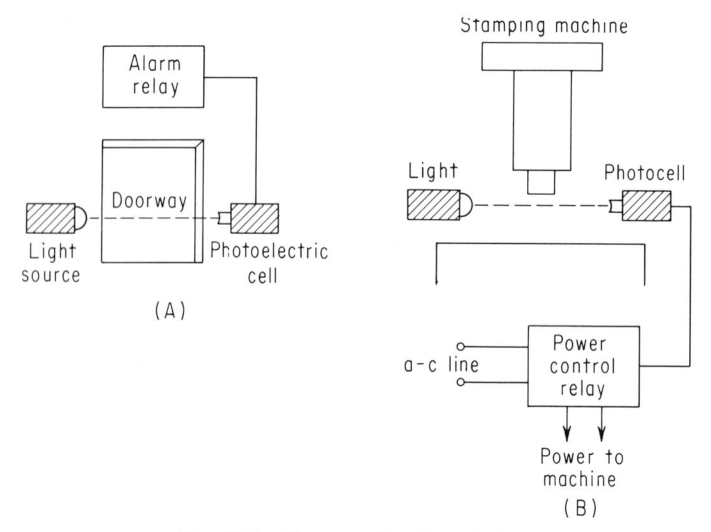

Fig. 14-1. Alarm and safety devices

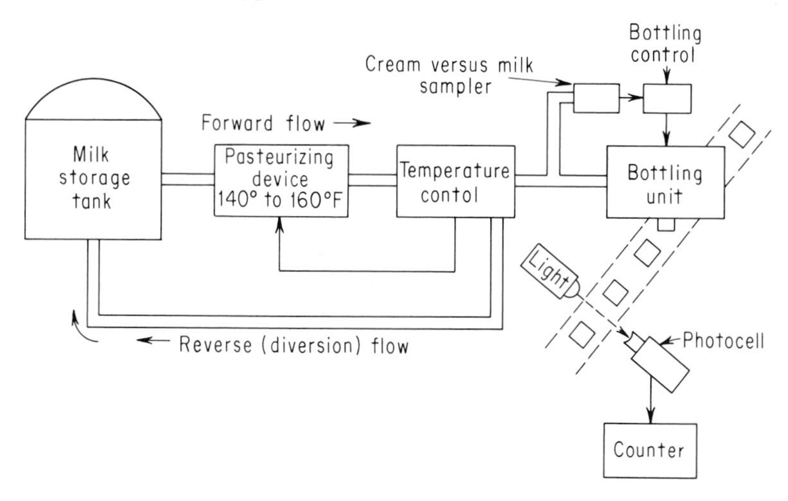

Fig. 14-2. Error detection in the dairy industry

In dairy processes, error detection can be employed in the pasteurization of milk. When the temperature falls below that at which the pasteurization process occurs, the error-detection devices can be used to divert the milk back to the main tank and thus stop the bottling process until the temperature is brought back to normal, as shown in Fig. 14-2. Error detection is also used to check for the accurate proportions of cream and milk during the bottling processes.

In the meat-packing industry, electronic error detection is employed for refrigeration temperature control, temperature control in smoke houses and meat-cooking devices, and the proper processing of meat for packaging.

In the metal-processing industry, error detection is utilized for temperature control of chemical electroplating processes, the temperature control of hardening processes, and the control of induction heating. In all these, deviations from the normal processes or normal states are sensed by electronic error-detecting devices so that correction can be made for any drift from standard.

In the petroleum industry electronic controls are extensively employed. Here, error-detecting devices must sense changes in petroleum flow through pipes; again, as in the case for chemicals, error detection is related to maintaining specific gravities, fluid densities, and liquid levels.

In the textile industry the error-detecting devices are applied to the boiling, dyeing, and bleaching processes. Error detection is also applied to temperature control of the processes which the textiles undergo during manufacture.

PROCESS CONTROL

Virtually in every instance where error-detecting devices are used, process control is also employed. Thus, in all the manufacturing processes previously mentioned under error-detection, the process-control phase of industrial electronics comes into play. Process control by electronic devices is utilized in the chemical industry, the food, beverage, and meat-packing industries, in the machinery and mechanical equipment industries, as well as in the petroleum, textile, utility, and other industries.

In general, process control would include the maintenance of material thicknesses, the protection of machine operators' hands by the use of photoelectric or other sensing devices, package-wrapping, weighing packages, and counting and sorting. Process control is also related to welding and to lathe, drill-press, and punch-press operation. Also in the process-control category is moisture control in concrete-block manufacturing as well as the control of brick drying temperatures. In lumber, process controls are applied to kiln-drying, sawing, and planing. In paper manufacturing, an electronic control is applied to the consistency of the paper during manufacture, the coating processes (if such are employed), and the speed and draw measurements for paper-processing machines.

In food and beverage processing, controls are applied to bottling and canning, sterilization and pasteurization, temperature control of ovens, and the refining, packaging, and sorting processes.

In other manufacturing processes, electronic control is applied to such operations as sequencing of chemicals or thermoprocesses; electroplating and galvanizing processes; temperature control in the manufacture of metals and other hard items, including the temperature control of the forging furnace, the open-hearth furnaces, and others.

COUNTING AND MEASURING

In the error-detection and process-control systems previously mentioned, many applications also require counting and measuring. Again, the three primary categories tend to overlap, because in some error-detection processes the error might be that of a count in excess of or below a certain amount. Or the error might be registered when a measurement indicates an excessive voltage, fluid level, or temperature, or a liquid level, voltage, or temperature below a preset standard.

There are, of course, instances where counting and measuring processes under electronic control simply indicate the status of a manufacturing process. The number of items going past a point on a moving belt may be counted and a record printed of the number produced per hour or per day, as covered in Chapter 12. Similarly, measurements may be made of the thickness of materials during manufacture, the density of ink during printing, the amount of smoke in certain combustion processes, as well as power and pressure levels. Measurements would, of course, also include weight and specific gravity as well as normal electronic measurements of voltage, current, resistance, and power.

In chemical processes, food processing, and fluid purification, mixture-consistency measurements are usually employed. In many commercial industrial processes, temperature measurements, both of high temperatures, and refrigerated temperatures, must be maintained. The distribution of gas and oil also requires flow measurement, and the volume of flow per minute, hour, or day must be recorded.

Counting is not only applied to items on an assembly line, but also to the number of times a welding or other mechanical process occurs. A count is often made of drill-press operation, stamping devices, and printing processes. When necessary, the measuring devices can be employed as error-detecting units, since a deviation from a preset standard or norm can be made to produce an error signal which can be utilized for correction purposes as discussed earlier.

SINGLE-PROCESS CONTROL SYSTEMS

The requirements of industry for electronic controls have led manufacturers to produce package units for convenience in setting up automatic counting, measuring, error-detecting, and control functions. Commercial package units for counting, measuring, and error detection have already been discussed, as well as package units for power control to motors and other load circuits. Besides these, however, a number of manufacturers offer control and error-detecting package units involving a single process or function. Among the latter are photoelectric alarm systems for protection of the premises against burglars, smoke, and fire. Photoelectric devices are also available in package form to protect employees from power tools, to open doors in supermarkets, and to perform counting procedures.

In package form also are single-process devices which will perform some function which is part of the entire automation manufacturing sequence. Such devices may consist of the necessary transducers plus appropriate circuitry and servos or motors as required. While such package units fit many applications without modification, most manufacturers have available an engineering department which will alter package units to meet the requirements which may arise in a specific installation.

Several single-process-control commercial devices and circuits are described next to acquaint the reader with typical items of this type. Multiprocess-control commercial packages are described later.

Edge and Position Control

When a continuously moving sheet of material is being processed during manufacture, it is often necessary to keep the material moving in a straight line without variation. This is necessary, for instance, in printing, particularly where colors are involved. Edge control is also necessary for moving sheets of metal which must be stamped or otherwise processed. In such cases, any variations of placement of the continuously moving sheet of material to either side must be controlled to prevent errors in the processing.

One method for control is to sense the deviations by use of photoelectric cells such as covered in Chapter 7. Any sideward movement is detected; and by use of null-indicating circuits, such as described in Chapter 10, a correction voltage is procured to control and vary the placement of the material as it moves down the line.

Another method is that shown in Fig. 14-3, the Atcotran Edge Guide Control system by Automatic Timing and Controls, Inc. It uses the Atcotran Edge Feeler shown earlier in Fig. 7-5 (Chapter 7). The lever arm of the transducer senses any lateral movement of the continuously moving sheet. Any variations picked up by the differential reactor, which in turn produces voltage variations, are amplified to the degree required to operate a servo-type motor as shown in Fig. 14-3. The servo motor rotates in one direction for one polarity of voltage generated by the transducer, and vice versa. The motor actuates a hydraulic valve which controls a piston as shown. Depend-

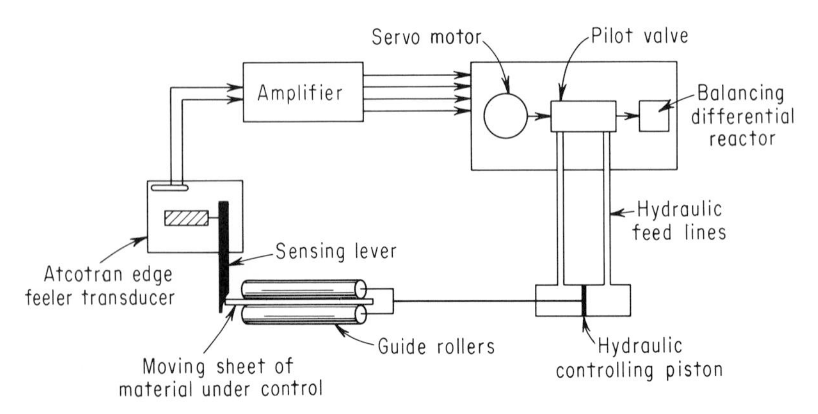

Fig. 14-3. Atcotran edge guide control (Automatic Timing & Controls, Inc.)

ing on the polarity of the voltage sensed by the transducer and the movement of the servo motor, the controlling piston moves in one direction or the other to establish the necessary correction for the deviation of the moving material.

If, for instance, the edge of the material moves slightly to the right, it pushes the lever attached to the differential reactor to the right and this is translated by the system and causes the piston to move to the left. Because the valve action regulates the positioning rollers, the material is pulled to the left until it again assumes the correct position. When the correct position prevails, the bridge circuit is balanced, a zero voltage prevails, and hence the piston no longer moves. A balancing reactor as well as the sensing reactor is used in a conventional null-indicating circuit (as described elsewhere herein) for controlling the servo motor. The balancing reactor is adjusted so that there is zero output when the material is in proper position on the line.

Omission Detection

The differential-reactor principle can also be employed to sense changes which are abrupt, rather than gradual as in edge control. Instead of a variable-core inductor, a fixed-core inductor is used which senses a change in terms of metal passing beneath the inductor. An a-c signal is applied to the reactor, and a magnetic field is generated around it. Thus, when a metal having magnetic properties passes beneath the reactor, the reactor's lines of force are cut and in consequence a slight change occurs in the reactor's circulating current.

A device of this type can sense omissions in an assembly line, and by producing appropriate signals can indicate such omissions. Another application is to sense a deviation from normal in the processed item; the deviation can be displayed on an indicating device and the signals produced can also be used for correction or rejection. A practical application is shown in Fig. 14-4, another Atcotran system. Here, filled and capped bottles are moving in an assembly line, and the system shown senses an error in terms of an uncapped bottle. This system is used in beverage-packing industries where a metal rather than plastic bottle cap is employed.

The error detection involves not only the sensing reactor; if it did, a signal would be obtained every time one of the metal bottle caps passed directly beneath the coil. The absence of a bottle cap would produce no signal; whereas from the practical design standpoint, the reverse condition should prevail—that is, a signal should be produced only when a bottle cap is missing.

For production of a signal in the absence of a bottle cap, the reactor (referred to as a *proximity cell*) is employed in conjunction with

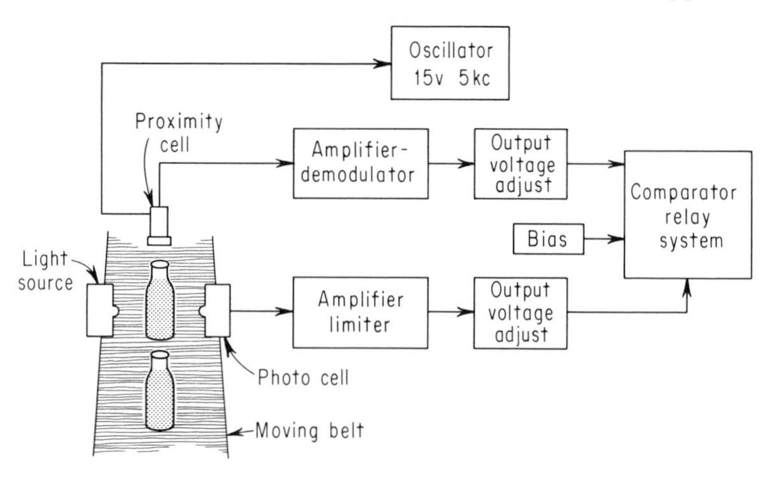

Fig. 14-4. Atcotran bottle cap control system

a photocell as illustrated, so that one unit with respect to the other forms a comparator circuit of the type described earlier in this text. The system shown is that devised by Automic Timing and Controls, Inc., for use with their proximity cell. The proximity reactor has applied to it a signal having a frequency of 5 kilocycles, and the signal generated by the proximity cell causes a variation in the amplitude of the 5-kilocycle oscillator frequency. The amplitude-modulated signal which is produced when a bottle cap is missing is amplified and then demodulated (detected) as shown. The uncapped bottle is between the light source and the photocell at the same time it reaches a position beneath the proximity cell.

The system uses a bias voltage as a comparison potential with respect to the signal produced by the photocell. The voltage from the photocell and that from the bias supply produce a difference frequency which has sufficient amplitude to trip a relay system which will initiate the physical removal of the uncapped bottle. If desired, the difference voltage can be employed to stop the conveyor belt for manual removal of the bottle. When a capped bottle is beneath the proximity cell, however, the voltage of the proximity cell opposes the difference voltage produced with respect to the photocell, and hence the two voltages cancel and no rejection or conveyor-belt stoppage is initiated.

By the foregoing process, uncapped bottles in beverage-packaging processes are detected electronically, and there is no need to sense the omission by mechanical means which would entail physical contact with the moving items.

Liquid-control System

A refractometer device for the processing and testing of liquids with respect to standards is also available commercially in package form. One such device is the Process Refractometer available from the Consolidated Electrodynamics Corp. The system was originally developed by the Phillips Petroleum Company to improve monitoring and control of its refinery processes. The Consolidated Electrodynamics Corp. manufactures and distributes this item for industrial usage.

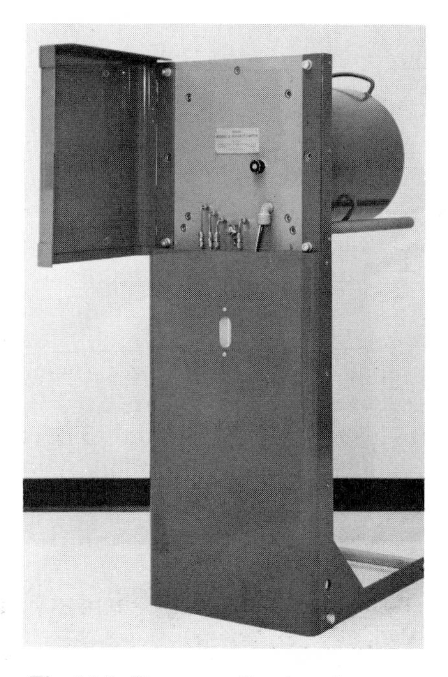

Fig. 14-5. Process refractometer (Consolidated Electrodynamics Corp.)

The process Refractometer unit is illustrated in Fig. 14-5. This device measures the difference in the refractive index between a liquid standard and a flowing liquid sample which is obtained directly from the process line. The manner in which it functions can be understood by reference to Fig. 14-6. A beam of light is bent as it passes from one medium to another having a different refractive index. The degree of beam deflection is proportional to the refractive index difference, and this is measured by the opti-

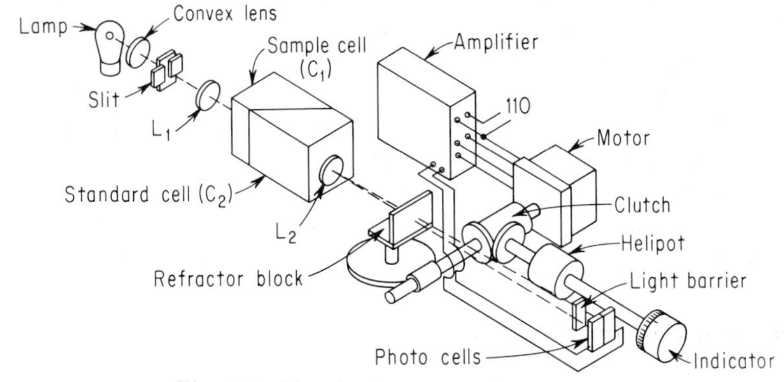

Fig. 14-6. Circuit of process refractometer

cal-servo system of the Refractometer. Because the refractive index is related to a liquid density, it provides a direct indication of relative composition changes in fluid mixtures.

The beam of light from the incandescent lamp is shaped by a slit as shown, plus a lense system L_1, and in going through the prism cells is bent in proportion to the refractive index. The beam is then focused by lense L_2 and redirected to dual photocells by a refractor block. The latter is mounted on a turntable which is positioned by the servo motor. The beam is split into two parts by a light barrier prior to reaching the photocells. When the system is balanced, the image of the split is evenly divided so that each photocell receives the same amount of light. When the refractive index of the liquid sample in prism C_2 changes, more light falls on one of the photocells. Because the photocells are connected in opposition to each other, the amplified difference signal will turn the positioning motor until each photocell receives an equal amount of light to restore balance. The displacement of the refractor block which is required to obtain balance is proportional to the difference in the refractive index between the sample fluid in cell C_2 and the standard liquid sample in cell C_1. The position of the refractor block is shown on a dial geared to the motor shaft. The motor shaft is also geared to operate a recorder device.

Because of the error signals involved, the Phillips Refractometer can be adapted to provide automatic control through conventional feedback servo-loop systems.

MULTIPROCESS CONTROL SYSTEMS

Control systems are available from various manufacturers for performing operations in sequential steps in industrial processes. Some of these systems simply involve small timing and control units, while others use devices that permit the programming of the individual steps which are involved with the manufacturing processes. The latter units then channel the information to various control sections which have amplifiers, servo and selsyn devices, and motors for performing the various functions in the sequence originally laid out. To illustrate the multiprocess system using small timers, a typical example of a commercial installation is given in this chapter. Multiprocess commercial systems of a more complex nature, involving automation and computer techniques, are covered in the latter part of the next chapter.

Automatic Molding Control

Automatic timers such as described in Chapter 12 can be used in combinations for sequential control of industrial processes. One such application is shown in Fig. 14-7, where Atcotrol Interval Timers

Fig. 14-7. Automatic molding control (Automatic Timing & Controls, Inc.)

(Automatic Timing and Controls, Inc.) are used to provide automatic operation of multi-die rubber-molding presses. By use of the timer system, one operator can work with a dozen or more presses simultaneously.

In the manufacture of rubber products, pressure molding is done by precisely timed applications of both heat and pressure, and the sequence of operations using timers starts with the placement of the rubber sheet in dies. A start button is then depressed to energize the first timer. (See Fig. 14-8.) The timer automatically closes the press for a predetermined initial heating cycle lasting several minutes.

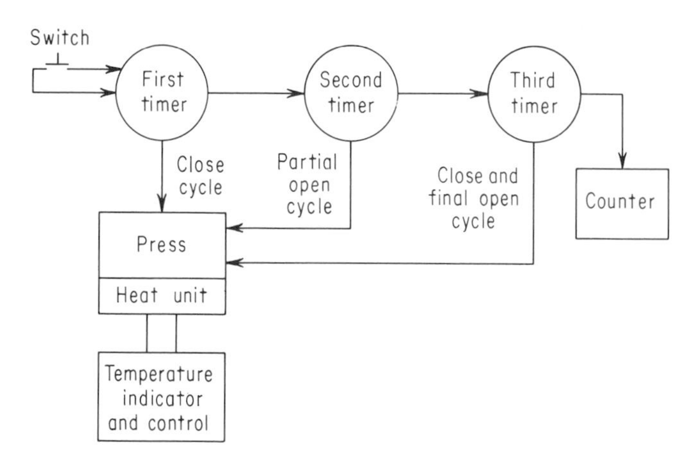

Fig. 14-8. Automatic molding control circuit

When the first timer completes its cycle, it automatically starts the second timer, and the latter causes the press to open partially for a specific time interval to permit degassing. After the degassing cycle, the second timer energizes the third timer which closes the press for a minute to permit curing. At the termination of the curing cycle, the third timer causes the press to open, for removal of the molded piece. The third timer also produces a signal output for triggering a digital counter to record the number of molding operations which have occurred. Duplications of the three-timer combinations will permit the simultaneous operation of a number of mold presses.

Review Questions for Chapter 14

1. List some typical applications for error-detecting devices.
2. Outline briefly what is involved in industrial process control.
3. Explain briefly the factors relating to process control in the milk-packaging industry.
4. For what purposes are error-detecting devices employed in petroleum and textile industries?
5. Explain what is meant by a *single-process control system* and give a typical example in block-diagram form.
6. How are differential reactors used in edge control for a moving sheet of material?
7. Briefly outline one omission-detection process.
8. Explain briefly how a light beam can be used to test liquids.
9. Show by block diagram how five timers in combination can turn on five machines in time-interval sequence, and count the number of times this process is completed.

15

Computer Systems

INTRODUCTION

Electronic computers are used in industrial applications for automation processes, control, data logging and calculation, and the storage of information such as the number of items processed, plus their unit value, the flow rate of fluids or gases, and the ratios of ingredients in mixing processes.

Typical applications of computers to industrial processes involve a variety of control functions. Some cement companies, for instance, use computers to compile statistics regarding the source of the raw material utilized, in terms of the proper proportions required in cement making. The computer also itemizes the various cost factors and retains in storage the amount and nature of chemical compositions and inventory. In electronic power-station applications, computers are used to maintain constant power levels by storing data regarding occurrence of periodic load changes and making calculations for the increase or decrease in power which is required to compensate for the variations. The computer also maintains a constant check on the many lines which route the power, and automatically selects alternate routes when overload occurs. It also automatically operates the closed-loop servo systems relating to the control of the temperature of steam, combustion, and water flow. In rolling and processing mills, computers are employed for controlling sequential operations of forming and processing as well as welding and stamping.

The versatility of the electronic computer makes it invaluable for many other industrial control, computing, and processing applications because sequential steps can be programed; that is, they can be entered into the storage section of the computer, after which the computer draws from the storage the information in sequence and—automatically and repeatedly as required—undertakes the processes or calculations involved.

COMPUTER TYPES

There are two specific types of computers—the analog and the digital. The digital computer is manufactured in two basic types, the general-purpose and the special-purpose. The special-purpose, such as the data-processing type, can be adapted to computations and automation; it is often an electronic filing system whereby various data are processed such as in inventory work. Items purchased and sold are stored or entered in the computer, which calculates total costs and can furnish any needed information in printed or tabular form as required.

The digital computers are more expensive than the analog, ranging in price from thousands of dollars well upwards to a million in some special large-size types. The digital computer handles numbers, or coded alphabetical characters, and performs with them computations, comparisons, and control functions. Digital computers are better suited to the obtaining of precision results. Generally, the techniques relating to the digital computer are more flexible than the analog and there is greater accuracy in computations. The analog computer, however, finds application in sensing variables and physical changes such as shaft positions, lever movements, and gear rotation, and can convert them to electric impulses or mathematical processes. The analog computer, working by analogy, can analyze electronically the relationship of mechanical variables to the device as a whole.

Digital computers, of whatever type, have the same general appearance. A control panel or desk is used for feeding information into the computer, and various cabinets contain the arithmetic circuitry, the storage devices, and the read-out units. Usually, the data-processing type has more external storage devices for handling the greater amount of information which it must inventory.

A typical digital computer is the IBM 705 electronic data-processing system shown in Fig. 15-1. This computer is designed particularly for commercial applications and combines the ability to calculate at extremely high speeds with its capacity for storing a vast quantity of data. The computer's circuitry performs calculations in millionths of a second and can make so-called "logical" decisions by indicating the best mathematical choice from literally thousands of possibilities. As shown in Fig. 15-1, magnetic tape units in the background are used for auxiliary storage devices.

Fig. 15-1. Computer (Courtesy International Business Machines, Inc.)

This computer has been designed to handle business data, and can simulate the entire operation of an oil refinery, or handle vast billing operations in minutes. It can also furnish inventory product control reports or process a personnel payroll of 50,000 people, including the computing of deductions, social security, and so on.

Fig. 15-2 shows the Elecom 125 general-purpose computer manu-

Fig. 15-2. Elecom 125 computer (Courtesy Underwood Corp.)

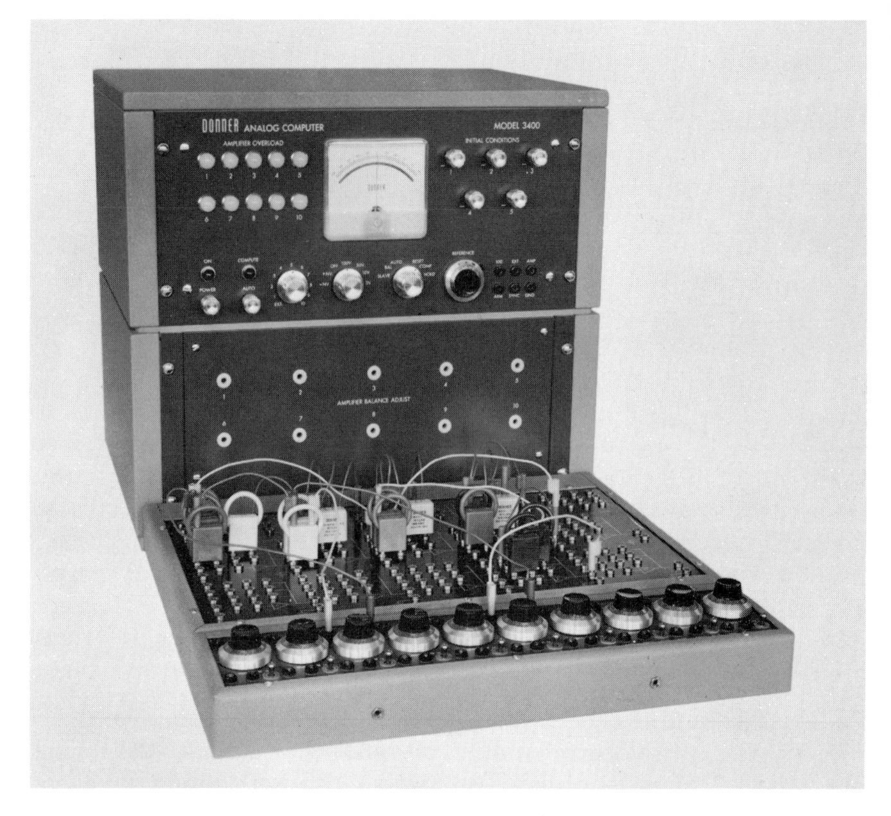

Fig. 15-3. Donner analog computer (Courtesy Donner Scientific Co.)

factured by the Electronic Computer Division of the Underwood Corp. Like other computers of its type, it has a wide variety of input and output facilities and is capable of solving highly intricate engineering problems.

An analog computer is shown in Fig. 15-3. This is the Model 3400 desk-top-type manufactured by the Donner Scientific Co. It is designed for applications in mechanical, industrial, chemical, nuclear, and other industrial fields as well as for process-control systems. It features a wide range of operating speeds, chopper-stabilized plug-in d-c amplifiers, and a removable problem board.

BASIC COMPUTERS

A basic computer contains the sections shown in Fig. 15-4. The problem to be solved or the processing procedures which the computer is to control must first be planned with respect to the sequential steps

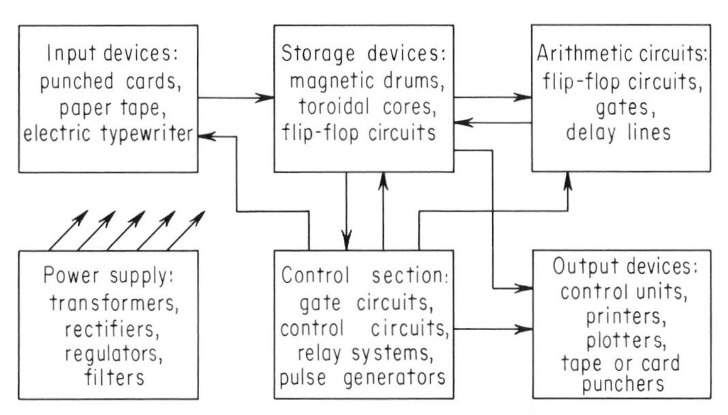

Fig. 15-4. Basic computer sections

involved. This is called *programming* and is necessary because the computer must be informed of the step-by-step procedures it is to undertake. Once the program has been established, it must be fed into the computer. This is usually done by typing out the program on a special electric typewriter which is linked electrically to the computer. As the sequential steps of the program are typed, pulse signals are produced which are fed directly to the internal storage section of the computer where they are retained until the program insertion has been completed. The operator then depresses a special start key, and the computer performs the indicated calculations or produces a series of control signals in proper sequence for control purposes. If a mathematical problem is being solved, the answer is printed out on the same electric typewriter used for program input, or the computer output can be channeled to printing devices, plotters which provide the information in graph form, or to external storage devices where it is held for future use.

The program involves use of a special code based on the binary numbering system to be described later. Computers of various manufacturers have codes which differ from each other, and familiarization with the particular code used is necessary before an operator can program for a given computer. Once the computer has assimilated the program, its internal electric processes employ only pulse signals having durations of a few microseconds or less. Consequently, the internal computer processes are extremely rapid, and problems can be solved in a fraction of the time it would take for a group of trained mathematicians to complete.

Because pulse-type signals are involved, the program can be entered into the computer from punched cards instead of an electric typewriter. The punched cards are prepared from the program using special card-punching equipment. Most of the electric typewriters used also perforate paper tape as the program is being typed out. Thus, the paper tape can be filed for future use and the same program re-run simply by feeding the paper tape through the electric typewriter mechanism.

While the computer is in operation, it may be necessary to hold some information temporarily while other data are being worked on. When this is the case, the computer must utilize its internal storage system. Because of the rapidity with which the computer works, it is necessary to have an internal storage into which information can be read very rapidly, or from which data can be procured without slowing down the calculation processes. Internal storage devices consist of magnetic drums, toroidal cores, and flip-flop circuits, as shown in Fig. 15-4. All have the necessary high-speed read-in and read-out characteristics.

Most computers also have external storage facilities, and these usually consist of magnetic tape similar to the type used in home tape recorders. External storage is used to hold information which does not need to be read out with the high speed necessary within the computer. Data-processing computers usually employ a number of magnetic-tape storage units which keep on file electronically an enormous amount of information. Typical external storage tape units were shown in Fig. 15-1.

As indicated in Fig. 15-4, the arithmetic sections of the computer contain the flip-flop circuits, as well as the pulse-handling and logical switching circuits. The control section houses the electronic gating devices and electronic relays which route the information according to the instructions contained in storage. As mentioned earlier, the output section of the computer can be an electric typewriter for printing out numerical or alphabetical information, plotters which graph statistical data, printers which can print on a continuously moving paper sheet (in duplicate or triplicate as desired), or control devices for initiating industrial processes. The data can also be punched on cards for future re-entry to the computer as required. The power-supply section contains the rectifiers, transformers, voltage regulators, and other similar circuits described earlier.

INTERNAL STORAGE

Internal storage systems are based on the magnetic principles previously outlined herein. The drum-type memory consists of a large cylindrical metal drum which has a thin coating of an oxide magnetic material. The drum is surrounded by an external shell which contains recording heads similar to the types found in home recorders. These recording heads are placed in rows, and those in any particular row are shifted slightly from the row above so that as much of the circumferential area of the drum is utilized as possible. Cables are then run to the various recording heads so that the pulses which represent numbers or alphabetical designations can be stored on the drum when it rotates. A typical magnetic drum assembly with the driving motor at the right is shown in Fig. 15-5. This is the Model 1110 magnetic storage drum manufactured by Remington Rand Univac, Division of Sperry Rand Corp. Drums come in various sizes, speeds, and storage capacities.

Fig. 15-5. Magnetic storage drum (Courtesy Remington Rand Univac)

As the drum rotates, each recording and playback head spans a narrow circumference track on the drum. Some drums have as many as 250 tracks, with each track capable of storing several thousand electronic pulses. Some drums have a diameter of only a few inches, while others have diameters of one foot or more. The revolutions per minute also vary, some turning only one or two thousand rpm, others spinning in excess of ten thousand rpm.

Another internal storage device is the magnetic core. Hundreds of tiny toroid cores made of ferrite are strung on a framework in a formation such as shown in Fig. 15-6. These tiny rings are magnetized in one of two directions, to indicate the zero or one as required. The magnetism which is thus created is retained until a demagnetizing current is applied.

As mentioned in Chapter 4, the ferrite materials and properties are such that the hysteresis loop is virtually a rectangle. This characteristic lends itself to switching and hence is of particular value in storing pulse information. Because of the rectangular hysteresis loop, the magnetic core becomes a bistable element. For storage purposes, when a magnetic field is created in a positive direction, it is assigned either *zero* or *one* as desired, with the negative magnetic field representing the opposite designation. For instance, if the plus direction is chosen to represent one, the minus magnetic field would represent zero. The manner in which the cores are wired may be seen by an inspection of Fig. 15-6. Individual insulated wires are run through the cores as shown, with the vertical series of wires intercepting the horizontal wires at the core centers. These horizontal and vertical wires are utilized for switching purposes, hence each magnetic ring has a pair of wires at intersection. The amplitude of the voltage applied to any single wire is maintained at a value low enough so that it

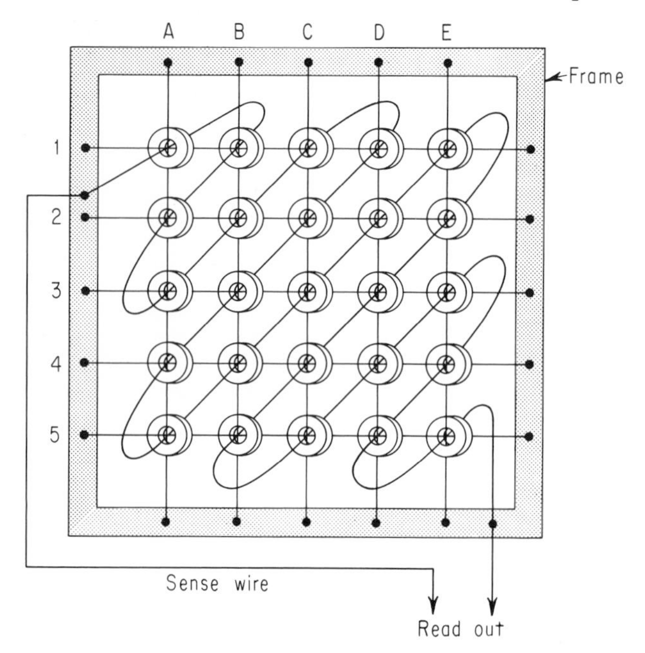

Fig. 15-6. Magnetic core storage

represents approximately one-half of the amplitude necessary to shift the magnetic field into its opposite direction.

Thus, if such a voltage is applied to the first vertical wire designated by A, it puts all the vertical cores in the A row at a point on the hysteresis loop as shown by P in Fig. 15-7. Assume that the horizontal wire no. 1 now has a voltage applied to it also. This, too, is also only about one-half the amplitude required to shift the field. The combination of the fields from the A wire and the no. 1 wire, however, is sufficient to switch the magnetic state of the core into its opposite direction, as shown by the Q symbol in Fig. 15-7. The no. 1 wire half-energized the first horizontal row of cores, and the A wire half-energized the first vertical row of cores. Only the first core was energized sufficiently to switch. Thus, by a proper selection of any two wires, a particular core can be pin-

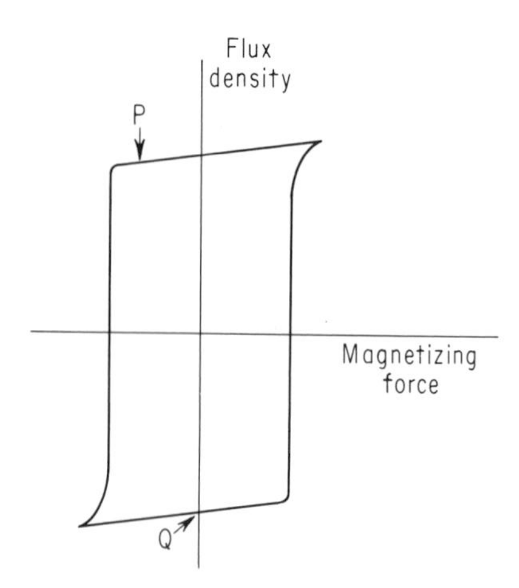

Fig. 15-7. Graph of magnetic core characteristics

pointed for switching. Thus, core no. 1 can be energized to represent 1, and by applying a reverse-polarity voltage to the A and no. 1 lines, the core can be energized in the opposite direction to represent zero. (Changing from the one state to the zero state is known as *clearing.*)

The information stored in any particular core is read out by the wire running diagonally through the cores; this is known as a *sense* wire. When a reverse voltage is applied at the intersection of a particular core to switch it, the shift in its magnetic state creates a changing magnetic field. The latter induces in the sense wire a voltage which is then present at the terminals for read-out purposes.

The ferrite cores are strung on frames, and a number of frames may be stacked to increase the number of pulse signals which can be retained.

THE BINARY SYSTEM

The notation system in a computer is not the ordinary, universally employed decimal notation. A different form of notation is necessary because the computer recognizes only two states, *zero* and *one.* This comes about because the flip-flop circuits, for instance, have the tubes or transistors operating either at cutoff (zero current) or saturation (maximum current). As detailed in Chapter 3, a single flip-flop stage can register either zero or one, and hence a system of notation is used which is known as *binary* notation.

Reference to Fig. 15-8 will show how the binary system of notation is established. Here, we have four flip-flop stages in cascade, with pulses applied to the first flip-flop at the *right,* and progressing through the stages to the *left.* When each flip-flop is in its "zero" state, it indicates that no pulses have entered the first flip-flop. The condition is as shown in the first horizontal line below the block diagram. The column at the right indicates the number of pulses entered, and the wide column at the left represents the "zero" or "one" state of each flip-flop circuit. (Reference should be made to Fig. 3-9 in Chapter 3 with respect to the *scaling principle* for a clearer understanding of this discussion.)

If one pulse is applied to the first flip-flop, this stage is turned on and the status of each flip-flop is as shown by the second horizontal indication below the block diagram. For the entry of another pulse, the first stage reverts to *zero* and the second stage changes to the *one* state as shown. Successive pulses will create the conditions as shown, up to the count of 16, when all four flip-flop stages revert to zero. At the count of 16, the fifth flip-flop in the cascade series would change to a one state.

An inspection of the various states which result indicates that

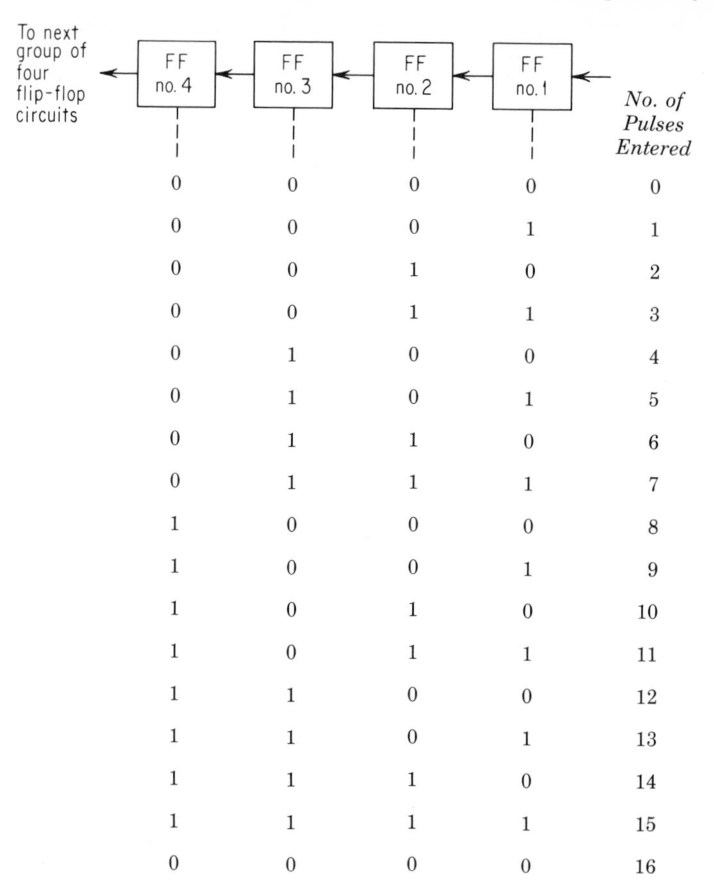

FF no. 4	FF no. 3	FF no. 2	FF no. 1	No. of Pulses Entered
0	0	0	0	0
0	0	0	1	1
0	0	1	0	2
0	0	1	1	3
0	1	0	0	4
0	1	0	1	5
0	1	1	0	6
0	1	1	1	7
1	0	0	0	8
1	0	0	1	9
1	0	1	0	10
1	0	1	1	11
1	1	0	0	12
1	1	0	1	13
1	1	1	0	14
1	1	1	1	15
0	0	0	0	16

Fig. 15-8. Computer binary system

when a continuous series of pulses is applied to the flip-flop system, the first stage alternately changes from zero to one. Note that the second stage remains in its zero position for two counts, then changes to its one state for two counts, and so on all down the line. The third flip-flop remains in its zero state for four entries and then changes to the one state and remains therein for four entries, and so on as shown. The fourth flip-flop remains in its zero state for eight entries and then remains in its one state for eight entries, etc.

From the foregoing, we can make up a list of decimal numbers and show the binary equivalent as follows:

Decimal Number	*Binary Equivalent*
0	00000
1	00001
2	00010
3	00011
4	00100
5	00101
6	00110
7	00111
8	01000
9	01001
10	01010
11	01011
12	01100
13	01101
14	01110
15	01111
16	10000
17	10001
18	10010
19	10011
20	10100

The list given above can be extended to as high a decimal value as desired by following the pattern of alternating the ones and zeros in the first column at the right; setting down, in groups of two, zeros and ones for the second column; and so on. Thus, every decimal number can be represented by its binary equivalent using only zeros and ones. This binary system is highly flexible despite its use of only two symbols, and the various operations of division, subtraction, addition, and multiplication can be performed.*

The system shown at Fig. 15-8 counts up to fifteen, then the fourth stage is triggered to the count of zero as shown for the sixteenth pulse which is entered. To facilitate the usage of the binary notation system, successive groups of four flip-flop stages are employed to resemble the decimal system, by appropriate circuit changes. Such circuit modifications consist of using feedback loops within the four stages to cause the four flip-flop circuits to trigger to zero at the count of ten instead of sixteen. When this is done, an equivalent decimal system is created even though binary notation is employed. This is evident by the grouping shown in Fig. 15-9.

In the aforementioned illustration, pulses are applied to the first group of flip-flops at the right, at the A terminal. Each successive group of four also has a separate pulse-entry terminal, marked B, C,

* For thorough analysis of binary arithmetical operations, see Matthew Mandl, *Fundamentals of Digital Computers* (Englewood Cliffs, N.J.: Prentice-Hall, Inc., 1958).

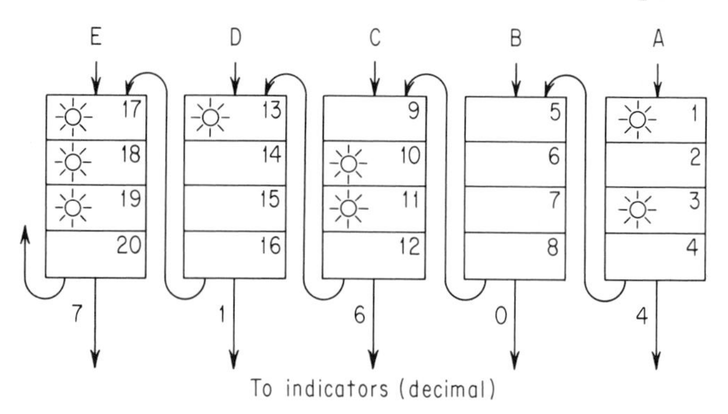

Fig. 15-9. Decade counters

D, and *E* in Fig. 15-9. With this system the number of pulses required to enter any decimal number into the cascade of flip-flops is limited to ten. Assume, for instance, that the number 71,604 is to be entered as shown in Fig. 15-9. This would simply require the entry of four pulses in the first group of four flip-flops, zero pulses in the second group, six pulses in the third group, one pulse in the fourth group, and seven in the fifth group. This group of pulses could be entered simultaneously at the *A, B, C, D,* and *E* terminals.

Each group of four flip-flops shown in Fig. 15-9 is known as a *decade counter* since each group of four counts to ten. If a neon indicator light is present in each flip-flop stage, the lights would be lit as shown in Fig. 15-9 for the number entered. Thus, the light in the first and third flip-flop *stages* would be lit to indicate the count of four. No lights would be lit in flip-flops five to eight in the second counter, and two lights would be lit in the tenth and eleventh flip-flops of the third group to indicate the binary number six, etc.

For this system, the binary notation would be broken up into groups to indicate the decimal equivalents. Thus, up to the count of nine, the binary notation is the same as shown earlier. From the decimal ten to any higher number, however, each digit of the decimal number would be represented by a separate binary number as shown below:

Decimal Number		*Binary-Coded Decimal*	
10		00001	00000
11		00001	00001
12		00001	00010
. . .	. . .	. . .	. . .
23		00010	00011
68		00110	01000
152	00001	00101	00010

The decade counter shown in Fig. 15-9 has several special characteristics. Any numbers which are entered will be retained (stored) for as long as power is applied to the circuits. All circuits can be erased by the application of appropriate clearing pulses to the individual flip-flop stages. In addition to the scaling function described in Chapter 3, the flip-flops will also accumulate counts, that is, they can act as basic adding devices. For this reason they are sometimes known as *accumulators* when they are strung in cascade in a particular grouping.

The adding feature can be understood by an inspection of Fig. 15-9. Assume that six additional pulses are entered at terminal A in the first group of flip-flops at the right. Since this reaches the count of ten for this decade counter, the latter trips to zero (each flip-flop of the four reverts to its zero state) and a pulse is applied to the next decade counter, leaving flip-flop no. 4 and entering flip-flop no. 5. This lights the neon light in flip-flop no. 5 and this second decade counter now registers one. Consequently, the stored number is now 71,610, and the system automatically has accepted the six additional pulses and added them to the number already stored within the system.

The outputs from the individual decade counters can be applied to any of the several indicators described in Chapter 12 for a visual decimal indication of the number stored within the decade counters. The entire system can be cleared of the stored number, and at the same time the number obtained from the output terminals can be routed to external storage for future usage. The number can also be channeled to the read-out devices such as the electric typewriters and printers mentioned earlier.

ANALOG TO DIGITAL CONVERSION

As mentioned earlier, the analog system relates to physical changes which must be sensed and channeled to a computer for processing. For digital application of the information obtained from physical changes, it is necessary to convert the analogical information into that representing the digital (binary notation) form. Devices for this purpose are known as *analog*-to-*digital* converters.

One type of analog-to-digital converter widely used is the binary-coded disk shown in Fig. 15-10, consisting of alternate sections of conduction and nonconduction. Another type used is similar in appearance, but consists of alternate transparent and nontransparent sections. Both types came in a variety of segment patterns to suit the particular requirements and type of code employed.

The coded disk shown produces a five-place output, such as the binary number 11011 or 01001, depending on the position of the shaft

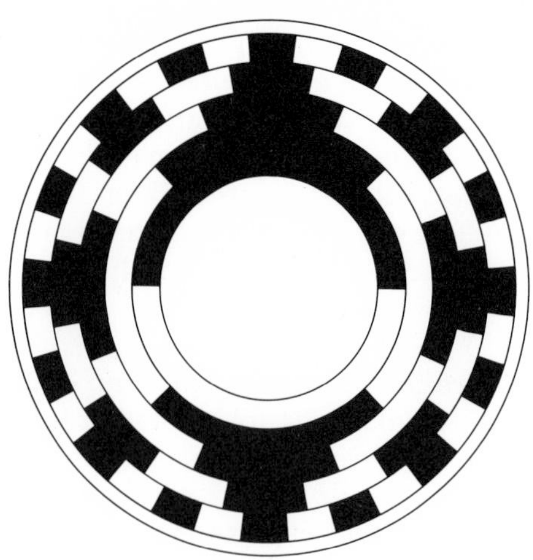

Fig. 15-10. Analog to binary encoding disk

to which the disk is mounted. Some disks in use have a greater number of output digits for production of a number involving a half-dozen or more places.

Methods for obtaining the binary digits from the disk converter (sometimes also referred to as an *encoder*) are illustrated in Fig. 15-11. At A the use of photosensitive cells is shown. A light source is directed to the back of the disk, and the photocells are aligned in a vertical row in front to intercept the light which goes through each slot (transparent area) and arrives in line with the photocell. As the shaft rotates, the five photocells generate pulses producing a five-part binary number. When one of the photocells receives no light, the binary zero is produced. If, for instance, the disk were in a position where slots (or transparent areas) were present only in the first and fifth rings, the output number would be 10001.

Another method for obtaining the binary number is shown at B, where alternate segments are conductive and nonconductive. Here

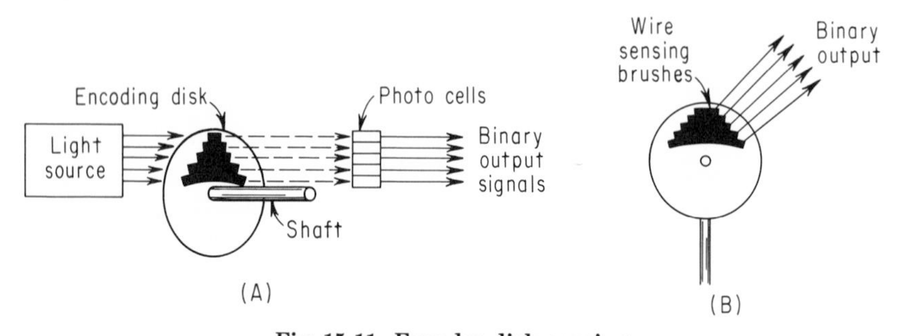

Fig. 15-11. Encoder disk sensing

five wire-brush "feelers" slide along the disk surface and produce a binary 1 every time a conductive area is traversed. The binary numbers thus obtained are channeled to flip-flop stages or other computer circuits for evaluation of the information as it relates to a shaft position for calculating or control purposes.

A commercial code disk assembly is shown in Fig. 15-11C. This is a product of Bendix-Pacific (Division of Bendix Aviation Corporation) and is used in their system of long-distance data transmission known as Electro-Span. The system permits digital measurement of the flow of fluids in pipelines as well as control of pumps, valves, and other devices at remote distances. The unit shown in Fig. 15-11C contains the brush-type feelers and the driving motor as well as the code disk. Use of this mechanism permits long-distance digital readings of electric power at three-second intervals with an accuracy of better than 1 per cent.

In the binary-notation principle there is often a change of more than one digit when going from one number to the next higher number. For example, when changing from the decimal number 3 (0011) to 4 (0100), three digits change. (The two 1's in 0011 must change to 0's and the third-place 0 must change to 1.) For greater accuracy in

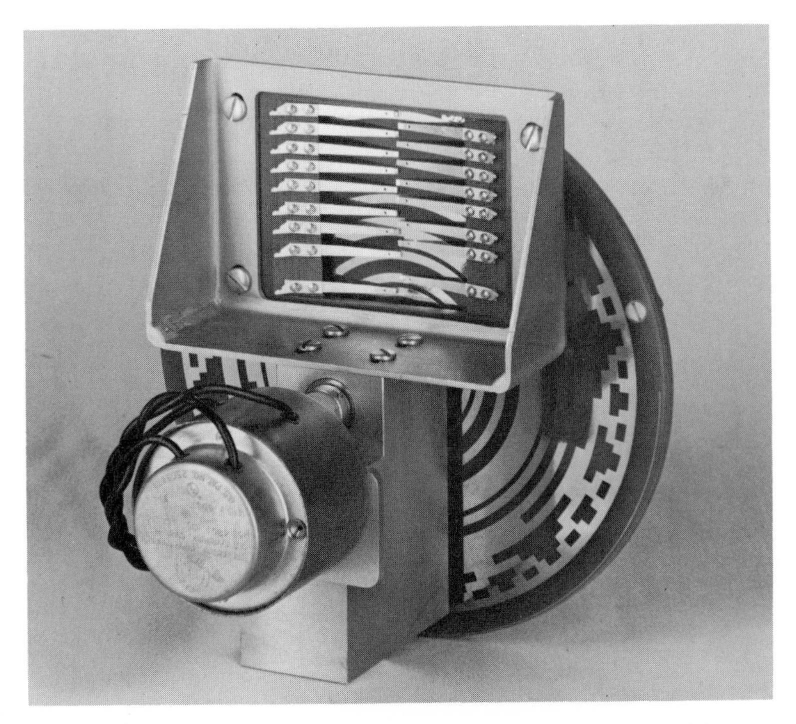

Fig. 15-11C. Commercial code disk (Courtesy Pacific Bendix)

analog-to-digital conversion, it is desirable to have only one digit change at a time when increasing a number progressively. When only a single digit changes, operational errors are considerably reduced. To accomplish the single-digit change, a code is frequently used which is known by various names: *Gray code, cyclic code, minimum-error code,* or *reflected binary.* The table below shows the Gray code in comparison with the pure binary, for a count up to 16.

Decimal Number	*Pure Binary*	*Gray Code*
0	00000	00000
1	00001	00001
2	00010	00011
3	00011	00010
4	00100	00110
5	00101	00111
6	00110	00101
7	00111	00100
8	01000	01100
9	01001	01101
10	01010	01111
11	01011	01110
12	01100	01010
13	01101	01011
14	01110	01001
15	01111	01000
16	10000	10000

Inspection will reveal that the same 16 binary numbers are present in both the pure binary and the Gray code, the only difference being the arrangement of the numbers. In the Gray code only one digit changes throughout, while in the pure binary there are a number of occasions where two or more digits change from one number to the next.

Automation

In the preceding chapter automatic control of industrial processes was shown, including examples of timer-initiated operations. Also shown was the way in which transducers (with their associated circuitry) and servos held the processes to close error-free tolerances. For *complete* automatic process control, however, one central machine acting as the "brain" must issue commands to the various processing devices. The latter, under direction of the master control unit, must be able to mold, shape, bend, punch, or drill the material not only in a certain predetermined sequence, but to certain tolerances under the control of the central machine.

When required, the central control device must be able to direct the shifting or positioning of a remote table by selsyn and servo devices so that certain processes can be applied to the unit being fabricated. During the manufacturing, the central control unit calculates the effect of variables, accumulated processes, or the total number of components manufactured, and either prints out such information or stores it in memory circuits for display as required.

Other devices continuously test the material being processed for flaws in structure or deviations in size, shape, or width, and either stop the industrial process or signal by alarm when the flaws or errors are sufficient to produce inferior results. All these functions fall under the electronic-computer category in terms of storage, control, and read-out. Also, initially, the entire process step-by-step must be programmed (entered) into the master control unit for proper usage by the latter for operation of the slave units. Typical commercial multiprocessing control and fabrication machines are discussed and illustrated in the remainder of this chapter to acquaint the reader with the practical aspects involved.

Automatic Coil Classifier

The installation shown in Fig. 15-12 illustrates the Systron Automatic Coil Classifier of the Systron Corporation. This assembly is for use in steel-mill quality control for coils of tinplate steel. It provides in-process inspection on a continuously moving steel coil at speeds up to 1500 feet per minute, and it is typical of the several automatic devices mentioned in the preceding paragraphs.

Fig. 15-12. Automatic classifier and control system (Courtesy Systron-Donner Corp.)

This Systron 130 system provides for visual as well as typewritten records of pinhole defects and variations in the coating thickness of the tinplate steel. It also computes automatically the total weight and length of the steel, and records the information. Storage of the defect information is also provided for, and the means for subsequent control of shearing and rejection of the defective material is included. A strip-chart record is made of the exact location of defects for subsequent analysis of the process involved, with appropriate warning-signal devices. The Systron system employs solid-state devices in its circuits, and visual read-out is by use of 1-inch Nixie indicators of the type discussed previously in Chapter 12.

Automatic Contouring Control System

An automatic system for controlling contouring operations in lathes, grinders, welders, and other such machines is produced by Electric Control Systems, a division of Stromberg-Carlson. This system utilizes a keyboard for entering the instructions to the machine regarding the machine process, plus a control unit for performing the command functions.

Initially, a specially printed Digimatic Planning Sheet is prepared, the latter having columns for entry of numerical information and other pertinent data relating to the exact process which is involved.

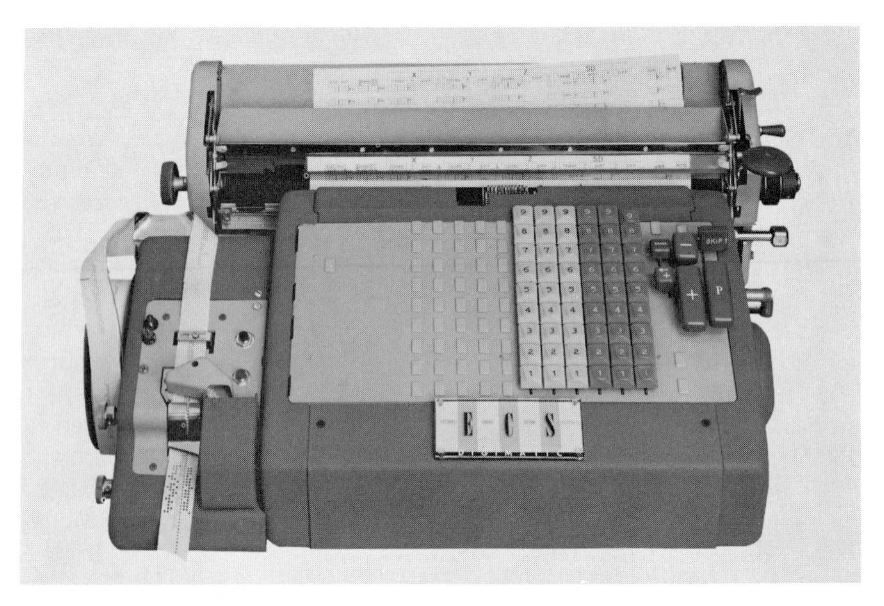

Fig. 15-13. Model 263 keyboard (Courtesy Electronic Control Systems)

Fig. 15-14. Control unit (Courtesy Electronic Control Systems)

The information placed on the planning sheet is procured from a drawing showing the part to be formed in terms of dimensions, material, type and size of cutter, feed rates, cutting speeds, etc. After the planning sheet has been prepared it is entered into the Model 263 Keyboard, and the data written in the small boxes and columns are entered on the keyboard. As soon as a given block of information has been entered into the machine and printed, a key is depressed which automatically assimilates the information and punches it on paper tape at the left of the machine (see Fig. 15-13). When all the planning-sheet information has been entered, the paper-tape data are transferred to magnetic tape by a special machine, or the paper tape is sent to the Electronic Controls Systems company for magnetic tape preparation.

The magnetic tape is used in conjunction with the Digimatic Model 191 Control Unit shown in Fig. 15-14. Information is played into the control unit from the magnetic tape in the form of pulse trains, each pulse controlling one-thousandth of an inch of motion.

As the tape is played back, the command data recorded on it are

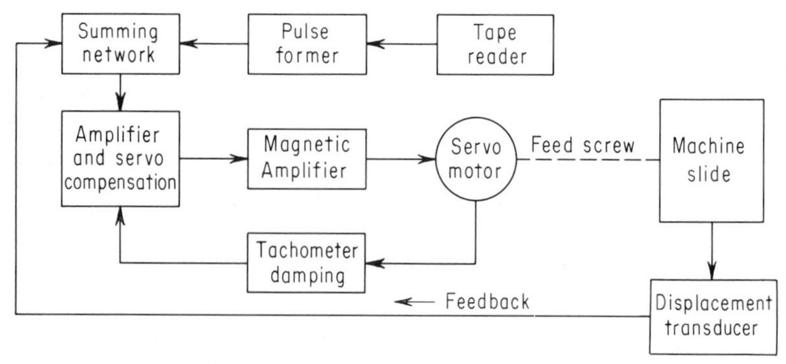

Fig. 15-15. Control unit block diagram

compared at all times with feedback signals supplied by position-sensing transducers which are connected to the machine-tool slides, as shown in the block diagram of the control unit in Fig. 15-15. The difference which is sensed between the motion of the lead screws and the commands initiating the movement gives an indication of the distance the cutter must move to reached a desired position. The distance is in the form of a signal voltage, and the control applies this signal to an electric or electrohydraulic drive, whichever is employed in a specific application. The drive then operates the feed mechanism controlling the table slides and moves them to the proper position. (A servo positioning table available from this company is described later.)

A novel and time-saving feature of the automatic contouring control system is the *reverse operation* process which can be utilized. In playing tape in the normal forward direction, the contouring steps are initiated as originally planned. By flipping a switch to reverse the tape reading, it is possible to reverse the contouring process. Hence, it is possible to machine a right-hand part or a left-hand opposite, or both. A typical example is the machining of airplane wing struts.

Automatic Point Positioning

When an item which is to be worked on is bolted to a work table, automation can control the lateral position of such a table in movements having a predetermined direction and sequence programmed into the control device. The process again begins with entry of the information into a tape-punching machine, and for this purpose a machine similar to the one shown earlier is utilized. The Electronic Control Systems company also has a system for automatic point positioning, using the Digimatic Model 264 keyboard in conjunction with the Model 202 Control Unit illustrated in Fig. 15-16. In contrast

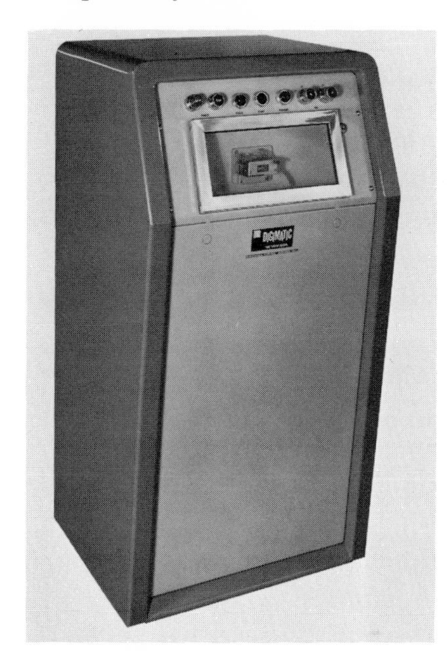

Fig. 15-16. Control unit (Courtesy Electronic Control Systems)

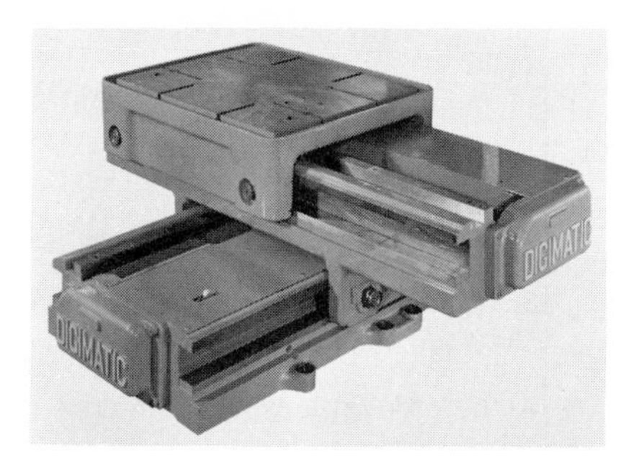

Fig. 15-17. Model 202 servo table (Courtesy Electronic Control Systems)

to the contouring control process, no magnetic tape is required for the point position control system, and the Model 202 control unit uses the paper tape just as it comes from the keyboard unit.

The control unit illustrated electronically controls the operation of the machine tool and the positioning of the Model 202 Compound Servo Table shown in Fig. 15-17. The control unit has seven operational controls on the front panel as shown. To operate the system, the punched tape is inserted into the reader of the control unit, and the power is turned on. Next, the start button is depressed and after the unit has completed the process, the program stop light comes on. At this time a new tape may be inserted for machining another part, or the tape already in the device can be rerun if the same work process is to be performed again. Two of the controls on the front panel are for positioning the table initially along any horizontal plane direction for setting up the work.

The compound servo table is composed of a base, a cross slide, and the table proper. Movement of the cross slide relative to the base permits one direction of motion, and movement of the table gives a motion at right angles to the cross slide. The a-c motors, clutches, and transducers necessary for operation are mounted within the table castings. Magnetic brakes hold the table position during the machining operations. The table is precisely machined for flatness and axis relationships, and can be adapted to existing machines used in industry.

Point positioning controls find applications in countersinking and drilling operations, spot facing, tapping, spot welding, riveting, and automatic assembly operations.

Review Questions for Chapter 15

1. List some of the uses for computers in industrial electronics.
2. Summarize briefly the basic computer types.
3. What two methods are used for internal storage in a digital computer? What method is used for external storage?
4. Briefly explain how a ferrite toroidal core is capable of storing a digit.
5. Explain the principles involved in reading out a number from a ferrite-core memory system using a sense wire.
6. (a) What are the decimal equivalents of the binary numbers 1010, 1110, 10000, and 10011?

   (b) What are the binary equivalents of the decimal numbers 4, 11, 17, and 20?
7. Briefly explain how a decade counter differs from an ordinary string of flip-flop stages.
8. Express the following numbers in binary-coded decimal notation: 14, 17, 18, 100, and 236.
9. Explain what is meant by an analog-to-digital encoder.
10. Explain briefly how a cyclic code differs from the pure binary code.
11. What is the necessity for using the cyclic code?
12. Express the decimal numbers 4, 8, 12, and 14 in both the pure binary code and the cyclic code.
13. In automation, what is meant by *programming?*
14. How are industrial machine operations performed automatically?

APPENDIX

Industrial Electronic Symbols

On occasion, some industrial electronic schematics may use symbols which differ somewhat from those generally employed in the radio-TV-audio-type drawings. Also, the reader may not be familiar with some of the symbols for industrial electronics because the items they illustrate may not usually be found in electronics involving communications-type circuitry. Consequently, the list which follows indicates the differences between the general and the industrial electronic symbols for the most common types encountered. Also, specific industrial symbols are shown for types which may not ordinarily be encountered in general electronics. Basic electronic symbols with which the technician is already familiar and which are identical with the industrial electronic types are not included herein.

Electronic symbols have been standardized in two publications, one by the American Standards Association and the other by the Institute of Radio Engineers, and should be consulted if additional symbol information is required. The publications are *Graphical Symbols for Electrical Diagrams* (ASA Y32.2-1954) and *Graphical Symbols for Semiconductor Devices* (57 IRE 21.S3).

LIST OF SYMBOLS

Device	*General Electronic Symbol*	*Industrial Electronic Symbol*
Capacitor	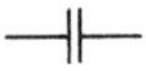 or 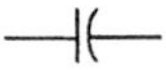	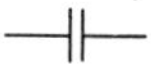 or 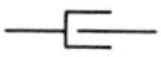
Coil (air-core)		 or 
Coil (magnetic core)	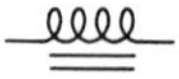	 or 
Coil (saturable core)	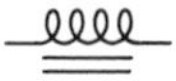	
Connector	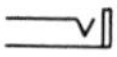	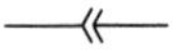
Contact (rotating, with brush)		
Contact (time sequential closing)		 or 
Counter (electromagnetically operated)		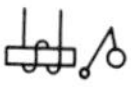
Fuse		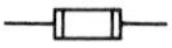
Ignitron		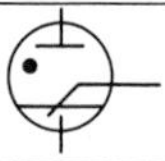
Lamp (neon)		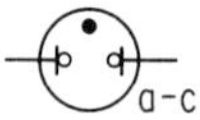 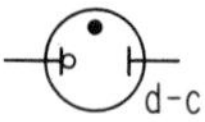 a-c d-c
Lamp (Pilot)	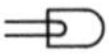	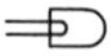 or  Letter for color
Relay (normally closed)		
Relay (normally open)		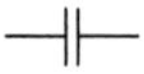
Relay (SPDT)		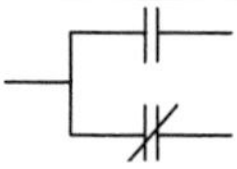
Resistor		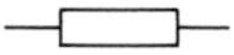

Device	*General Electronic Symbol*	*Industrial Electronic Symbol*
Resistor (tapped)		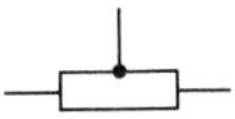
Resistor (adjustable)	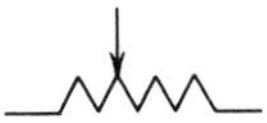	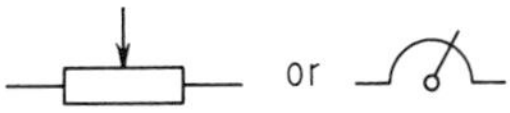 or
Thermostat (normally closed) (break)		
Thermostat (normally open) (make)		
Transformer	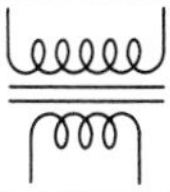	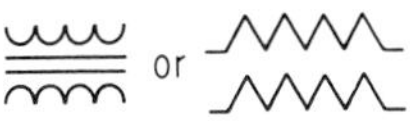 or
Transformer (3-phase)		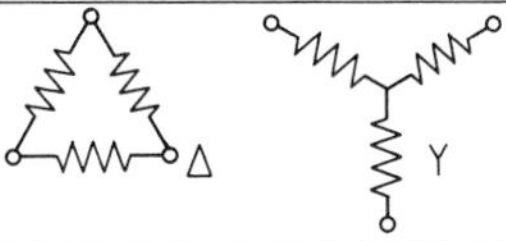 Δ Y
Transformer (adjustable inductance)	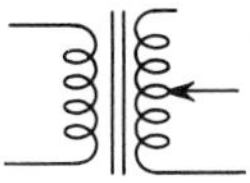	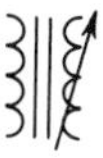
Transformer (auto-type)	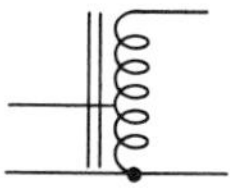	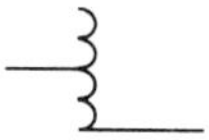
Switch (single throw)		
Switch (double throw)		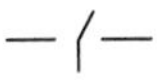

Standard Abbreviations

a-c	alternating-current
amp	ampere
amp-hr	ampere-hour
cp	candlepower
cm	centimeter
cgs	centimeter-gram-second (system)
cir mils	circular mils
cond	conductivity
cemf	counter-electromotive force
db	decibel
C	degree centigrade
F	degree Fahrenheit
K	degree Kelvin
d-c	direct-current
emf	electromotive force
ft-c	foot-candle
hp	horsepower
hp-hr	horsepower-hour
ihp	indicated horsepower
ID	inside diameter
i-p	intermediate-pressure
j	joule
kc	kilocycles per second
kv	kilovolt
kva	kilovolt-ampere
kw	kilowatt
kwhr	kilowatthour
L	lambert
l-p	low-pressure
l	lumen
l-hr	lumen-hour
lpw	lumens per watt
mep	mean effective pressure
mhcp	mean horizontal candle power
μa	microampere
μf	microfarad
μμf	micromicrofarad
mv	millivolt
NEC	National Electrical Code
Ω	ohm
OD	outside diameter
ppm	parts per million
psf	pounds per square foot
psi	pounds per square inch
pf	power factor
rpm	revolutions per minute
rps	revolutions per second
rms	root mean square
shp	shaft horsepower
sp gr	specific gravity
sq cm or cm^2	square centimeter
std	standard
ts	tensile strength
va	volt-ampere
whr	watthour
wpc	watts per candle

Index

N

O

P

R

S